STUDY GUIDE TO ACCOMPANY

FUNDAMENTALS OF
MICROBIOLOGY

I. Edward Alcamo

PREPARED BY

Robert V. Miller

Stritch School of Medicine
Loyola University of Chicago
for
P.S. Associates, Inc.
Brookline, Massachusetts

▲

ADDISON-WESLEY PUBLISHING COMPANY

Reading, Massachusetts
Menlo Park, California
London · Amsterdam · Don Mills, Ontario · Sydney

PREFACE

It has been said that if all matter in the world were destroyed, leaving only microorganisms, all of the features of the earth, including cities, plants, and animals, could still be identified because all of these features would be outlined by microorganisms. Much of the biological world is invisible to the naked eye and we can see it only with the aid of a microscope. Microbiology is the study of these organisms, which are found ubiquitously throughout the world in the air, water, and soil, and, as parasites, in larger organisms.

In your study of Fundamentals of Microbiology by Edward Alcamo, you will be introduced to the bacteria, the viruses, the fungi, and other members of the microbial world. In the last 150 years, since the work of Pasteur and Koch, the sciences of microbiology, immunology, virology, biochemistry, and molecular biology have been born and have flourished from the study of these tiny organisms. Your textbook will first describe the physiology, metabolism, taxonomy, and genetics of microorganisms. These discussions will be followed by an in-depth look at the interactions of pathogenic microorganisms and their hosts. Particular attention will be given to the types of organisms that cause infectious diseases and the diseases they cause. The immune response of the host will be discussed in detail and its importance as a major defense mechanism will be pointed out. Finally, a discussion of microorganisms in public health, as well as their usefulness in industrial processes will be described.

The story of the microbial world is an exciting one, but it is also a difficult one--one that requires diligent study to be fully understood. This Study Guide is designed to help you with your study of microbiology. It is intended to help you organize the information in your textbook and to increase your understanding of the material. Each chapter in the textbook is accompanied by a chapter in this guide. The materials included here are not intended to replace your textbook, but rather to enhance it.

Each chapter provides a variety of approaches to the subject matter of the text. The Chapter Outline begins the chapter. It is followed by an Overview that touches on the important subject matter of the chapter, and by a number of Objectives which point out things you should be able to do after completing your study of the chapter. A set of multiple-choice questions in the form of a Pre-Test follows. This test should be used as a preliminary test of your knowledge and understanding of the text chapter. A series of Practice Exercises is then presented. These items feature true-false, fill-in-the-blank, matching, and other exercises and problems to test your knowledge in more detail and to serve as reinforcement drills. In this section, you are often asked to interpret information in tables and figures. The Practice Exercises are particularly important because they present information in ways that are often encountered by the microbiologist and related professional personnel. The next section, Concept Exercises, asks you to go somewhat beyond the information given, to make connections between chapter contents and real or hypothetical situations. A Post-Test consisting of a second set of multiple-choice questions rounds out the exercises. Answers to all items appear at the end of each chapter. References to the pages in the text where the information is covered are also given in the answer section. Often references in the answer sections will be to tables and figures. This has been done to make checking your answers more convenient. If you miss a question, however, you should reread the section of the text that covers this material. You should not depend on the materials summarized in the tables and figures to supply all of the information you need to fully understand the materials covered in the chapter.

The order in which you complete the components of each Study Guide chapter is up to you. It is suggested that the Pre-Test be used as an initial test of your knowledge. After completing this test, turn to the answer section in the guide and see how you have done. You might want to reread sections of the text at this point. The Post-Test can be used as a final appraisal of your knowledge after you have completed the drill offered by the Practice Exercises.

You should read each item carefully before answering; if you chose an incorrect response, make the effort to correct your error by reviewing the appropriate pages of your text or by consulting your instructor.

We come into contact with the microbial world every moment of our lives, from before we are born until after our death. Its study is a vital concern and the uses being made of the knowledge gained are exciting and often amazing. I wish you much success in your study of Fundamentals of Microbiology and hope that you will find this Study Guide useful.

Robert V. Miller

1st Exam covering chapters 1-4, omitting ch. 2.

5. Pasteur's studies proved that wine was produced by the fermentation of grape juice by:
   a. bacteria.
   b. yeast.
   c. algae.
   d. a natural chemical process not involving living organisms.

6. Pasteur first suggested that bacteria could cause disease in humans by showing that they could cause diseases in:
   a. animals.
   b. plants.
   c. wine.
   d. canned foods.

7. Walter Reed determined that yellow fever was transmitted by:
   a. flies.
   b. mosquitos.
   c. rats.
   d. bats.

8. Alexander Fleming discovered:
   a. antibodies.
   b. bacterial flagella.
   c. penicillin.
   d. drugs.

9. Pasteur considered one of his greatest accomplishments in applying the work of science to practical problems in medicine to be the:
   a. discovery of penicillin.
   b. development of a vaccine for the rabies virus.
   c. disproving the theory of spontaneous generation.
   d. discovery of phagocytosis.

10. Shibasaburo Kitasato working in Koch's laboratory was able to demonstrate that the tetanus bacillus would grow only:
    a. in pure culture.
    b. at 37° C.
    c. in the absence of oxygen.
    d. on solid surfaces.

PRACTICE EXERCISES

1. List Koch's postulates:
   a. _Microorganism must be present every time disease occurs_
   b. _M. must be isolated from dise. host + grown in a pure culture med._
   c. _After M. is reproduced it must be injected into A healthy host._
   d. _M. must be recovered again from infected host_

2. Each of the following persons was associated with Robert Koch. Identify one contribution that each made to microbiology.

a. Fanny Eilshemius _Suggested agar be used_ _for growth of bacterie on a solid media._

b. Richard Pfeiffer _Isolated organisms thought_ _to cause influenza_

c. Emil von Behring _Treated diphtheria with_ _antitoxin_

d. Richard Petri _Developed the petri dish_

e. Friedrich Loeffler _Isolated organism that_ _causes diphtheria_

3. Underline True or False

Decide whether each of the following statements is true or false; then place a T for true or an F for false on the line provided.

F a. The first person to receive the Nobel Prize in medicine was Louis Pasteur.

T b. Marcelo Malpighi described the cells of the brain, spleen, and kidney tissues, and depicted the development of the chick embryo.

T c. Many of Anton van Leeuwenhoek's "wee beasties" can be identified as protozoa and bacteria.

T d. The first person to identify the shapes of bacteria as rods, spheres, and spirals was van Leeuwenhoek.

F e. Pasteur's "swan-necked flask" experiments proved once and for all that spontaneous generation takes place to produce bacteria and other microorganisms.

F f. Final proof that bacteria cause disease was given when Robert Koch observed the organism that causes anthrax.

T g. Agar is an excellent substance for the growth of bacteria because it mixes easily with liquids, does not melt until it reaches a temperature of 90°C, and does not gel until a much lower temperature (about 45°C).

F h. Marcello Malpighi was the first person to observe protozoa with a microscope he made himself.

4. Match the name in the left-hand column with the event in the

4

right-hand column by placing the correct number in the space provided.

_2_ a. van Leeuwenhoek

_7_ b. Edward Jenner

_3_ c. John Snow

_6_ d. Louis Pasteur

_1_ e. Robert Koch

_4_ f. Emil von Behring

_5_ g. Jules Bordet

1. Established the germ theory of
    disease.

2. Reported his observation of
    to the Royal Society.

3. Determined that cholera was
    spread through contaminated
    water.

4. Won the first Nobel Prize for
    his work on diphtheria.

5. Devised the complement-fixation
    test.

6. Developed a vaccine for rabies.

7. Protected people from smallpox
    by infecting them with cowpox.

CONCEPT EXERCISES

1. Recently the World Health Organization declared smallpox extinct.
   How did the discoveries of Louis Pasteur, Robert Koch, and their
   co-workers lay the foundations for the medical war that led to
   the erradication of this disease?

   _____

   _____

   _____

   _____

   _____

   _____

2. In March and April 1982, a large number of cans of salmon were
   recalled because it was found that several individuals had contracted botulism poisoning after eating the salmon. Botulism is
   caused by a toxin produced by an organism that is closely related

to the anthrax bacillus. How do you think that this organism
could grow in a can of salmon? _____

_____

_____

_____

_____

_____

_____

_____

_____

_____

POST-TEST

1. Edward Jenner found that he could protect people from _____
   by inoculating them with _____.
   a. rabies; bacteria.
   b. smallpox; virus.
   c. anthrax; virus.
   d. cholera; purified water.

2. The physician who developed what is probably the most important
   staining procedure in microbiology was:
   a. Louis Pasteur.
   b. Robert Koch.
   c. Richard Pitri.
   d. Christian Gram.

3. Nicholas Appert was among the first to use heat to preserve food.
   He carried out his studies in the early:
   a. 1700s.
   b. 1800s.
   c. 1850s.
   d. 1900s.

4. Charles Nicolle of the Pasteur Institute worked with typhus and
   proved that transmission of the disease was by infected:
   a. lice.
   b. rats.
   c. dogs.
   d. mosquitos.

5. In 1859, the publication of a book showed that Europeans would
   accept the human body as a creature susceptible to the laws of
   nature. This book was:

    a.   On the Origin of Species.
    b.   The Little Animals.
    c.   The Human Species.
    d.   The Diseases of Wine.

6. Anton van Leeuwenhoek is considered the first person to describe:
    a.   brain cells.
    b.   the development of the chick embryo.
    c.   bacteria.
    d.   the breathing system of insects.

7. Much of the initial work in immunology was carried out in the laboratory of:
    a.   Louis Pasteur.
    b.   Anton van Leeuwenhoek.
    c.   Robert Koch.
    d.   Robert Jenner.

8. Emil von Behring used antitoxin to treat:
    a.   cholera.
    b.   diphtheria.
    c.   anthrax.
    d.   rabies.

9. The typhoid bacillus was successfully grown in the laboratory by:
    a.   Robert Koch.
    b.   George Gaffky.
    c.   Emile Roux.
    d.   Emil von Behring.

10. Yeasts are responsible for the:
    a.   fermentation of wine.
    b.   anthrax.
    c.   tobacco mosaic disease.
    d.   cholera.

ANSWERS TO EXERCISES

Pre-Test

1. b   6. c

2. b   7. b

3. a   8. c

4. c   9. b

5. b   10. c

Practice Exercises

1. a.   The microorganism must be present in every case of the disease.

b. The microorganism must be isolated from the diseased host and grown in pure culture.

c. The specific disease must be reproduced when a pure culture of the microorganism is inoculated into a healthy susceptible host.

d. The microorganism must be recoverable once again from the experimentally infected host.

2. a. Suggested agar for growth of bacteria on solid media.

b. Isolated organisms thought to cause influenze.

c. Treated diphtheria with antitoxin.

d. Developed the pertri dish for the cultivation of bacteria.

e. Isolated organism that causes diphtheria.

3. a. F; b. T; c. 3; d. 6; e. 1; f. 4; g. 5.

Concept Exercises

1. Several different discoveries are important here. The two most important are probably (a) the development of the germ theory of disease by Koch and his group and (b) the development of the science of immunology by Pasteur and his group.

2. The botulism organism, which is closely related to the anthrax organism, produces heat-resistance spores. If these spores enter the can after the canning process (through a hole perhaps) or if the cans were improperly sterilized, these spores can germinate. Since the bacteria can grow anaerobically (without air), they can grow and produce the toxin that causes poisoning when the food is eaten.

Post-Test

1. b

2. d

3. b

4. a

5. a

6. c

7. a

8. b

9. b

10. a

In the middle of the last century, the focus on biological investigation was moving—in pursuit of the the steadily greater resolving power of the microscope and then outrunning it—down from the organ and the tissue to the cell. For a hundred years or more, the cell and its contents were to be the domain of the biochemists, whose interest lay in what they could detect and infer about the subtle flux of materials and energy therein.

Biochemists early sorted out the principal distinctive substances they found in living beings into four broad categories—fats (the lipids), sugars and starches (the polysaccharides), proteins, and nucleic acids. The nucleic acids were the last of these to be isolated.

> Horace Freeland Judson, The Eighth Day of Creation: Makers of the Revolution in Biology. New York: 1979, Simon and Schuster.

CHAPTER OUTLINE

    C. Proteins

    D. Nucleic Acids

OVERVIEW AND OBJECTIVES

To understand successfully the life processes, biologists must have a thorough understanding of chemistry. In this chapter, the fundamental concepts of chemistry are presented to lay a foundation for the discussion of microbiology that follows.

There are 92 naturally occurring elements. These elements make up all living and nonliving things on earth. The major elements found in bacteria, and all living cells, are carbon (C), hydrogen (H), nitrogen (N), oxygen (O), phosphorus (P), and sulfur (S). The smallest indivisible part of an element is the atom, which is, itself, made up of various particles. Atoms combine to form molecules. Atoms in a molecule are held together with bonds. Ionic bonds form when electrons are moved from one atom to another, whereas in covalent bonds, atoms share electrons. Hydrogen bonds are weak bonds that form between protons and nearby pairs of electrons. Chemical reactions occur when bonds are broken in molecules and re-formed into new molecules. In the living cell, these reactions are catalyzed by enzymes, which are themselves protein molecules.

Molecules important to organisms include: (a) carbohydrates, which are used for energy and as structural components of the cell; (b) lipids, which include fats that are used for energy and components of the cell membrane; (c) proteins, which are structural components of the cell and enzymes; and (d) nucleic acids, which include DNA and RNA—compounds that contain the genetic information.

After reading Chapter 2 of your textbook, you should be able to:

1. Define or identify the following terms: element, atom, nucleus, proton, neutron, electron, atomic number, atomic weight, isotope, ion, shell, oxidation, reduction, electropositive, electronegative, molecule, molecular weight, ionic bond, mole, covalent bond, hydrocarbon, functional group, hydrogen bond, acid, base, pH, reactant, product, enzyme, carbohydrate, saccharide, dehydration reaction, lipid, fat, glycerol, fatty acid, saturated, unsaturated, protein, amino acid, peptide bond, nucleic acid, ribose, deoxyribose, phosphate, nitrogenous base, ribonucleic acid, and deoxyribonucleic acid.

2. Describe the components that make up the atom and explain how the atomic number and atomic weight of an atom is calculated.

3. Distinguish among ionic, covalent, and hydrogen bonds.

4. Explain what acids and bases are, and how their presence in a solution can influence the pH of the solution.

5. Outline the structure and functions of the chemical compounds important to organisms.

PRE-TEST

1. The smallest indivisible part of an element is the:
   a. atom.
   b. proton.
   c. electron.
   d. neutron.

2. When two ions are attracted and become held fast together by electrical charges, they are said to have formed a(n):
   a. covalent bond.
   b. hydrogen bond.
   c. ionic bond.
   d. strong bond.

3. The dense center of an atom is called the:
   a. proton.
   b. neutron.
   c. nucleus.
   d. orbit.

4. The atomic number of an element indicates the number of:
   a. electrons.
   b. protons.
   c. neutrons.
   d. neutrons and protons.

5. The atomic weight indicates the number of:
   a. electrons.
   b. protons.
   c. neutrons.
   d. neutrons and protons.

6. When two atoms join together, they form a(n):
   a. ionic bond.
   b. solution.
   c. covalent bond.
   d. molecule.

7. The <u>direct</u> cause of cavities in the teeth is:
   a. eating sweets.
   b. bacteria in the mouth.
   c. acid produced by bacteria.
   d. not brushing properly.

8. The sequence of amino acids in a protein is referred to as its:
   a. primary structure.
   b. secondary structure.
   c. tertiary structure.
   d. quaternary structure.

9. Uracil is one of the:
   a. amino acids.
   b. carbohydrates.

c. nitrogenous bases.
d. fats.

10. The simplest carbohydrates are the:
    a. polysaccharides.
    b. monosaccharides.
    c. disaccharides.
    d. dehydrated carbohydrates.

11. Lipids that contain double bonds because hydrogen atoms are missing
    are said to be:
    a. unsaturated.
    b. fatty acids.
    c. saturated.
    d. glycerol.

12. Proteins are formed when amino acids are joined together by a de-
    hydration reaction. The bond formed between amino acids is referred
    to as a:
    a. hydrocarbon bond.
    b. peptide bond.
    c. primary bond.
    d. hydrogen bond.

13. Acids are compounds that:
    a. release hydrogen ions.
    b. take up hydrogen ions.
    c. tast bitter.
    d. have a pH greater than 7.0.

14. Ninty-seven percent of the dry weight of bacteria is made of atoms
    that include all of the following elements, <u>except</u>:
    a. hydrogen.
    b. oxygen.
    c. carbon.
    d. helium.

15. Particles that are negatively charged and make up part of the atom
    are:
    a. electrons.
    b. neutrons.
    c. protons.
    d. isotopes.

PRACTICE EXERCISES

1. Refer to Table 2.1. Using this table, provide the atomic number
   and atomic weight for each of the elements listed below.

Element	1. Atomic number	2. Atomic weight
a. O	_____	_____
b. C	_____	_____

c.   H   _____   _____

d.   N   _____   _____

e.   Fe   _____   _____

2. For each of the elements listed in Exercise 1 by their atomic symbol, write the name of the element on the corresponding line below.

a. _____

b. _____

c. _____

d. _____

e. _____

3. True or False

Decide whether each of the following statements is true or false; then place a T for true or an F for false on the line provided.

_____ a. An atom of an element having a different number of neutrons than other atoms of the same element is referred to as an isotope of the element.

_____ b. An atom that has lost or gained an electron is referred to as an ion.

_____ c. An ion that has gained an electron has a negative charge.

_____ d. Oxidation is the gaining of electrons.

_____ e. The element is the smallest indivisible part of an atom.

_____ f. Each atom has a dense center called a nucleus, which is composed of protons and neutrons. A third particle, the electron, revolves around the nucleus.

4. Fill in the blanks. When atoms join together to form molecules, they are said to have formed a chemical (a) _____.
There are several types of these chemical (b) _____:
The (c) _____ _____ develops when two ions are attracted together and become held fast by (d) _____ charges. No transfer of electrons takes place when a (e) _____ _____ is formed.
Instead the electrons are (f) _____ by the two atoms.
(g) _____ _____ are weak bonds that form between protons and nearby pairs of electrons.

5. Identify each of the following complex ions and radical groups.

a.   —OH   _____   _____ .

b. $PO_4{}^{-3}$ _____   _____ .

c.   —COOH   _____   _____ .

d.   —NH_2 _____   _____ .

6. Match each of the following biologically important types of compounds with the descriptive statements that follow by placing the appropriate number on the line provided. Some terms may be used more than once and some may not be used at all.

  1. carbohydrates   3. proteins

  2. lipids   4. nucleic acids

____a. Made up of amino acids held together with peptide bonds.

____b. The simplest form of this compound is the monosaccharide.

____c. These compounds are utilized principally as energy sources but they are also important compounds in the structural makeup of cellular structures.

____d. These compounds are made up of a glycerol molecule attached to one, two, or three long-chain fatty acids.

____e. These compounds are made of repeating subunits called nucleotides.

____f. These compounds are structural components of chromosomes where they carry the genetic information and direct its expression.

____g. These compounds play a critical role in living cells where they act as enzymes that stimulate chemical reactions to occur.

CONCEPT EXERCISES

1. Recently it was reported in many newspapers that amino acids had been found in meteorites that had fallen to earth. Why was this such an important discovery? Does it change your mind about the possibility of life on other planets? Why or why not? _____

    _____

    _____

    _____

    _____

    _____

    _____

2. Until the model of DNA proposed by Watson and Crick (see Figure 2.17 in your textbook) gained acceptance, most scientists believed that the genetic material <u>must</u> be protein. What features of the chemical composition of DNA and protein might lead someone to this conclusion? _____

_____

_____

_____

_____

_____

_____

_____

_____

POST-TEST

1. The physical universe as we know it is composed of a finite number of naturally occurring elements. There are _____ elements.
   a. 50
   b. 32
   c. 92
   d. 106

2. Fatty acids that contain double bonds are referred to as:
   a. unsaturated.
   b. saturated.
   c. glycerol.
   d. saccharides.

3. An atom may contain each of the following, <u>except</u>:
   a. nucleus.
   b. proton.
   c. neutron.
   d. electron.

4. When an atom (A) captures the escaped electrons from another atom (B), atom A is said to be:
   a. oxidized.
   b. bonded.
   c. reduced.
   d. acidified.

5. When an atom (A) captures electrons from another atom (B), atom B is said to be:

a. oxidized.
b. electropositive.
c. reduced.
d. electronegative.

6. In a dehydration reaction:
   a. water is removed in the formation of the bond.
   b. monosaccharides are produced from polysaccharides.
   c. water is incorporated into a molecule.
   d. water is removed from a bacterial cell.

7. A chemical bond formed between the electropositive sodium ion and the electronegative chloride ion is a(n):
   a. covalent bond.
   b. hydrogen bond.
   c. biological bond.
   d. ionic bond.

8. The carboxyl group is important biologically. Its chemical formula is:
   a. —OH.

   b. —COOH.

   c. —CHO.

   d. —NH$_2$.

9. Weak bonds that form between protons and nearby pairs of electrons are:
   a. ionic bonds.
   b. covalent bonds.
   c. hydrogen bonds.
   d. peptide bonds.

10. When a protein is denatured, the:
    a. tertiary structure is destroyed.
    b. amino acid sequence is changed.
    c. peptide bonds are hydrated.
    d. amino groups of certain amino acids are removed.

11. All of the following nitrogenous bases are found in RNA except:
    a. adenine.
    b. thymine.
    c. uracil.
    d. cytosine.

12. In the chemical reaction $2Na + Cl_2 \longrightarrow 2NaCl$, the product(s) is (are):
    a. Na and Cl$_2$.

    b. Cl$_2$ only.

    c. Na only.

d. NaCl.

13. Molecules that catalize biological reactions are known as:
   a. nucleic acids.
   b. enzymes.
   c. carbohydrates.
   d. fats.

14. Nucleic acids are composed of all the following simpler molecules
   except:
   a. phosphate.
   b. carbohydrate.
   c. amino acids.
   d. fats.

15. Bacterial toxins are composed of:
   a. nucleic acids.
   b. carbohydrates.
   c. proteins.
   d. fats.

ANSWERS TO EXERCISES

Pre-Test

1. a   6. d   11. a

2. c   7. c   12. b

3. c   8. a   13. a

4. b   9. c   14. d

5. d   10. b   15. a

Practice Exercises

1. a. 1. 8, 2. 16 (all answers can be found in Table 2.1);

   b. 1. 6, 2. 12;

   c. 1. 1, 2. 1;

   d. 1. 7, 2. 14;

   e. 1. 26, 2. 56.

2. a. oxygen (all answers can be found in Table 2.1);

   b. carbon; c. hydrogen; d. nitrogen; e. iron.

3. a. T; b. T; c. T; d. F; e. F;

   f. T.

4. a. bond; b. bond; c. ionic bond; d. electric;

   e. covalent bond; f. shared; g. Hydrogen bonds.

5. a. hydroxyl group; b. phosphate ion; c. carboxyl group;

   d. amino group.

6. a. 3; b. 1; c. 1; d. 2; e. 4; f. 4; g. 3.

Concept Exercises

1. Amino acids are the building blocks of one of the <u>most important</u>
   biological macromolecules--proteins. Finding them in a meteorite
   suggests that life "as we know it" <u>might</u> be found in outer space.

2. DNA is made up of only four types of building blocks, whereas proteins are made up of 20 different building blocks. It was hard to
   understand how molecules made up of so few different precursors
   could code for the diversity needed to be the genetic material.
   When Watson and Crick published their model of DNA, scientists
   could understand how the linear array of bases in the molecule
   could act as a coded message for a large number of different traits.

Post-Test

1. c	6. a	11. a
2. a	7. d	12. d
3. a	8. b	13. b
4. c	9. c	14. c
5. a	10. a	15. c

3 Basic Concepts of Microbiology

The variations on a theme are so extensive among the protista, that it behooves every bacteriologist to pay attention to those morphologically unusual bacteria which may, in the long run, provide answers to some of the basic questions of suborganismic biology for which ordinary bacteria are unsuited as experimental material. Certainly, rational exploration of the development and behavioral biology of bacteria necessitates such attention, . . .

> M. P. Starr, and V. B. D. Skerman. 1965. Bacterial diversity: The natural history of selected morphologically unusual bacteria. Annual Review of Microbiology 19;407-454.

CHAPTER OUTLINE

I. A Brief Survey of Microorganisms

    A. Bacteria

    B. Viruses

    C. Protozoa

    D. Fungi

    E. Algae

II. Classification

    A. Modern classification

III. Nomenclature

IV. Size Relationships

V. Microscopy

    A. Bright-field microscopy

    B. Dark-field microscopy

    C. Phase-contrast microscopy

    D. Fluorescent microscopy

    E. Electron microscopy

OVERVIEW AND OBJECTIVES

The microbial world contains one of the most diverse sets of organisms classified in any taxonomic group. During the short history of micro-biology, organisms that the microbiologist studies have been included in the plant kingdom, the animal kingdom, and in their own kingdom, the protista. None of these classification systems was completely satisfactory. Do you classify the alga _Euglena_ as a plant because it photosynthesizes or as an animal because it is motile? Are the blue-green algae plants because they carry out plant photosynthesis, or bacteria because they are prokaryotic cells? Questions such as these have led to the modern method of classification used in biology, which includes five kingdoms. Members of the microbial world are to be found in four of the five kingdoms. With such a diversity of organisms, the microbiologist must have some basic knowledge of classification and taxonomy and be able to apply it to the many species of bacteria. In this chapter, the basic groups of microorganisms are introduced and placed in their taxonomic relationships to each other.

In addition, the chapter introduces the basic instrument of micro-biology, the microscope. Actually there are several types of micro-scopes, each of which is best used for specific purposes. Since micro-biologists cannot see the organisms they work with without the aid of a microscope, it is necessary for them to understand the basic principles of the microscope and to understand its strengths and weaknesses in order to be able to evaluate the information obtained through its use. To this end, the chapter discusses some of the basic features of the physics of microscopy including magnification, resolving power, and real and virtual images.

Bacteria are prokaryotic in nature. They do not have nuclear mem-branes or membrane enclosed organelles. The bacteria along with the blue-green algae and viruses are classified in the kingdom _Monera_. The fungi are eukaryotic and include the molds and yeasts. They are classified in their own kingdom, _Fungi_. The protozoa are eukaryotic animals that are classified in the kingdom _Protista_, which also includes the slime molds, some eukaryotic algae, and other one-celled eukaryotes. Some of the larger algae are classified in the kingdom _Plantae_, and can be very large indeed. Some of the giant kelp reach lengths of 20 feet or more.

Bergey's Manual of Determinative Bacteriology is the recognized system of bacterial taxonomy. The latest edition, the eighth, separates the _Monera_ into two divisions: 1. _Cyanobacteria_, and II. _Bacteria_. The bacteria are further divided into 19 parts, loosely based on morphological and metabolic characteristics. Bacteria are named by the _binomial system_ commonly used to name organisms in biology. This system uses the capitalized "genus" name and the uncapitalized "species" name of the organism. The names are written in italics or underlined to indicate that they should be italicized (e.g., _Escherichia coli_).

Since the time of Anton van Leeuwenhoek, the microscope has become a highly technical instrument. Several types of microscopes have been developed and are available to the microbiologist, ranging from the bright-field microscope which is the most basic of the instruments to the electron microscope which is capable of identifying objects as small as a single thread of DNA. The size of the object that can be observed in any particular microscope is a measure of both its total magnification and its resolving power. The resolving power of a microscope is a measure of its ability to separate two closely spaced objects, and is in turn dependent on the microscope's numerical aperture and the wave length of the source of illumination. The high resolution obtained with the electron microscope is due to the fact that its source of illumination, a beam of electrons, has such a short wave length.

After reading Chapter 3 of your textbook, you should be able to:

1. Define or identify the following: prokaryotic, eukaryotic, bacteria, rickettsiae, chlamydiae, mycoplasmas, viruses, protozoa, fungi, molds, yeasts, algae, chloroplasts, taxonomy, Protista, Lower Protists, Higher Protists, Monera, Fungi, Animalia, Plantae, species, genus, family, order, class, phylum, kingdom, Bergey's Manual of Determinative Bacteriology, Prokaryotae, Cyanobacteria, binomial nomenclature, micrometer, nanometer, bright-field microscope, objective lens, ocular lens, real image, virtual image, compound microscope, magnification, resolving power, numerical aperture, wavelength, working distance, dark-field microscope, phase-contrast microscope, fluorescent microscope, fluorescein, ultraviolet light, fluorescent-antibody technique, transmission electron microscope, and scanning electron microscope.

2. Distinguish among the various kinds of microorganisms and identify the kingdoms in which each kind is classified.

3. Distinguish between the prokaryotes and the eukaryotes.

4. Describe each of the major types of microscopes, the sources of illumination, and their major uses.

5. Explain the difference between magnification and resolving power and be able to calculate each for a specific microscope.

PRE-TEST

1. Cells that do not contain nuclei or membrane-enclosed organelles are said to be:
   a. prokaryotic.
   b. eukaryotic.
   c. animal.
   d. fungal.

2. An investigator isolates an organism from beer which is unicellular, is eukaryotic, and is neither photosynthetic nor capable of movement. The organism is likely to be classified as a(n):
   a. bacterium.
   b. yeast.
   c. protozoan.
   d. alga.

3. Organisms that do not grow or show any nutritional patterns and have no observable activity except replication which can only be accomplished in the cytoplasm of a living cell are the:
   a. bacteria.
   b. protozoa.
   c. algae.
   d. viruses.

4. Bergev's Manual separates the kingdom Monera into two divisions. The blue-green algae are found in the division called:
   a. Bacteria.
   b. Cyanobacteria.
   c. Protista.
   d. Chlamydiae.

5. The smallest division in modern taxonomy is the:
   a. kingdom.
   b. order.
   c. genus.
   d. species.

6. A nanometer is what part of a meter?
   a. 1/10
   b. 1/1000
   c. one millionth
   d. one billionth

7. The correct way to write the name of a bacterium in the Binomial System is:
   a. coli.
   b. Escherichia coli.
   c. Escherichia coli.
   d. E. coli.

8. Photosynthetic microorganisms that are eukaryotic but unicellular are placed in the kingdom:
   a. Protista.
   b. Monera.
   c. Plantae.
   d. Fungi.

9. A microscope that has an ocular lens with a magnification of 10 X and an objective lens with a magnification of 40 X has a total magnification of:
   a. 10 X.
   b. 400 X.
   c. 50 X.
   d. 40 X.

10. The specification of a lens, usually printed on the lens by the manufacturer, which relates to the size of the cone of light that will enter the objective and to the medium in which the lens is suspended, is the:
    a. magnification.
    b. resolving power.

c. numerical aperature.
d. working distance.

11. A microscope that has a dark background, with only the object under observation illuminated, is the:
a. bright-field microscope.
b. electron microscope.
c. dark-field microscope.
d. phase-contrast microscope.

12. The modern classification system recognizes five kingdoms. Each of the following is one of these kingdoms, except:
a. Fungi.
b. Prokaryotae.
c. Monera.
d. Protista.

13. If a lens has a numerical aperture of 0.25 and is illuminated with light of 500 nm, its resolving power is:
a. 0.25 um.
b. 0.50 um.
c. 1.00 um.
d. 2.00 um.

14. In the classification of humans as Homo sapiens, the term Homo is the human:
a. species name.
b. class name.
c. genus name.
d. family name.

15. In one microscopic technique, a fluorescent dye is chemically joined to antibodies, and these tagged antibodies are mixed with an unknown organism. They are then observed in the fluorescent microscope. If the antibodies are specific for the organism, the:
a. organism will appear darker than the background.
b. background will fluoresce.
c. organism will fluoresce.
d. ribosomes of the organism will be visable.

PRACTICE EXERCISES

1. For each group of organisms listed below, indicate which of the five modern kingdoms it is classified under by placing the proper number on the line provided.

1. Monera   4. Animalia

2. Fungi   5. Plantae

3. Protista

4 a. Cat.

23

_1_ b. Escherichia coli.

_5_ c. Pine tree.

_2_ d. Brewer's yeast.

_3_ e. Slime mold.

_3_ f. Amoeba (a protozoan).

_1_ g. SV40 virus.

_8_ h. Blue-green algae.

_3_ i. A single-celled eukaryotic alga.

_2_ j. Bread mold.

2. Identify each of the following organisms as bacteria, blue-green algae, protozoa, or fungi.

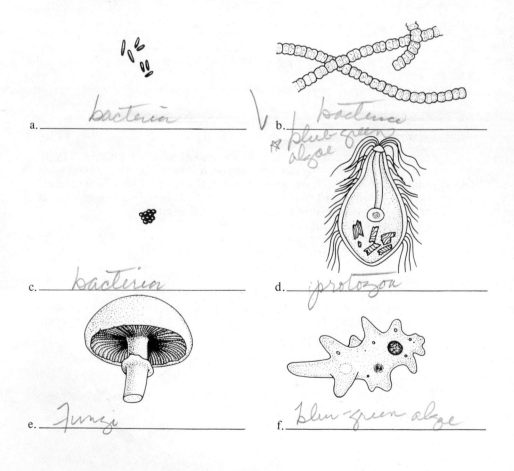

a. _bacteria_   b. _bacteria_ / _blue green algae_

c. _bacteria_   d. _protozoa_

e. _Fungi_   f. _blue-green algae_

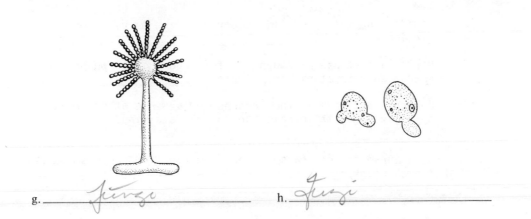

g. ___*fungi*___   h. ___*fungi*___

3. For each set of conditions given below give the total magnification of the microscope and the resolving power of the objective lens.

   a. Ocular lens = 10 X; objective lens = 400 X; NA = 1.25; wavelength of light = 600 nm.

   _____

   _____

   b. Ocular lens = 10 X; objective lens = 100 X; NA = 0.75; wavelength of light = 550 nm.

   _____

   _____

   c. Ocular lens = 15 X; objective lens = 1000 X; NA = 1.5; wavelength of light = 10 nm.

   _____

   _____

4. Refer to Table 3.3 of your textbook. For each of the bacteria described below, indicate which of the 19 Parts of Division II of the Kingdom <u>Monera</u> it is classified under in <u>Bergey's</u> <u>Manual</u> <u>of</u> <u>Determinative</u> <u>Bacteriology</u>.

   a. Aquatic bacteria that produce carbohydrates from CO_2 using photosynthesis pigments. _____

   b. Spheres that give a negative reaction on gram staining.

   _____

c. Slender, helically coiled bacteria moving by rotation of flexion of the cell. _____

d. Bacteria that use nitrogen, sulfur, and iron compounds for energy and structural components. _____

e. Spheres that live in the presence or absence of oxygen and that give a positive reaction on gram staining.

_____

5. On the diagram of the transmission electron microscope shown below, label each blank.

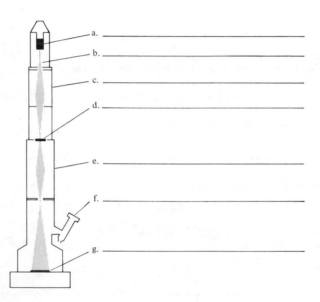

a. _____

b. _____

c. _____

d. _____

e. _____

f. _____

g. _____

6. True or False.

Decide whether each of the following statements is true or false; then place a T for true or an F for false on the line provided.

___T___ a. An eukaryotic cell has a nuclear membrane and other organelles enclosed in membranes.

___T___ b. The electron microscope has the greatest resolving power of any of the types of microscopes now in use.

___F___ c. Eukaryotic algae are placed in the Kingdom Monera in the modern classification system.

___F___ d. The electron microscope has great resolving power because its numerical aperature is so large.

26

___T___ e. Bacteria that are rodlike or spherical in shape and form endo-
       spores during their life cycles are placed in Part 15 of the
       Division Bacteria.

___F___ f. A _nanometer_ is one millionth of a meter.

7. Fill in the blanks. According to some microbiologists, the (a)
   _____ are too simple to be considered prokaryotes.
   Most researchers question whether they are even (b) _____.
   Other "small" bacteria include the (c) _____, which
   are tiny rods that are transmitted by arthropods, and the (d)
   _____, which are among the smallest bacteria. The
   latter organisms were considered viruses until their properties
   were clearly understood. The (e) _____ are the
   smallest organisms that can be cultivated outside living tissue.
   Certain ones are involved in lung disease. Besides the bacteria
   and the groups just mentioned, the Kingdom _Monera_ includes the
   group of photosynthetic organisms known as the (f) _____-
   _____ _____.

CONCEPT EXERCISES

1. On June 15, 1982, the National Public Radio program "Morning
   Edition" reported that a microbiologist at the University of
   Connecticut had discovered that bacterial forms had been found
   deep in the earth's crust—at levels many times lower than pre-
   viously believed that organisms could live. There are also the
   levels at which the earth's groundwater table is found, and it is
   now believed that the organisms may help to purify water by digesting contaminating organic and inorganic molecules. If you
   were assigned the task of classifying these organisms into one of
   the 19 Parts of the Division Bacteria, what characteristics of the
   organisms would you want to identify in order to classify them?

   _____

   _____

   _____

   _____

   _____

   _____

   _____

   _____

   _____

   _____

2. As suggested by the author of your text, many microbiologists
   believe that viruses should not be considered "living organisms."

Other scientists argue just as strongly that viruses should be considered living. List the characteristics of viruses you consider to be evidence that they are alive and, alternatively, that they are not alive. Now try to decide which side of the question you are on. Save your list and review it after you have studied Chapters 8, 9, and 10, which deal with viruses in detail.

_____

_____

_____

_____

_____

_____

3. Before 1962, it was believed that bacteria were only parasitized by viruses known as bacteriophages. Then two microbiologists, Stolp and Petzold, reported that a bacterium could also parasitize other bacteria, causing the death of the host bacteria. This bacterium, later named Bdellovibrio causes a "disease" of the host bacterium that cannot be distinguished from the diseases of bacteria caused by viruses. If you suspect that a strain of bacteria you are working with in the laboratory might be infected with either bacteriophage or Bdellovibrio, how could you determine whether the infection is viral or bacterial in nature?

_____

_____

_____

_____

_____

_____

POST-TEST

1. After storing some fruit in a warm, damp place, you discover that the fruit has begun to decay. You take a sample of the fruit and observe it under a light microscope. You find that the fruit sample contains some single-celled organisms, which appear to have no nucleus or membrane-bound intracellular organelles. The organisms you have discovered are most likely some type of:
   a. bacteria.
   b. yeast.
   c. protozoa.
   d. algae.

2. Immersion oil is used with the light microscope because it has a
   _____ similar to that of glass.
   a. magnification index
   b. refractive index
   c. numerical aperature
   d. wave length

3. A microscope with a series of special filters and diaphragms that
   split the light beam and throw the rays slightly out of phase is
   the:
   a. dark-field microscope.
   b. compound microscope.
   c. phase-contrast microscope.
   d. electron microscope.

4. A researcher has just isolated a small bacterium. It is a rod-
   shaped cell and appears to cause a disease that is transmitted by
   arthropods. The bacterium will multiply only within a host cell.
   The researcher would most likely classify this organism under which
   Part of the Division Bacteria? (You may wish to refer to Table
   3.3 of your textbook while answering this question.)
   a. Part 15, Endospore-forming rods and cocci
   b. Part 19, The mycoplasma
   c. Part 5, The spirochaetes
   d. Part 18, The rickettsias

5. The algal cells contain organelles in which photosynthesis takes
   place. The organelles are called:
   a. chlorophyll.
   b. chloroplasts.
   c. chromosomes.
   d. mitochondria.

6. In the bacterial name Bacillus subtilis the word subtilis represents which level of taxonomic classification?
   a. species
   b. genus
   c. family
   d. kingdom

7. The smallest unit of size in the list below is the:
   a. meter.
   b. millimeter.
   c. micrometer.
   d. nanometer.

8. If a lens has a numerical aperature of 1.25 and uses light having
   a wave length of 550 nm, then its resolving power is:
   a. 220 nm.
   b. 220 um.
   c. 0.22 nm.
   d. 0.22 mm.

9. If the total magnification of a microscope is 15,000 X and its

29

objective lens has a magnification of 1000 X, the ocular lens must
have a magnification of:
   a. 10 X.
   b. 14,000 X.
   c. 15 X.
   d. 150 X.

10. Eucaryotic one-celled animals are:
    a. protozoa.
    b. prokaryotae.
    c. algae.
    d. fungi.

11. Each of the following is among the most commonly used criteria
    used in the indentification and classification of bacteria, <u>except</u>:
    a. pH requirements.
    b. size and shape.
    c. natural habitat.
    d. nitrogenous-base content of the bacterial chromosome.

12. A microscope that allows surfaces of objects to be seen in their
    natural state and which can give a sense of dimension to the ob-
    served object is the:
    a. dark-field microscope.
    b. fluorescent microscope.
    c. scanning electron microscope.
    d. transmission electron microscope.

13. When the fluorescent microscope is used, microorganisms are coated
    with a fluorescent dye such as fluorescein. They are then ob-
    served in the microscope illuminated with:
    a. electrons.
    b. white light.
    c. ultraviolet light.
    d. colored light.

14. In the bacterial taxonomy of Ernst H. Haeckel, all microscopic
    organisms were placed in one kingdom the <u>Protista</u>. Eukaryotic
    organisms were later placed in the subgroup:
    a. "Higher protists."
    b. "Lower protist."
    c. "Monera."
    d. "Protozoa."

15. You have isolated and classified a new organism. You are going to
    name it, and you give it the genus name "bacillus" because it is
    an aerobic spore former. You give it the species name "Maryius"
    after your mother. In correct binomial nomenclature, you should
    write the name of your new organism:
    a. Maryius bacillus.
    b. Bacillus maryius.
    c. <u>bacillus</u> <u>Maryius</u>.
    d. <u>Bacillus</u> <u>maryius</u>.

ANSWERS TO EXERCISES

Pre-Test

1. a	6. d	11. c
2. b	7. c	12. b
3. d	8. a	13. c
4. b	9. b	14. c
5. d	10. c	15. c

Practice Exercises

1. a. 4; b. 1; c. 5; d. 2; e. 3; f. 3; g. 1; h. 3;
   i. 3; j. 2.

2. a. bacteria; b. blue-green algae; c. bacteria; d. protozoa;
   e. fungi; f. protozoa; g. fungi; h. fungi. (All answers to
   this exercise can be found in Figure 3.2.)

3. a. magnification = 4,000 X. resolving power = 240 nm = 0.24 um;
   b. magnification = 1,000 X. resolving power = 367 mn = 0.367 um;
   c. magnification = 15,000 X. resolving power = 3.3 nm = 0.003 um.

4. a. Part 1; b. Part 10; c. Part 5; d. Part 12; e. Part 14.
   (All answers to this exercise can be found in Table 3.3.)

5. a. electron source; b. electron beam; c. condensing lens;
   d. specimen; e. magnetic lens; f. viewing eyepiece; g. image.
   (All answers to this exercise can be found in Figure 3.13.)

6. a. T; b. T; c. F; d. F; e. T; f. F.

7. a. viruses; b. alive; c. rickettsiae;
   d. chlamydiae; e. mycloplasmas; f. blue-green algae.

Concept Exercises

1. Among the things you might want to know are the organism's shape and size; its oxygen, pH, and temperature requirements; and laboratory culture characteristics. Also: whether the organism is photosynthetic (not likely—why?), whether it produces a capsule or spores, its type of movement, and its staining reaction. You might want to know what carbohydrates it can digest and the nitrogenous-base content of its chromosome.

2. On the pro side of life, viruses do have nucleic acid (the genetic material) and can reproduce. On the con side, they cannot metabolize or reproduce outside their host, and and they use the host cell's metabolic enzymes and organelles to carry out these functions.

3. The best way would be to look at a sample of the infected bacteria in the electron microscope. If the infection were viral, you would expect to see particles of virus. If it were bacterial, you would expect to see parasitic bacteria inside the host bacterium's cell.

Post-Test

1. a	6. a	11. c
2. b	7. d	12. c
3. c	8. a	13. c
4. d	9. c	14. a
5. b	10. a	15. d

4 Morphology and Growth of Bacteria

The fourth sort of little animals . . . were incredibly small; nay so small, in my sight, that I judged that even if 100 of these very wee animals lay stretched out one against another, they could not reach to the length of a grain of coarse sand; and if this be true, then ten hundred thousand of these living creatures could scarce equal the bulk of a coarse sand-grain.

A. van Leeuwenhoek, 18th letter to the Royal Society, 9 October 1676.

CHAPTER OUTLINE

I. Morphology of the Bacteria

II. Fine Cellular Structure

    A. Flagellum

    B. Pili

    C. Capsule

    D. Cell wall

    E. Cell membrane

    F. Cytoplasm

    G. Spores

III. Bacterial Reproduction

    A. Bacterial growth curve

IV. Bacterial Nutrition

    A. Cultivation of the bacteria

    B. Patterns of nutrition

    C. Intermicrobial relationships

    D. Temperature

    E. Oxygen

    F. Acidity/alkalinity

V. Staining of Bacteria

A. Simple stain technique

B. Negative stain technique

C. Gram stain technique

D. Acid fast technique

E. Special stain techniques

OVERVIEW AND OBJECTIVES

While the prokaryotic cell appears simple compared to the eukaryotic cell under the light microscope, you should not make the mistake of thinking that bacteria are simple creatures capable of carrying out only a limited number of functions. The bacterial cell is capable of carrying out all the life functions of higher organisms. And, as we will see in subsequent chapters, it is able to metabolize many compounds that higher organisms are incapable of using as energy sources or as a source of raw materials for the production of cell components. In fact it is a generally held belief among bacteriologists that a bacterium can be found which will degrade any compound; that if you cannot find one now, just leave the compound in the environment for a few years and a bacterium capable of digesting it will evolve. In addition, these organisms can carry out this function without having to develop the many subcellular organelles that eukaryotic cells need.

In this chapter the morphology of prokaryotic organisms is discussed. Morphology is a general term used to describe the physical properties of an organism, including its size, shape, what internal organelles it possesses, and what external appendages it may have. In addition, this chapter describes the kinetics of bacterial growth and the various chemical and physical parameters necessary for the growth of bacteria. These conditions include the nutrients necessary for cultivation of bacteria as well as temperature, oxygen, and pH requirements of microorganisms. The chapter ends with a discussion of the types of stains used to increase the visibility of bacterial cells and their morphological features in the microscope. Without stains, the microbiologist would be unable to identify many of the structures of the bacterial cell in the light microscope or even in the electron microscope. Stains can also be important diagnostic aids.

After reading Chapter 4 of your textbook, you should be able to:

1. Define or identify the following terms: morphology, bacillus, coccus, diplococcus, streptococcus, sarcinae, staphylococcus, spirillum, spirochete, flagellum, monotrichous, lophotrichous, amphitrichous, peritirichous, swarmer, pilus, fimbriae, capsule, cell wall, peptidoglycan, lysozyme, penicillin, gram(-), gram(+), cell membrane, plasma membrane, mitochondria, mesosomes, cytoplasm, ribosomes, volutin, metachromatic granule, bacteriochlorophyll, photosynthesis, chromosome, nucleoid, plasmid, spore, vegetative cell, dipicolinic acid, binary fission, generation time, growth curve, lag phase, logarithmic (log) phase, stationary phase,

decline phase, nutrient agar/broth, selective media, differential media, autotroph, heterotroph, saprobe, parasite, pathogen, symbiosis, nitrogen fixation, mutualism, commensalism, synergism, parasitism, mesophile, psychrophile, thermophile, aerobe, anaerobe, facultative, microaerophilic, simple stain, heat fixation, negative stain, Gram stain, differential stain, acid-fast stain, Mycobacterium, tergitol, spore stain, capsular stain and Center for Disease Control (CDC).

2. List and describe the major morphological features of the bacterial cell. Identify which are common to all bacteria and which may be found in only certain groups of organisms.

3. Describe the physiological role(s) of each organelle you listed.

4. Draw a bacterial growth curve, label all the parts, and explain why you think that the rapid increase of cells is described by a logarithmic function.

5. Outline the various types of media for the cultivation of bacteria and describe the major uses of each.

6. List some of the environmental parameters that must be considered when setting up a bacterial culture.

7. Describe the important types of intermicrobial relationships and distinguish among them.

8. Describe the various types of bacterial stains and their taxonomic and diagnostic uses.

PRE-TEST

1. Spherical bacteria that remain in pairs are called:
   a. cocci.
   b. diplococci.
   c. bacilli.
   d. streptococci.

2. You are observing a bacterium in the microscope which has a single whiplike appendage that allows it to move through the medium. This organism would be said to be:
   a. monotrichously flagellated.
   b. peritrichously flagellated.
   c. monotrichously piliated.
   d. peritrichously piliated.

3. The location of the enzymes for energy production in the prokaryotic bacterial cell is the:
   a. mitochondrium.
   b. cell wall.
   c. cell membrane.
   d. ribosome.

35

4. Bacterial cytoplasm contains all of the following, <u>except</u>:
   a. ribosomes.
   b. chromosomes.
   c. plasmids.
   d. mitochondria.

5. A soil sample is added to a culture medium that has been designed to promote the growth of the genus <u>Pseudomonas</u> while inhibiting the growth of fungi. This test utilizes a(n):
   a. nutrient medium.
   b. natural medium.
   c. differential medium.
   d. minimal medium.

6. Bacteria reproduce by a process known as:
   a. meiosis.
   b. binary fission.
   c. mitosis.
   d. spontaneous generation.

7. The time interval required for all cells in a bacterial population to grow and divide is known as the:
   a. generation time.
   b. lag time.
   c. log time.
   d. division time.

8. You want to increase your ability to see a bacterium in the light microscope and do so by staining the bacterium. The stain you chose leaves the bacterium unstained and accumulates around the cell. You have used a(n):
   a. negative stain.
   b. simple stain.
   c. differential stain.
   d. spore stain.

9. <u>Bergey's</u> <u>Manual</u> classifies in Part 5 those organisms which contain long axial filaments that extend the length of the cell and con- tract to allow motion. These spiral-shaped organisms are known as:
   a. spirilla.
   b. cocci.
   c. spirochetes.
   d. sarcinae.

10. The cell wall contains a rigid macromolecule that is the site of attack by the enzyme lysozyme. This complex molecule is known as:
   a. cell membrane.
   b. penicillin.
   c. Gram's compound.
   d. peptidoglycan.

11. Small molecules of DNA exist in bacteria as circular units. They contain few genes but are extremely important since they carry

traits for drug resistance. These molecules are known as:
a. chromosomes.
b. nucleoids.
c. plasmids.
d. nucleoli.

12. Endospores are heat-stable resting forms of all of the bacteria listed below, except:
a. Bacillus anthracis.
b. Escherichia coli.
c. Clostridium perfringens.
d. Clostridium botulinium.

13. A bacterium characterized as a sarcina has which of the following morphological shapes?
a. rod
b. spherical in long chains
c. spherical in packets of eight
d. spherical

14. A diagnostic stain for Mycobacterium, the organism that causes tuberculosis, is the:
a. acid-fast stain.
b. spore stain.
c. gram stain.
d. negative stain.

15. Bacteria that can grow only in the absence of oxygen are said to be:
a. aerobic.
b. microaerophilic.
c. facultative.
d. anaerobic.

PRACTICE EXERCISES

1. Fill in the blanks. Rod-shaped bacteria are known as (a) _bacilli_ _____, whereas spherical bacteria are said to be (b) _cocci_ _____. Spherical bacteria can be found in several configurations. If they are found in pairs, they are said to be (c) _diplococci_ _____ but if they are found in packets of eight, they are referred to as (d) _sarcina_ _____. (e) _staphylococci_ _____ are found in irregular clusters, which resemble bunches of grapes. Long chains of spherical bacteria are called (f) _streptococci_ _____. Spiral-shaped bacteria are called (g) _spirilla_ _____ or, if they have a long axial filament that extends the length of the cell, as (h) _spirochetes_ _____.

2. On the lines provided identify the type of flagellation exhibited by the cells pictured.

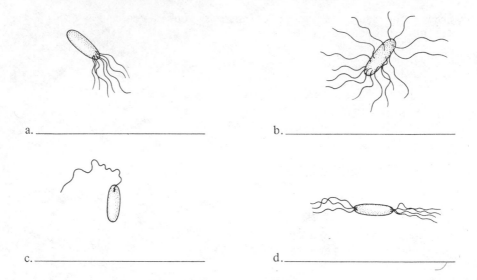

a. _____

b. _____

c. _____

d. _____

3. Identify each of the bacterial cell structures described in the phrases below.

a.   The site of the synthesis of proteins.   *Ribosomes*

b.   The circular molecule of DNA that contains the cell's genes.
     Chromosome

c.   A cell appendage found on many bacterial species. It does not function in motility but has been demonstrated to anchor bacteria to various surfaces.   *pili*

d.   An outer layer of carbohydrates and small proteins that is secreted by the bacterium and adheres to the cell.
     Capsule

e.   The site of energy production in the bacterial cell. It is composed of two layers of protein floating on a double layer of phospholipid material.   *Cell membrane*

f.   Contains the peptidoglycan.   *cellwall*

4. Make a drawing of a typical bacterial growth curve. Label (a) the lag phase, (b) the log phase, (c) the stationary phase, and (d) the decline phase.

start

log

De.

lag

5. Matching. Match the term in the left-hand column with the
   descriptive phrase in the right-hand column.

_1_ a. nutrient agar   1. standard bacterial medium

_4_ b. psychrophile   2. differential medium

_6_ c. aerobe   3. grows at 20 - 45°C

_2_ d. mannitol salts agar   4. grows below 20°C

_3_ e. mesophile   5. grows from 45 - 90°C

_7_ f. anaerobe   6. grows in the presence of
                                    oxygen
_5_ g. thermophile
                                7. will not grow in oxygen
_8_ h. microaerophile
                                8. grows best in reduced
                                    oxygen

6. True or False.

   Decide whether each of the following statements is true or false;
   then place a T for true or an F for false on the line provided.

_T_ a. If two organisms establish a relationship in which they live
       together in a mutually beneficial manner, the relationship is
       symbiotic.

_F_ b. If one organism derives benefit from a relationship while the
       other obtains no benefit or damage, the relationship is a
       parasitic one.

_T_ c. In a synergistic relationship two organisms accomplish together
       what neither can accomplish alone.

_T_ d. A parasitic relationship is established when one organism
       feeds on or in a host and often causes injury to the host.

_F_ e. The relationship of certain autotrophic bacteria with the
       roots of pod-bearing plants where the bacterium fixes nitrogen
       for the plant and the plant provides a stable environment to
       the bacterium is an example of commensalism.

39

7. <u>Fill in the blanks.</u> In the simple stain a (a) _____
such as crystal violet is used. This (b) _____-
_____ dye is attracted to the bacterial cytoplasm which has a (c) _____, and staining
of the cell takes place. Before the stain is applied to the sample,
a droplet of water containing the bacteria must be placed on a
glass slide and (d) _____. Next
the slide is passed through a flame in a process called (e) _____
_____-_____, which bonds the
cells to the slide. The (f) _____
_____ works in an opposite manner, in which the stain
collects around the cell because it is an (g) _____
dye.

8. Fill in the following table, which differentiates between gram-
positive and gram-negative bacteria. (Refer to Table 4.2 if necessary.)

Property	Gram-positive	Gram-negative
Penicillin susceptibility	a._____	b._____
	c._____	d._____
Amount of cell wall lipid	e._____	f._____
	g._____	h._____
Lysozyme susceptibility	i._____	j._____
	k._____	l._____
Toxin produced		
Streptomycin susceptibility		
Typical bacteria		

9. Indicate whether each of the following statements describes the
bacterial flagellum (F) or the bacterial pilus (P); place the appropriate letter on the line provided.

____ a. A structure of adjacent fibrila with no regular pattern.

____ b. Used for motion.

____ c. Occurs on many gram(-) rods and cocci.

____ d. Is needed for conjugation and attachment of the cell to surfaces.

40

_P_ e. It is made up of wound fibers with a hollow center.

_F_ f. It is composed of a protein called flagellin.

_P_ g. It is narrower (0.007 um to 0.008 um in width) and somewhat shorter (0.5 um to 20 um in length).

CONCEPT EXERCISES

1. In her research, a microbiologist has isolated a mutant (genetic variant) of a motile strain of bacteria that no longer can swim. When she observes the bacteria after staining them with a special staining procedure which stains flagella, she cannot identify any flagella. She reasons that the mutation could lead either to the loss of the ability of the cell to make the proteins necessary for the production of flagella or to the loss of the ability to as- semble the flagellar components into mature flagella. What techni- ques could the microbiologist use to determine whether the cell is making flagellar components, and for which flagellar components would she look?

_____

_____

_____

_____

_____

_____

2. Utilizing the knowledge you have gained to date in your study of microbiology, what morphological features of the following bacteria could you predict from their scientific name?

a. Bacillus megaterium:

_____

b. Sarcina littoralis:

_____

c. Bacillus sterothermophilus:

_____

d. Streptococcus pyogenes:

_____

e. Clostridium butyricum:

f. _Paraspirillum_ <u>vejdovskii</u>:

3. An organism has been discovered living in a hot spring well below
   the earth's surface. There is little organic material in the hot
   spring; the water from the hot spring is quite acidic. A team of
   researchers wants to grow this organism in your laboratory. They
   have been working with an organism isolated from the blood of a
   patient in a nearby hospital, and they want to make sure the cultures of the hot-spring organism do not become contaminated with
   the blood organism. What culture conditions might they set up to
   favor the growth of the hot-spring organism and inhibit the growth
   of the blood organism?

POST-TEST

1. An organism that grows at 5°C is classified as a(n):
   a. mesophile.
   b. psychrophile.
   c. thermophile.
   d. facultative organism.

2. All of the following are characteristics of the bacterial flagellum,
   <u>except</u>:
   a. It is composed of flagellin.
   b. It has a hooklike insertion to a basal granule inside the cell
      wall.
   c. It is used in conjugation.
   d. It is composed of adjacent fibrils with no regular pattern.

3. You have isolated an organism from the human intestinal tract and
   find that it grows better when you stopped the culture flask with
   a semiporous plug than when you use a plug which is completely

permeable to oxygen. This organism should be classified as a(n):

a. aerobe.
b. anaerobe.
c. facultative organism.
d. microaerophile.

4. Spherical organisms arranged in random groups of cells that resemble bunches of grapes are referred to as:
a. staphylococci.
b. streptococci.
c. sarcinae.
d. cocci.

5. An organism that has flagella over its entire surface is classified as:
a. monotrichous.
b. lophotrichous.
c. peritrichous.
d. amphitrichous.

6. A relationship between two organisms together can accomplish things that neither one of them can accomplish alone is called:
a. symbiotic.
b. commensal.
c. mutualistic.
d. synergistic.

7. The internal environment of most bacteria is at pH:
a. 7.0
b. 4.0
c. 9.0
d. 2.0

8. Penicillin is an antibiotic that prevents the synthesis of the bacterial:
a. cell membrane.
b. ribosomes.
c. cell wall.
d. flagella.

9. You have isolated a bacterium that has the ability to trap light energy and convert it to chemical energy. You would expect this organism to contain which of the following compounds that would not be expected in cells which do not have the ability to photo-synthesize?
a. ribosomes
b. bacteriochlorophyll
c. nucleoids
d. plasmids

10. Traditionally, tomatoes could be canned without fear of botulism poisoning. Today, however, people must be more careful in canning tomatoes because of the development of new strains of tomatoes. Which of the following properties of the new strains is the cause

11. Bacteria that retain crystal violet-iodine stain after treatment with the decolorizer alcohol-acetone are classified as:
    a. gram(-).
    b. gram(+).
    c. acid fast.
    d. spore formers.

12. The federal agency specifically charged with protecting the public health of the nation by providing leadership and direction in the prevention and control of disease and other preventable conditions is known as:
    a. National Institutes of Health.
    b. United States Public Health Service.
    c. Walter Reed Hospital.
    d. Center for Disease Control.

13. As nutrients are depleted and waste products accumulate in a bacterial culture tube, bacterial death begins to slow the population's growth, and the culture enters the:
    a. lag phase.
    b. log phase.
    c. stationary phase.
    d. decline phase.

14. As a culture of Clostridium enters the decline phase of growth the vegetative cells will have developed into:
    a. inviable cells.
    b. endospores.
    c. stationary vegetative cells.
    d. aerobic variants.

15. A medium that selects for one species or group of bacteria while at the same time selecting against other groups of organisms is said to be:
    a. differential.
    b. natural.
    c. synthetic.
    d. enriching.

ANSWERS TO EXERCISES

Pre-Test

1. b	6. b	11. c
2. a	7. a	12. b
3. c	8. a	13. c
4. d	9. c	14. a
5. c	10. d	15. d

Practice Exercises

1. a. bacilli; b. cocci; c. diplococci; d. sarcina;
   e. Staphylococci; f. streptococci; g. spirilla;
   h. spirochetes.

2. a. lophotrichous; b. peritrichous; c. monotrichous;
   d. amphitrichous. (All answers to this exercise can be found
   in Figure 4.3.)

3. a. ribosome; b. chromosome; c. pili;
   d. capsule; e. cell membrane; f. cell wall.

4.

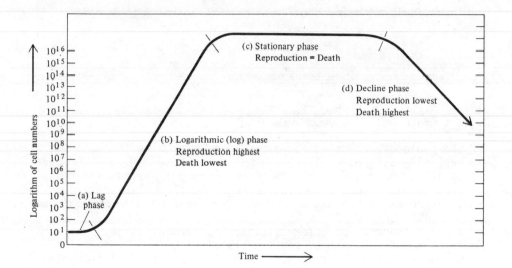

5. a. 1;   b. 4;   c. 6;   d. 2;

   e. 3;   f. 7;   g. 5;   h. 8;

6. a. T;   b. F;   c. T;   d. T;   e.   f.

7. a. basic dye; b. positive-charged; c. negative charge;

   d. air dried; e. heat-fixation; f. negative stain; g. acid.

8. a. more susceptible; b. less susceptible; c. low;

   d. high; e. more susceptible; f. less susceptible;

   g. exotoxin; h. endotoxin; i. less susceptible; j. more

   susceptible; k. spore-forming rods, many cocci; l. many

   intestinal rods, few cocci.

9. a. F; b. F; c. P; d. P; e. P; f. F; g. P.

Concept Exercises

1. She could use the electron microscope to examine the cell for
   partially assembled flagella. She might look for hooks or basal
   bodies. She could also develop an antiserum against the flagellin
   protein of the bacterium and test the nonflagellate strain to see
   if it contains protein molecules which reacted with the antibody.

2. a. Rod-shaped, spore former, aerobic, perhaps large.
   b. Cocci in packets of eight cells.
   c. Rod-shaped, spore former, aerobic, probably is a thermophile.
   d. Cocci in long chains.
   e. Rod-shaped, spore former, anaerobic.
   f. spiral-shaped cells.

3. Grow at a high temperature (above 45°C) because it is probably a
   thermophile. Grow anaerobically (probably anaerobic, since it is
   found deep inside the earth). Grow on a synthetic medium, as it
   probably does not require many organic compounds. Grow at an acid
   pH because the water from which it was isolated was acidic and it
   can probably tolerate low pH. The blood organism is most likely
   a mesophile, aerobic, requires several to many organic nutrients,
   and grows best at pH 7.0.

Post-Test

1. b	6. d	11. b
2. c	7. a	12. d
3. d	8. c	13. c
4. a	9. b	14. b
5. c	10. b	15. a

5   Bacterial Metabolism

The immediate principles of living bodies would be, to a degree, indestructible if, of all the organisms created by God, the smallest and apparently most useless were to be suppressed. And because the return to the atmosphere and to the mineral kingdom of everything which had ceased to live would be suddenly suspended, life would become impossible.

Louis Pasteur

CHAPTER OUTLINE

   I. Enzymes and Cellular Energy Reactions

      A. Enzymes

      B. Energy

  II. Catabolism of Carbohydrates

      A. Carbohydrate catabolism by aerobic respiration

      B. Glycolysis

      C. The Krebs cycle

      D. Oxidative phosphorylation

      E. Catabolism of other carbohydrates

      F. Carbohydrate catabolism by anaerobic respiration

      G. Fermentation

 III. Catabolism of Proteins and Fats

  IV. Anabolism of Carbohydrates and Fats

      A. Photosynthesis in microorganisms

      B. Anabolism of fats

   V. Anabolism of Proteins

      A. Transcription

      B. Translation

      C. Control of protein anabolism

OVERVIEW AND OBJECTIVES

In Pasteur's famous quote above, he points out that the bacteria have
an important place in the cycling of elements. It is their responsi-
bility to degrade organic materials and return the important elements
they contain to the inorganic reservoirs to be reused for new life.
It is from the decay of organic materials that the bacterium obtains
its energy for life. The spectrum of organic compounds that can be
degraded by bacteria is almost unlimited. In fact, the story is told
that when the famous bacterial physiologist and taxonomist C. B. Van Neil
was surveying the metabolism of the microbial world, he would go into
the laboratory and pull a chemical off the shelf at random. He would
then incorporate it into a growth medium, sprinkle a little dirt in
the culture and isolate a bacterial species that could use the compound
to supply its energy needs. In other words, the metabolism of bacteria
taken as a whole is very diverse. It does follow certain patterns,
however, and this chapter will introduce the major themes that are repeated, with variations, throughout the microbial--and indeed the entire biological--world.

Metabolism is divided into two general processes: catabolism, the
digestion of organic materials; and anabolism, the biosynthesis of
organic compounds. To live, an organism must carry out both of these
processes. The major metabolic tool of the cell is the enzyme. Enzymes
are biological catalysts that increase the speed of a reaction without
entering into it themselves (see Chapter 2).

The major function of catabolism is to gain for the cell the energy
stored in the high-energy phosphate bonds of adenosine triphosphate
(ATP). This energy can be released when needed by splitting ATP into
adenosine diphosphate (ADP) and inorganic phosphate. When a biological
process releases energy that can be trapped in ATP, it is referred to
as respiration. Catabolic processes that occur in the presence of
oxygen are referred to as aerobic respirations; those that take place
in the absence of oxygen are anaerobic respirations. Major respiratory
processes in the catabolism of carbohydrates are: (a) glycolysis,
which splits a 6-carbon glucose molecule into two 3-carbon pyruvic acid
molecules; (b) the Krebs cycle, which under aerobic conditions converts
the pyruvate produced in glycolysis into carbon dioxide; (c) oxidative
phosphorylation, which utilizes important coenzymes that are chemically
reduced in the Krebs cycle to produce ATP; and (d) fermentation, which
under anaerobic conditions converts the pyruvate produced in glycolysis
into other organic materials extracting some energy as ATP in the process. Proteins and fats are also catabolized by bacteria to produce
energy.

Anabolic processes are usually energy-requiring but some, such as
photosynthesis, produce energy and are, hence, a form of respiration.
In bacterial photosynthesis light energy from the sun is trapped by
bacteriochlorophyll to produce ATP. This energy can then be used to
reduce CO_2 to carbohydrate [$(CH_2O)_n$]. Carbohydrate can be stored in
the form of fat for use at a later time.

The anabolism of proteins by the cell is an important and involved process. Proteins are important as enzymes and structural components of the cell. Their function is determined by the specific sequence of amino acids that make them up. The information for the synthesis of these specific sequences is stored in the DNA of the cell and converted into protein by a two-step process. In the first step, transcription, an exact complementary ribonucleic acid (RNA) copy of the DNA is made. In the second step, translation, the message in the RNA is converted into a sequence of amino acids. Translation takes place on the ribosome.

After you have read Chapter 5 of your textbook, you should be able to:

1. Define or identify each of the following terms: metabolism, anabolism, catabolism, enzyme, substrate, end product, cofactor, coenzyme, adenosine triphosphate (ATP), aerobic respiration, anaerobic respiration, glycolysis, Embden-Meyerhof Pathway, Krebs cycle, oxidative phosphorylation, nicotinamide adenine dinucleotide (NAD), flavin adenine dinucleotide (FAD), cytochromes, fermentation, deamination, fatty-acid spiral, photosynthesis, chlorophyll, ferredoxin, bacteriochlorophyll, deoxyribonucleic acid (DNA), ribonucleic acid (RNA), gene, transcription, translation, swivelase, RNA polymerase, ribosomal RNA (rRNA), ribosomes, messenger RNA (mRNA), codon, genetic code, transfer RNA (tRNA), anticodon, peptide bond, guanosine triphosphage (GTP), structural gene, operator gene, repressor gene, operon, repressor protein, and inducer.

2. Describe the importance of enzymes to the cell and explain how they carry out their functions.

3. Explain how the cell stores energy for use at a later time.

4. Outline the major processes of aerobic and anaerobic respiration in the bacterial cell and tabulate the amount of ATP obtained from each.

5. Describe the process of bacterial photosynthesis and explain how the process is carried out without the liberation of O_2.

6. Discuss the anabolism of proteins and explain how the process is controlled.

PRE-TEST

1. Any process that releases energy is referred to as:
   a.   metabolism.
   b.   respiration.
   c.   catabolism.
   d.   anabolism.

2. Proteins that bring about chemical changes while remaining essenti- ally unchanged are best referred to as:
   a.   enzymes.
   b.   catalysts.
   c.   coenzymes.

d.   cofactors.

3. Energy is stored in the cell for later use as:
   a.   ADP.
   b.   carbohydrates.
   c.   ATP.
   d.   fats.

4. The essential step in the catabolism of amino acids is a process
   known as:
   a.   glycolysis.
   b.   the Krebs cycle.
   c.   deamination.
   d.   fermentation.

5. In the operon, genes that code for enzyme proteins are called:
   a.   structural genes.
   b.   operator genes.
   c.   repressor genes.
   d.   inducer genes.

6. The production of RNA from DNA is known as:
   a.   transduction.
   b.   transformation.
   c.   translation.
   d.   transcription.

7. The catabolic process in which glucose is converted into pyruvic
   acid is:
   a.   glycolysis.
   b.   the Krebs cycle.
   c.   fermentation.
   d.   oxidative phosphorylation.

8. A bacterium that utilizes glucose as an energy source has been
   isolated. The bacterium will grow in an anaerobic environment.
   After the growth of the bacterium, the pH of the growth medium is
   measured and found to be very acidic. When analyzed, the medium
   is found to have a high concentration of lactic acid. This
   bacterium is most likely metabolizing by a process known as:
   a.   aerobic respiration.
   b.   the Krebs cycle.
   c.   oxidative phosphorylation.
   d.   fermentation.

9. If you measured the net number of moles of ATP produced per mole
   of glucose metabolized by the organism in exercise 8, you would
   probably find the number to be:
   a.   2.
   b.   38.
   c.   4.
   d.   19.

10. In oxidative phosphorylation, _____ moles of ATP

are produced from each molecule of $NADH^+ + H^+$.
a. 1
b. 2
c. 3
d. 4

11. The molecule containing the codon is:
a. tRNA.
b. mRNA.
c. rRNA.
d. DNA.

12. In the general reaction for the catabolism of carbohydrates, the six moles of water are produced during:
a. glycolysis.
b. fermentation.
c. the Krebs cycle.
d. oxidative phosphorylation.

13. The process that produces the most ATP during the catabolism of glucose is:
a. glycolysis.
b. fermentation.
c. the Krebs cycle.
d. oxidative phosphorylation.

14. A nonphotosynthetic autotrophic bacterium that oxidizes ammonium ions into nitrite to form ATP has been isolated. This organism is classified in the genus:
a. Rhodopseudomonas.
b. Nitrobacter.
c. Nitrosomonas.
d. Pseudomonas.

15. The information for the synthesis of enzymes if ultimately stored in:
a. DNA.
b. RNA.
c. protein.
d. carbohydrate.

PRACTICE EXERCISES

1. Refer to Figure 5.1. Write the reactions in glycolysis at which ATP is either (a) utilized or (b) produced.

a. _____

_____

b. _____

_____

2. For each of the reactions listed below, determine how many mole of ATP are <u>ultimately</u> produced either directly or through oxidative phosphorylation. You may wish to refer to Figures 5.4, 5.5, and 5.8 of your textbook as you answer this question.

   a. Alpha-ketoglutaric acid ⟶ succinic acid: _____

   b. Fructose-6-phosphate ⟶ fructose-1-6-diphosphate: _____

   c. Malic acid ⟶ oxaloacetic acid: _____

   d. Succinic acid ⟶ funaric acid: _____

   e. Phosphoenolpyruvic acid ⟶ pyruvic acid: _____

   f. Pyruvic acid ⟶ lactic acid: _____

3. <u>True or False</u>. Decide whether each of the following statements is true or false; then place a T for true or an F for false on the line provided.

   __F__ a. During the complete aerobic respiration of one mole of glucose to carbon dioxide and water, 19 moles of ATP are produced.

   __T__ b. Any process of catabolism or anabolism that leads to the production of energy is called respiration.

   __T__ c. The process of <u>translation</u> can be summarized by the general reaction: RNA ⟶ protein.

   __F__ d. Each of the 64 codons of the genetic code is translated into one and only one amino acid.

   __F__ e. Yeast carries out a fermentation that converts pyruvic acid into lactic acid.

   __T__ f. In the Embden-Meyerhof Pathway a net synthesis of two moles of ATP per mole of glucose takes place.

4. <u>Fill in the blanks</u>. In order for a (a) chemical _____ reaction to take place, (b) energy _____ must be supplied to the system. This is because (c) covalent _____ bonds are not easily rearranged unless the (d) electrons _____ are energized, and the atoms are forced apart into new combinations. (e) _____ enzymes _____ play an important role in the chemistry of the cell because they (f) lower _____ the amount of (g) _____ energy _____ required for a reation to take place.

5. For each of the codons listed below give (1) the amino acid for which it codes and (2) the anticodon found in the tRNA. (Refer to Table 5.1, if necessary.)

   a. UUU: 1. _____   2. _____

b. UGU: 1. _____   2. _____

c. UAG: 1. _____   2. _____

d. AUG: 1. _____   2. _____

e. UUC: 1. _____   2. _____

6. Each of the following statements describes the role of a certain molecule or structure in the anabolism of protein. Identify the molecule or structure.

a. This molecule contains the genes that code for proteins.
   _____

b. This enzyme links the components of RNA into an exact copy of the gene. _____

c. These molecules contain the codons. _____

d. This structure is part of the tRNA, which interacts with the codon. _____

e. The organelle on which translation takes place.
   _____

f. Although transcribed, this molecule is not translated but becomes a structural part of the ribosome. _____

g. The triplet of bases that code for an amino acid.
   _____

h. The enzyme that unwinds DNA during transcription.
   _____

i. The process described by the general reaction: DNA ——→ RNA.
   _____

j. The energy source for peptide-bond formation. _____

7. Identify each of the following reactions as occurring in glycolysis (G), the Krebs cycle (K), fermentation (F), protein anabolism (P) fat catabolism (FC), or fat anabolism (FA); place the appropriate letter on the line provided.

_____ a. 2 amino acids ——→ amino acid-amino acid

_____ b. Malic acid ——→ oxaloacetic acid

_____ c. Citric acid ——→ alpha-ketoglutaric acid

_____ d. Glucose ——→ glucose-6-phosphate

_____ e.   Pyruvic acid ⟶ acetaldehyde

_____ f.   Pyruvic acid ⟶ lactic acid

_____ g.   Pyrivic acid ⟶ acetyl-CoA

_____ h.   Glycerol + fatty acids ⟶ fats

_____ i.   Phsophoenolpyruvic acid ⟶ pyruvic acid

_____ j.   Fatty acid ⟶ ⟶ acetyl-CoA

CONCEPT EXERCISES

1. The metabolism of an aerobic bacterium that is able to catabolize
   fats as a source of energy is being studied. Reactions in this
   process are followed through the use of radioactive tracers. As-
   sume that the organism is fed fats labeled as indicated below. In
   what compounds would you expect to find the radioactivity and why?

   a.   Fats containing [^{14}C]glycerol:

   _____

   _____

   _____

   b.   Fats containing [^{14}C]fatty acids:

   _____

   _____

   _____

2. Yeasts are facultative organisms. Explain why it is important to
   the production of wine to keep the environment free of oxygen.

   _____

   _____

   _____

3. The enzyme beta-galactosidase carries out the reaction:

   lactose ⟶ glucose + galactose.

   It has been found that if Escherichia coli is grown in a medium
   containing glucose, little of this enzyme can be found in the cell.
   If E. coli is grown in a medium containing lactose in place of
   glucose, very high levels of this enzyme are found. Explain these
   observations.

POST-TEST

1. The digestion of organic material is referred to collectively as:
   a. anabolism.
   b. catabolism.
   c. deamination.
   d. glycolysis.

2. The aerobic bacterium Pseudomonas aeruginosa is fed glucose and the products from the bacterial respriation is measured. You would expect to find:
   a. CO_2.
   b. ATP.
   c. CO_2 and H_2O.
   d. CO_2, H_2O, and ATP.

3. After inspecting Figure 5.4, identify the reaction(s) in which ATP is utilized.
   a. Fructose-6-phosphate $\longrightarrow$ fructose-1-6-diphosphate
   b. Diphosphoglyceric acid $\longrightarrow$ 3-phosphoglyceric acid
   c. Phosphoenolpyruvic acid $\longrightarrow$ pyruvic acid
   d. Alpha-ketoglytaric acid $\longrightarrow$ succinic acid

4. Bacterial photosynthesis can be distinguished from plant photo-synthesis because it fails to produce:
   a. ATP.
   b. glucose.
   c. reducing power.
   d. oxygen.

5. Inorganic ions that compose parts of enzymes are referred to as:
   a. coenzymes.
   b. substrates.
   c. cofactors.
   d. collaborators.

6. Enzymes that transfer phosphate from one molecule to another are called:
   a. kinases.
   b. transaminases.
   c. oxidases.
   d. peptidases.

7. You are studying an anaerobic organism. Which of the following pathways would you expect to be carried out in this organism?
   a. the Krebs cycle
   b. glycolysis
   c. oxidative phosphorylation
   d. the respiration of fatty acids

8. The reaction that allows the catabolism of galactose through glycolysis is:
   a. Glucose-1-phosphate————>glucose-1-6-diphosphate.
   b. Galactose-1-phosphate————>galactose-1-6-diphosphage.
   c. Galactose-1-phosphate————>glucose-1-phosphate.
   d. Galactose-1-phosphate————>fructose-1-phosphate.

9. The number of moles of ATP produced per mole of glucose by the Krebs cycle is:
   a. 38.
   b. 2.
   c. 28.
   d. 34.

10. In anaerobic respiration, all of the following molecules can be used as final electron acceptors, except:

   a. NO_3^-.

   b. O_2.

   c. $SO_4^=$.

   d. NO_2^-.

11. The general reaction amino acids————>Protein is carried out on the:
    a. chromosome.
    b. ribosome.
    c. cell membrane.
    d. pili.

12. The mRNA that codes for a particular protein will have _____ _____ nucleotides for each amino acid in the protein.
    a. 1
    b. 2
    c. 3
    d. 4

13. The removal of an amino group from an amino acid with the substitution of a hydroxyl group is known as:
    a. deamination.
    b. dehydroxylation.
    c. peptidation.
    d. peptide bond formation.

14. The structure and function of a protein is ultimately controlled

by the sequence of:
   a. amino acids.
   b. nucleotides in DNA.
   c. nucleotides in mRNA.
   d. nucleotides in tRNA.

15. The energy for protein anabolism is supplied by:
   a. ATP.
   b. ADP.
   c. GTP.
   d. GDP.

ANSWERS TO EXERCISES

Pre-Test

1. b	6. d	11. b
2. a	7. a	12. d
3. c	8. d	13. d
4. c	9. a	14. c
5. a	10. c	15. a

Practice Exercises

1. a. ATP is utilized in the following reactions:

   Glucose ———→glucose-6-phosphate

   Fructose-6-phosphate———→fructose-1,6-diphosphate

   b. ATP is generated in the following reactions:

   Diphosphoglyceric acid———→3-phosphoglyceric acid

   Phosphoenolpyruvic acid———→pyruvic acid

   (All answers to this exercise can be found in Figure 5.1.)

2. a. 4 (Figure 5.5); b. 0 (Figure 5.4); c. 3 (Figure 5.5);
   d. 2 (Figure 5.5); 3. 1 (Figure 5.4); f. o (Figure 5.8).

3. a. F;   b. T;   c. T;   d. F (Table 5.1);
   e. F;   f. T.

4. a. chemical; b. energy; c. covalent; d. electrons;
   e. Enzymes; f. lower; g. energy.

5. a. 1. phenylalanine, 2. AAA; b. 1. cysteine, 2. ACA;
   c. 1. chain terminator, 2. since this does not code for an amino

acid, there is no anticodon;
d. 1. methinonine, 2. UAC;
e. 1. phenylalanine, 2. AAG. (All answers to this exercise can be found in Table 5.1 and on page 46.)

6. a. DNA;   b. RNA polymerase;   c. mRNA;
   d. anticodon;   e. ribosome;   f. rRNA;
   g. codon;   h. swiverlase;   i. transcription;
   j. GTP.

7. a. P;   b. K (Figure 5.5); c. K (Figure 5.5);
   d. G (Figure 5.4); e. F (Figure 5.8); f. F (Figure 5.8);
   g. K (Figure 5.5); h. FA (Figure 5.21); i. G (Figure 5.4);
   j. FC.

Concept Exercises

1. a. Glycerol enters glycolysis at dihydroxyacetone phosphate and from there will continue through glycolysis and the Krebs cycle. The radioactivity will end up as carbon dioxide.

   b. The fatty acids will enter the pathway at acetyl-CoA and continue through the Krebs cycle. The radioactivity will again end up as carbon dioxide.

2. Aerobically, yeast will metabolize glucose through the Krebs cycle to carbon dioxide and water. To obtain alcohol, the yeast must carry out the anaerobic fermentation of glucose to ethyl alcohol.

3. The synthesis of the enzyme beta-galactosidase is under the control of an operon. Its synthesis is induced by the presence of lactose in the cell environment. When E. coli is grown on glucose, lactose is not present and the synthesis of the enzyme is repressed. When the bacteria are grown on lactose, the synthesis of the enzyme is induced and large amounts are found in the cell.

Post-Test

1. b	6. a	11. b
2. d	7. b	12. c
3. a	8. c	13. a
4. d	9. d	14. b
5. c	10. b	15. c

6 Bacterial Genetics

Rigorous proof that the gene is DNA and not protein appeared in 1944, when Oswald Avery and fellow workers at the Rockefeller Institute in New York published a paper in The Journal of Experimental Medicine about inheritable transformations that occur in a strain of pneumonia bacteria when they are mixed with DNA extracted from a different strain. Avery's paper is today universally cited as fundamental, always with the reservation that the proof took years to be credited. In February 1944, when the paper appeared, Crick was working for the British Admiralty as a physicist, designing naval mines, and Watson was a precocious college boy in Chicago, consumed by ornithology the way another might have been absorbed in railway timetables. When they met, seven years later, both knew of Avery's work, though then and for several years more it was still generally believed and widely asserted that genes are protein.

> Horace Freeland Judson, The Eighth Day of Creation: Makers of the Revolution in Biology. New York: Simon and Schuster, 1979.

CHAPTER OUTLINE

   I.   The Bacterial Chromosome

    A.   Duplication of the chromosome

  II.   Bacterial Mutation

    A.   Types of mutations

    B.   Effect of mutations

 III.   Bacterial Recombination

    A.   Transformation

    B.   Conjugation

    C.   High frequency recombination

    D.   Plasmids

    E.   Transduction

  IV.   Genetic Engineering

    A.   Sticky-ends and plasmids

    B.   Modern applications

OVERVIEW AND OBJECTIVES

In 1944, Avery, MacLeod, and McCarty stated in the discussion of their
paper on the transformation of pneumonia cocci: "If however, the
biologically active substance [DNA] isolated . . . actually proves to
be the transforming principle, as the available evidence strongly suggests, then nucleic acids of this type must be regarded not merely as
structurally important but as functionally active in determining the
biochemical activities and specific characteristics of pneumococcal
cells." At that time they had no idea of the revolution they would
cause in the scientific world. Before publication of the paper, biologists believed that protein was the "genetic material" and nucleic
acid was only a kind of framework that held the chromosome together.
Yet within ten years, Watson and Crick had defined the structure of
DNA and explained how it might code for the information needed to con-
struct an entire living cell; geneticists were well on their way to
understanding the chemical nature of Gregor Mendel's "genetic markers."
This chapter examines DNA and the mechanisms by which variation in the
genetic information are introduced into bacteria and other cells. In
addition, it describes one of the most important developments in modern
genetics: development of the techniques of genetic engineering.

DNA replicates by a semiconservative mechanism, which ensures that
exact copies of the molecule are made. A mechanism for the exact
replication of DNA is important because DNA controls all biochemical
activities of the cell through its role as the genetic material.
Variation can be introduced into the molecules, however, through the
processes of mutation and recombination. This variation is important
because it allows for biological evolution and the ability of organisms
to adapt to changing environments.

Mutations result from modifications of the sequence of bases in
chromosomal DNA so that the sequence of amino acids in the protein
product is altered. Mutations may involve only one base pair (point
mutations) or large segments of DNA (generalized mutations).

Recombination refers to a process in which a piece of DNA from
one source (e.g., a bacterial cell) is inserted into another molecule
of DNA (e.g., the chromosome of another bacterial cell). In bacteria
the transfer of DNA can take place by three different processes: (1)
transformation--the absorption of free DNA from the external environment; (2) conjugation--a parasexual process where a donor (male) cell
transfers DNA to a recipient (female) cell through cell-to-cell contact;
and (3) transduction--the transfer of DNA from one cell to another
through a bacteriophage intermediate.

One of the most revolutionary developments in biology during the
1970s was the introduction of techniques that allow the insertion of
genetic material into a bacterial chromosome by biochemical means.
These techniques are referred to collectively as genetic engineering
or recombinant DNA techniques. These techniques have already been
used successfully in medical, agricultural, and industrial applications.

After you have read Chapter 6 of your textbook, you should be able to:

1. Define or identify the following terms: gene, chromosome, DNA, mutation, recombination, genetic engineering, locus, DNA polymerase, Okazaki fragements, DNA ligase, semiconservative replication, nucleoid, mutagen, mutant, point mutation, generalized mutation, spontaneous mutation, environmental mutagen, induced mutation, analogs, lethal mutation, transformation, conjugation, F+ cell, F- cell, fertility factor, Hfr cell, F-prime, sexduction, diploid, haploid, plasmid, episome, transferable drug resistance factors, transduction, bacteriophage, lytic cycle, virulent phage, repressor protein, prophage, lysogeny, temperate phage, specialized trans-duction, generalized transduction, endonuclease, restriction enzyme, "sticky-ends," chimeras, and reverse transcriptase.

2. Outline the process of semiconservative replication of DNA, and list the enzymes involved.

3. Explain how the process of mutation introduces variation into the genetic material.

4. Describe the various mechanisms of DNA transfer found in bacteria.

5. Distinguish between generalized and specialized transduction.

6. Distinguish among F+, F-, Hfr, and F-prime cells.

7. Identify the "tools" of genetic engineering and describe how they work, and list some of the uses to which genetic engineering has been put in the fields of medicine and agriculture.

PRE-TEST

1. Mutations arising from chance events in the environment are known as:
   a. point mutations.
   b. spontaneous mutations.
   c. environmental mutations.
   d. induced mutation.

2. You have carried out a conjugation and discovered that the recipient cells have almost all become donors, but that no chromosomal genes have been transferred. The male cell in the original mating was a(n):
   a. F+ cell.
   b. Hfr cell.
   c. F- cell.
   d. F-prime cell.

3. Avery, MacLeod, and McCarty demonstrated that pneumonia cocci could absorb DNA directly from the medium surrounding them. This is an example of:
   a. mutation.
   b. conjugation.

c. transduction.
d. transformation.

4. In one form of DNA transfer in bacteria, the DNA is transferred from one cell to another in a bacteriophage. If all fragments of the bacterial chromosome are transferred with equal frequency, the process is referred to as:
a. specialized transformation.
b. specialized transduction.
c. generalized transformation.
d. generalized transduction.

5. Through the techniques of genetic engineering, you have produced a plasmid that contains a gene for human insulin. Such a plasmid is called a(n):
a. episome.
b. chimera.
c. F-prime.
d. endonuclease.

6. Diphtheria organisms contain a bacteriophage that codes for toxin produced during disease. This is a consequence of the phenomenon known as:
a. lytic growth.
b. genetic engineering.
c. lysogeny.
d. temperate growth.

7. An enzyme that synthesizes DNA from mRNA is:
a. DNA polymerase.
b. DNA ligase.
c. restriction endonuclease.
d. reverse transcriptase.

8. Plasmids that can attach to the bacterial chromosome are called:
a. episomes.
b. prophage.
c. chimeras.
d. F factors.

9. A phage that cannot establish lysogeny in its host is referred to as:
a. lytic.
b. virulent.
c. generalized transducing.
d. specialized transducing.

10. When a bacteriophage DNA integrates into the host cell's chromosome, it is called a(n):
a. episome.
b. temperate phage.
c. prophage.
d. lytic phage.

11. A mutant that will grow under laboratory conditions but will not
    survive if it escapes into the environment is referred to as a(n):
    a. safe mutant.
    b. environmental mutant.
    c. lethal mutant.
    d. point nutant.

12. The enzyme that joins together the DNA fragments produced during
    DNA replication is called:
    a. DNA ligase.
    b. DNA polymerase.
    c. Okazaki enzyme.
    d. the restriction enzyme.

13. The chromosome region of a bacterial cell is referred to as the:
    a. nucleus.
    b. nucleolus.
    c. nucleoid.
    d. nuclear body.

14. The sequence of bases in a DNA molecule is changed by all of the
    following processes, except:
    a. recombination.
    b. duplication.
    c. genetic engineering.
    d. mutation.

15. One process by which pathogenic bacteria acquire drug resistance
    from harmless organisms is termed:
    a. conjugation.
    b. transferable drug resistance.
    c. transformation.
    d. transduction.

PRACTICE EXERCISES

1. Diagram the semiconservative replication of DNA through two
   generations of cell growth.

2. Fill in the blanks. If an incorrect base exists on the DNA molecule, the (a) _____ _____ will be miscoded, and the correct (b) _____ _____ will not be matched into position on the (c) _____ molecule. This is known as a (d) _____ _____. Other, more (e) _____ _____ occur from physical damage to the (f) _____, such as breaks in the molecule, deletion of entire sets of genes, or rearrangement of the genes. Mutations are classified as one of two types. Mutations arising from chance events in the environment are known as (g) _____ mutations. (h) _____ mutations are the second major type of mutations. These mutations are brought about by subjecting the (i) _____ to mutagens under controlled laboratory conditions.

3. For each type of conjugational mating described below, indicate (1) the frequency of recipient cells that will become donors and (2) the approximate fraction of chromosomal genes that can be transferred.

   a. F+ X F-:   1. _____   2. _____

   b. Hfr X F-:   1. _____   2. _____

   c. F-prime X F-: 1. _____   2. _____

4. Match the term in the left-hand column with the correct statement in the right-hand column by placing the correct number on the line provided.

   __6__ a. F-prime   1. phage-mediated DNA transfer

   __3__ b. Transformation

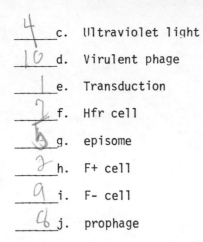

___4___ c. Ultraviolet light

___10__ d. Virulent phage

___1___ e. Transduction

___7___ f. Hfr cell

___6___ g. episome

___2___ h. F+ cell

___9___ i. F- cell

___6___ j. prophage

2. F factor separate from chromosome

3. absorbtion of DNA from environment

4. environmental mutagen

5. plasmid in chromosome

6. F factor containing part of the chromosome

7. F factor in chromosome

8. viral DNA in chromosome

9. recipient cell

10. can establish lysogeny

5. Show with a diagram how each of the mutagens listed below can cause mutation in DNA.

   a. Nitrite ions:

   b. Ultraviolet light:

6. Fill in the blanks. Interest in genetic manipulations was heightened in the 1960s with the isolation of a group of enzymes called (a) _____. These enzymes could split a DNA molecule at a specific point and could therefore open a plasmid where scientists wished. These enzymes are also known as (b) _____ enzymes because they operate at (c) _____ points on the molecule. These enzymes have been used to insert foreign DNA into (d) _____, creating recombined molecules known as (e) _____. This technique is referred to as (f) _____ _____.

7. True or False. Decide whether each of the following statements is true or false; then place a T for true or an F for false on the line provided.

_F_ a. No matter what kind of DNA is taken up by the cell during transformation, only double-stranded DNA is incorporated into the bacterial chromosome.

_F_ b. When the male cell in a conjugation in an Hfr, almost all of the recipient cells in the mating will be converted into donors.

_T_ c. F factor stands for "fertility factor" because, under the right conditions, it promotes transfer of the bacterial chromosome.

_T_ d. A cell having two copies of each gene is referred to as diploid.

_T_ e. Because it is an episome the F factor is essential for the growth of the bacterial cell.

_T_ f. Enzymes that split DNA at specific points are called restriction endonucleases.

_F_ g. Chemical compounds known collectively as "analogs" cause mutations because they closely resemble amino acids in structure.

_T_ h. As an environmental mutagen, ultraviolet light is capable of
causing "spontaneous mutations."

_T_ i. Three important medical compounds now being produced through
genetic engineering are insulin, interferon, and human growth
hormone.

_T_ j. In 1980, the U.S. Supreme Court decided that laboratory-engineered
organisms were patentable.

CONCEPT EXERCISES

1. A biologist is working with a bacterial species that has not pre-
viously been reported to have a DNA transfer system. He discovers
that DNA is being transferred from one strain to another. What
kinds of experiments might he do to determine whether this "gene-
transfer" system is (a) transformation, (b) conjugation, or (c)
transduction?

a._____

_____

_____

_____

b._____

_____

_____

_____

c._____

_____

_____

_____

2. In their famous experiment, Meselson and Stahl determined that DNA
replicates "semiconservatively". At the time many scientists believed that DNA must be replicated in a "conservative" manner.
(a) What do you think the scientists meant by this designation?
(b) Redraw Figure 6.2 of your textbook so that it represents "conservative" replication.

a._____

_____

_____

b.

3. Figure 6.3 of your textbook demonstrates how penicillin can be
used to "select" for the rare penicillin-resistant mutant in a
population of penicillin-sensitive bacteria. Penicillin can also
be used to help "select" for mutants unable to synthesize an essential anabolic precursor such as an amino acid. Calling on your
knowledge of the way in which penicillin kills bacterial cells,
how do you think penicillin could be used to select an alanine
auxotroph (an organism unable to synthesize its own alanine) from
a population of alanine prototrophs (organisms able to make their
own alanine).

_____

_____

_____

_____

_____

_____

_____

_____

_____

_____

POST-TEST

1. Compounds that act as mutagens because they are closely related to
nitrogenous bases in structure and are incorporated into DNA in
place of the normal bases are called:
   a. analogs.
   b. environmental mutagens.

69

    c. point mutagens.
    d. lethal mutagens.

2. In an experiment in bacterial gene transfer, it is found that if
   two strains of <u>Escherichia coli</u> are mixed together in a liquid
   medium, recombination takes place. If, however, a semipermeable
   membrane is placed between the two strains, allowing free flow of
   the medium but not the bacterial cells, no recombination can be
   observed. These E. <u>coli</u> are transferring DNA by:
    a. transformation.
    b. specialized transduction.
    c. generalized transduction.
    d. conjugation.

3. During the process of transformation, the only types of DNA incorporated into the recipient chromosome is :
    a. phage DNA.
    b. single-stranded DNA.
    c. plasmid DNA.
    d. double-stranded DNA.

4. The enzymatic process by which a portion of one DNA molecule is incorporated into another DNA molecule is:
    a. transduction.
    b. conjugation.
    c. transformation.
    d. recombination.

5. Griffith's 1928 experiments on the transfer of virulence in pneumonia
   cocci were the first demonstration of what is now known as:
    a. transduction.
    b. conjugation.
    c. transformation.
    d. recombination.

6. In a conjugation experiment, you discover that a male strain of E.
   <u>coli</u> will only transfer <u>certain</u> chromosomal genes to the recipient
   cell. The donor strain you are working with is most likely a(n):
    a. F+.
    b. F-prime.
    c. F-.
    d. Hfr.

7. Extrachromosomal DNA elements that do not contain genes essential
   to the growth of the cell and which <u>do not</u> integrate into the
   bacterial chromosome are called:
    a. episomes.
    b. plasmids.
    c. prophage.
    d. transducing particles.

8. Box 6.1 in your textbook describes how Roy Curtiss constructed his
   "safe microbe" for genetic engineering experiments. He did so by
   manipulating the bacterial genome so that it contained a number of

_____ mutations.
  a. environmental
  b. spontaneous
  c. lethal
  d. point

9. Bacteria are normally:
  a. haploid.
  b. diploid.
  c. triploid.
  d. tetraploid.

10. The genes of an organism are strung along its chromosomes in a
    linear array. The point on the chromosome where any particular
    gene is to be found is referred to as its:
  a. position.
  b. place.
  c. marker.
  d. locus.

11. One very important environmental mutagen is ultraviolet light. It
    exerts its mutagenic effect by forming a(n) _____
    in the DNA.
  a. nitrite ion
  b. analog
  c. thymine dimer
  d. photon

12. The enzyme responsible for the synthesis of DNA from a DNA template
    is:
  a. DNA polymerase.
  b. DNA lygase.
  c. DNA endonuclease.
  d. DNA reverse transcriptase.

13. In an Hfr X F- cross, how much of the chromosome can be transferred
    from the male to the female cell?
  a. none of it
  b. all of it
  c. only a small, specific section of it
  d. any 2% of it

14. One type of DNA transfer in bacteria takes place when viral DNA
    enters the lytic cycle and incorporates a fragment of the host's
    DNA into the virus instead of viral DNA. This is a random occur-
    rence, which may involve any of the bacterial genes. This process
    is referred to as:
  a. transformation.
  b. conjugation.
  c. generalized transduction.
  d. specialized transduction.

15. An important property of restriction endonucleases that makes them
    particularly useful for genetic engineering is that many of them:

71

a. cleave DNA.
b. produce "sticky-ends" on the DNA.
c. synthesize DNA.
d. are restricted to certain kinds of DNA.

ANSWERS TO EXERCISES

Pre-Test

1. b	6. c	11. c
2. a	7. d	12. a
3. d	8. a	13. c
4. d	9. b	14. b
5. b	10. c	15. b

Practice Exercises

1. (Answer to this exercise can be found in Figure 6.2.)

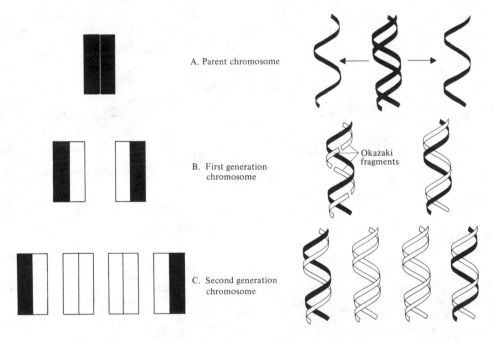

A. Parent chromosome

B. First generation chromosome

Okazaki fragments

C. Second generation chromosome

2. a. messenger RNA; b. amino acid; c. protein;

   d. point mutation; e. generalized mutations; f. chromosome;

   g. spontaneous; h. Induced; i. chromosome.

3. a. 1. high, 2. none; b. 1. few, if any, 2. all can be transferred; c. 1. high, 2. only a small, specific region can be transferred.

4. a. 6; b. 3; c. 4; d. 10; e. 1;

   f. 7; g. 5; h. 2; i. 9; j. 8.

5. (All answers to this exercise can be found in Figure 6.4.)

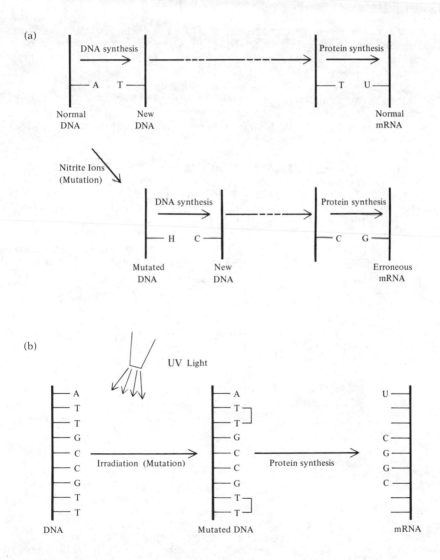

6. a. endonucleases; b. restriction; c. restricted:

d. plasmids; e. chimeras; f. genetic engineering.

7. a. F;   b. F;   c. T;   d. T;   d. T;

e. F;   f. T;   g. F;   h. T;   i. T;

j. T.

Concept Exercises

1. a. To test for transformation he could check the culture medium for DNA chemically. He could also see whether treatment of the culture medium with a nuclease (DNase) would inhibit the gene transfer event.

   b. To test for transduction he could see whether he could identify phage particles in the electron microscope. Also, the insertion of a semipermeable membrane between the two strains of bacteria should not inhibit the process.

   c. To test for conjugation he should see whether the insertion of a semipermeable membrane between the two strains will inhibit the transfer process. Also, he should check to see whether the transfer is unidirectional (i.e., strain 1 [male] ⟶ strain II [female], but not strain II ⟶ strain I).

2. a. conservative replication refers to a process where one double-stranded molecule directs the synthesis of a second, completely new molecule.

   b.

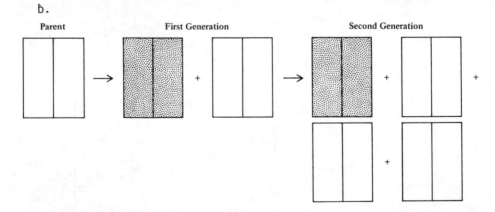

| Parent | First Generation | Second Generation |

3. Penicillin kills bacteria by inhibiting the synthesis of the peptidoglycan layer of the cell wall (See Chapter 4). Hence, only growing bacteria that are actively synthesizing cell wall material are killed by this antibiotic. Unless alanine is supplied to an

alanine auxotroph in the culture medium, the cell will not grow. Therefore it <u>will</u> <u>not</u> <u>be</u> <u>killed</u> by penicillin. To do the experiment, you would withhold alanine from a culture at the same time you added penicillin. The alanine prototrophs (which can grow) would be killed, thereby <u>enriching</u> for the auxotrophs. To isolate the auxotrophs, you would then transfer them to a medium containing alanine but not containing penicillin. This technique is known as <u>penicillin</u> <u>enrichment</u>.

Post-Test

1. a	6. b	11. c
2. d	7. b	12. a
3. b	8. c	13. b
4. d	9. a	14. c
5. c	10. d	15. b

7   The Rickettsiae and Chlamydiae

The first known case of rickettsialpox in medical history turned up in
the winter of 1946, in New York City . . . . It is among the few
identified ailments that bear scientifically illuminating names. . . .
Rickettsialpox, as a name, not only gives a good idea of one of the
disease's most notable manifestations, a spotty rash, but indicates its
cause, a microorganism of the genus Rickettsia. . . . The cause of
rickettsialpox and its means of transmission were established just
seven months and seven days after its first known victim, and eleven-
year-old boy, came down with it on the afternoon of February 23, 1946.

Berton Roueché, _Eleven Blue Men_.   New York:
Berkley Publishing Corp., 1955.

CHAPTER OUTLINE

I.   Structure and Growth of the Rickettsiae

II.   Rickettsial Diseases

A.   Rocky Mountain spotted fever

B.   Epidemic typhus

C.   Endemic typhus

D.   Recrudescent typhus

E.   Tsutsugamushi

F.   Rickettsial pox

G.   Q fever

H.   Trench fever

I.   Boutonneuse fever

III.   Structure and Growth of the Chlamydiae

IV.   Chlamydial Diseases

A.   Trachoma

B.   Inclusion conjunctivitis

C.   Nongonococcal urethritis

D.   Lymphogranuloma venereum

E. Psittacosis

OVERVIEW AND OBJECTIVES

For many years after they were first described by Howard Ricketts in
1909, the rickettsiae were considered a form of life less developed
than the bacteria. Many biologists thought that the organisms were
viruses. The reason for these beliefs was the fact that the rickettsiae
could not be cultivated outside their host organism. In recent years
research has shown that they possess the characteristics of a bacterium
and, in fact, one member, the rickettsiae organism that causes trench
fever, has been cultivated on synthetic medium. The major characteristics
of the rickettsiae, which led to their inclusion in Part 18 of the
current edition of Bergey's Manual, are that:

1. They multiply by binary fission.

2. They contain both DNA and RNA.

3. They possess enzymes of the Krebs cycle, of electron transport,
   and of protein synthesis.

4. They possess cell walls like those of free-living gram(-) bacteria.

5. They have ribosomes similar in size to those of bacteria.

6. Their growth is inhibited by a variety of antibacterial agents.

Several of these characteristics are shared by a second group of
similar organisms, the chlamydiae. The chlamydiae are also classified
in Part 18 of Bergey's Manual.

The rickettsiae cause a number of diseases in humans. These vary
in severity from epidemic typhus, which at times has come close to
eliminating the human species, to the relatively benign rickettsialpox,
which often runs its course without the victim realizing that he or
she has the disease. Regardless of their severity, all reckettsial
diseases have several characteristics in common. These include: (1)
high fever, (2) maculopapular rash, (3) transmission by an arthropod
vector, and (4) treatment with antibacterial chemotherapy. In addition,
many produce an enscar at the organism's site of entry.

The chlamydiae possess an antigen which is not shared with the
rickettsiae. The chlamydiae also cause several diseases in humans,
including diseases of the eye and the reproductive organs.

After you have read Chapter 7 of your textbook, you should be able
to:

1. Define or identify the following terms: Rocky Mountain spotted
   fever, rickettsiae, chlamydiae, coccobacillus, pleomorphic, obligate intracellular parasite, arthropod, vector, transovarian infection, macule, papule, maculopapular rash, Weil-Felix reaction,
   heterophile antigen, Rickettsia rickettsii, mortality rate, epi-

demic typhus, Rickettsia prowazekii, endemic typhus, murine typhus, Rickettsia typhi, tabardillo, recrudescent typhus, Brill-Zinnser Disease, tsutsugamushi, scrub typhus, Rickettsia tsutsugamushi, eschar, rickettsialpox, Rickettsia akari, Q fever, Coxiella burnetti, trench fever, His-Werner disease, Rachalimaea quintana, xenodiagnosis, boutonneuse fever, Rickettsia conori, tache noir, elementary body, initial body, inclusion, Chlamydia trachomatis, Chlamydia psittaci, trachoma, TRIC agent, conjunctiva, inclusion conjunctivitis, blennorhea, nongonococcal urethritis, lymphogranuloma venereum, LGV agent, proctitis, psittacosis, and ornithosis.

2. Describe the growth of rickettsiae and chlamydiae.

3. List the characteristics of rickettsiae and chlamydiae that require their classification as bacteria.

4. Outline the symptoms and other characteristics the rickettsial diseases share.

5. Describe the chlamydial diseases of humans.

PRE-TEST

1. Rickettsiae are obligate intracellular parasites. This means that they:
   a. must be infected by viruses before they can grow.
   b. will grow on selective medium only if serum is added to the medium.
   c. can grow only inside tissue cells.
   d. do not grow unless an extract of tissue cells is added to the culture medium.

2. a patient comes to a physician with the following symptoms: fever, rash, and eschar. The patient lives in an area infested by mice. The doctor orders a Weil-Felix test, which proves to be negative. Of the following, the patient probably has:
   a. Rocky Mountain spotted fever.
   b. Q fever.
   c. rickettsialpox.
   d. scrub typhus.

3. The TRIC agent causes all of the following diseases, except:
   a. lymphogranuloma venereum.
   b. trachoma.
   c. inclusion conjunctivitis.
   d. nongonococcal urethritis.

4. When a chlamydia first infects a cell, it is called an:
   a. inclusion.
   b. elementary body.
   c. initial body.
   d. entry body.

5. Each of the following rickettsial diseases cause an eschar, except:

a. boutonneuse fever.
b. rickettsialpox.
c. scrub typhus.
d. epidemic typhus.

6. The organism that causes Rocky Mountain spotted fever was first described by:
a. Howard Taylor Ricketts.
b. Robert Koch.
c. Anton van Leeuwenhoek.
d. Louis Pasteur.

7. Rickettsia akari is the causative agent of:
a. recrudescent typhus.
b. endemic typhus.
c. Q fever
d. rickettsialpox.

8. An eschar is a:
a. tick that transmits Rocky Mountain spotted fever.
b. blackened crust which forms at the site of entry of the organisms that cause several rickettsial diseases.
c. skin rash of pink spots.
d. pink-red spot which resembles a pimple.

9. The Weil-Felix reaction depends on a heterophile antigen. The presence of this antigen in the patient's serum is identified in the Weil-Felix reaction by its ability to agglutinate:
a. Rickettsia.
b. Proteus.
c. Chlamydia.
d. Coxiella.

10. The vectors for rickettsial diseases are:
a. rodents.
b. birds.
c. arthropods.
d. humans.

11. Q fever is unique among the rickettsial diseases for several reasons. These include all of the following, except:
a. The organism that produces it is among the most resistant of all bacteria.
b. It elicits a negative Weil-Felix reaction.
c. It does not require an arthropod vector.
d. The organism that produces it survives outside living cells for long periods of time.

12. Particles may be seen in the cytoplasm of cells infected by chlamydiae. These granule-like particles are called:
a. inclusions.
b. elementary bodies.
c. initial bodies.
d. eschars.

13. In the diagnosis of trench fever, laboratory-reared lice are al-
    lowed to feed on the patient, after which the insects are examined
    for the presence of rickettsiae. This procedure is known as:
    a. Weil-Felix diagnosis.
    b. His-Werner diagnosis.
    c. tache noir diagnosis.
    d. xenodiagnosis.

14. Lymphogranuloma venereum is caused by the:
    a. LGV agent.
    b. TRIC agent.
    c. His-Werner agent.
    d. Q agent.

15. Chlamydiae cause an eye disease in newborns which is acquired during
    the birth process from a woman who has an infection of the repro-
    ductive tract. This disease of newborns if known as:
    a. gonorrhea.
    b. blennorhea.
    c. nongonococcal urethritis.
    d. trachoma.

PRACTICE EXERCISES

1. Diagram the transmission of a typical rickettsiae from the primary
   host to the secondary host and back again.

2. In the list below, indicate the characteristics that rickettsiae
   share with other bacteria by placing an X on the appropriate lines.

_____a. Pili may be present.

_____b. Contain both DNA and RNA.

_____c. Cell wall similar to gram(-) bacteria.

_____d. Produce endospores.

_____e. Can reproduce extracellularly.

_____f. Contain ribosomes.

_____g. Divide by binary fission.

_____h. Can carry out the reaction
succinic acid $\longrightarrow$ fumaric acid.

_____i. Produce an extracellular capsule.

_____j. Have the enzyme of the electron transport system.

3. True or False. Decide whether each of the following statements is true or false; then place a T for true or an F for false on the line provided.

_____ a. The Weil-Felix reaction depends on the fact that rickettsiae and the genus _Proteus_ share a common antigen.

_____ b. The high fever caused by rickettsial infection is referred to as a macule fever.

_____ c. The vector for trench fever is the louse.

_____ d. Another name for endemic typhus is murine typhus. This name comes from the fact that the disease is prevalent among rodent populations.

_____ e. The mortality rate represents the percent of victims who succumb to an untreated disease.

_____ f. Boutonneuse fever does not display the typical pink rash but rather a black rash known as tache noir.

_____ g. After the initial infection of a cell by an elementary body, the chlamydial cell enlarges to form an initial body.

_____ h. Of all the rickettsial diseases, endemic typhus is probably the most notorious because it has such a high mortality rate.

_____ i. His-Werner disease debilitated more than a million men during World War I and, except for the great influenza pandemic of 1918-1919, was probably the most devastating disease of the period.

_____ j. There is no way to distinguish between gonorrhea and nongonococcal urethritis and the two diseases must be treated in the
same way.

4. For each of the rickettsial diseases listed below, indicate (1)
the causative agent, (2) the vector, and (3) the natural reservoir.

   a. Rocky Mountain spotted fever. 1. _____, 2. __
      _____, 3. _____

   b. Q fever. 1. _____, 2. _____ 3.
      _____.

   c. Epidemic typhus. 1. _____, 2. _____
      ____, 3. _____.

   d. Rickettsialpox. 1. _____, 2. _____
      ___, 3. _____.

   e. Trench fever. 1. _____, 2. _____
      3. _____

5. Fill in the blanks. Reproduction by the chlamydiae is a complex
process that occurs in the (a) _____ of an in-
fected cell. The chlamydia, called an (b) _____
_____, enlarges to form an (c) _____
_____ that divides by (d) _____
_____ and forms a series of small, dense particles
called (e) _____. These are a characteristic feature of the (f) _____. They develop into highly
infectious (g) _____ _____. The
process takes place over a 24-hour period.

6. Identify the rickettsial or chlamydial disease best described by
each set of symptoms (syndrome) listed below.

   a. An infection of the eye common in newborns. _____

   b. Fever, rash, eschar, mite bite, negative Weil-Felix reaction.

      _____

   c. Fever, no rash or eschar, tick bite, negative Weil-Felix re-
      action. _____

   d. Fever, rash, eschar, mite bite, positive Weil-Felix reaction.

      _____

   e. Epididymis in males with copious amounts of purulent dis-
      charge. _____

CONCEPT EXERCISES

1. In 1946, the first class of rickettsialpox was reported in New
York City. More recently, Legionnaire's disease appeared

suddenly. From time to time throughout history, new diseases have appeared. What are some of the factors that can lead to this phenomenon?

_____

_____

_____

_____

_____

_____

_____

_____

_____

_____

_____

2. Rickettsialpox, like many other rickettsial diseases, resembles several viral diseases, including chickenpox, smallpox, and infectious mononucleosis. There is one symptom, however, that separates this disease from the viral diseases. What is it? How does the treatment of rickettsialpox differ from the treatment of viral diseases?

_____

_____

_____

_____

_____

_____

3. If a physician suspects that a patient has a rickettsial disease, what important questions should she ask the patient while taking a medical history? What other symptoms should she look for and what laboratory tests should she employ to determine which of the rickettsial dieases the patient has?

_____

_____

_____

_____

_____

_____

POST-TEST

1. The causative agent for trachoma is:
   a. Chlamydia trachomatis.
   b. Chlamydia psittaci.
   c. Rickettsia rickettsii.
   d. Rickettsia trachomatis.

2. Endemic typhus is acquired through the bite of a:
   a. louse.
   b. flea.
   c. mite.
   d. tick.

3. The measure of the percentage of victims who die of a disease is the disease's:
   a. morbidity rate.
   b. cure rate.
   c. mortality rate.
   d. success rate.

4. A rash which begins as pink spots and progresses to pink-red spots that resemble pimples is called a(n):
   a. macular rash.
   b. eschar rash.
   c. papular rash.
   d. maculopapular rash.

5. All of the following diseases are spread by arthropod vectors, except:
   a. Rocky Mountain spotted fever.
   b. trachoma.
   c. tsutsugamushi.
   d. boutonneuse fever.

6. In the eighth edition of Bergey's Manual the chlamydiae are classified with the:
   a. viruses.
   b. blue-green algae.
   c. spore-forming bacteria.
   d. rickettsiae.

7. Soon after your son comes in from playing in the rice paddies that surround your Indonesian home, you remove a tick from his leg.

Shortly thereafter he develops a headache, fever, and a rash. A black spot appears where the tick bit him. You rush him to a physician, who gives him a Weil-Felix text. The test is positive. You are worried and ask the physician what the chances are that your child will die. The physician tells you that the child has:
a. Rocky Mountain spotted fever and there is a high probability that he will die.
b. Rocky Mountain spotted fever, which has a variable mortality rate.
c. boutonneuse fever and the chances are very good that he will live.
d. boutonneuse fever and there is a high probability that he will die.

8. The federal government's facility responsible for the investigation of possible rickettsial diseases is the:
   a. U.S. Public Health Service.
   b. Center for Disease Control in Atlanta, Georgia.
   c. Rocky Mountain Laboratory.
   d. Walter Reed Hospital.

9. The proper sequence of events in a chlamydial infection is:
   a. elementary body $\longrightarrow$ initial body $\longrightarrow$ inclusion $\longrightarrow$ elementary body.
   b. initial body $\longrightarrow$ elementary body $\longrightarrow$ inclusion $\longrightarrow$ initial body.
   c. inclusion $\longrightarrow$ initial body $\longrightarrow$ elementary body $\longrightarrow$ inclusion.
   d. elementary body $\longrightarrow$ inclusion $\longrightarrow$ initial body $\longrightarrow$ elementary body.

10. If two unrelated organisms produce the same antibody-inducing substance, this substance is referred to as a:
    a. generalized antigen.
    b. family antibody.
    c. heterophile antigen.
    d. heterophile antibody.

11. The organism that causes Rocky Mountain spotted fever is:
    a. Rickettsia rickettsii.
    b. Rickettsia prowazecki.
    c. Rochalimea quintana.
    d. Rochalimea rickettsii.

12. The rickettsial disease which shares with plague, smallpox, and cholera the distinction of having caused pandemics that have significantly reduced the human population is:
    a. scrub typhus.
    b. endemic typhus.
    c. epidemic typhus.
    d. Nigerian typhus.

13. A venereal disease caused by Chlamydia trachomatis TRIC varient is:
    a. nongonococcal urethritis.
    b. lymphogranuloma venereum.

c.   gonorrhea.
c.   syphilis.

14. Of the following, the <u>best</u> description of the rickettsiae and
    chlamydiae is as:
    a.   pathogens.
    b.   fastidious organisms.
    c.   obligate intracellular parasites.
    d.   obligate intercellular parasites.

15. The rickettsiae are described as short rods with rounded edges.
    This shape is called:
    a.   bacillus.
    b.   coccus.
    c.   coccobacillus.
    d.   sarcina.

ANSWERS TO EXERCISES

Pre-Test

1. c	6. a	11. b
2. c	7. d	12. a
3. a	8. b	13. d
4. b	9. b	14. a
5. d	10. c	15. b

Practice Exercises

1. The answer to this exercise can be found in Figure 7.3.

2. The shared characteristics are: b., c., f., g., h., and j.

3. a. T; b. F; c. T d. T; e. T; f. F

   q. T; h. F; i. T; j. F.

4. a. 1. <u>Rickettsia rickettsii</u>, 2. tick, 3. ticks, rodents;

   b. 1. <u>Coxiella burnetti</u>, 2. tick, dairy products, dust, drop-

   lets, 3. domestic livestock; c. <u>Rickettsia prowazecki</u>, 2.

   lice, 3. humans; d. <u>Rickettsia akari</u>,

   2. mite, 3. mite, house mice, other rodents; e. <u>Rochalimea</u>

quintana, 2. lice; 3. humans.

5. a. cytoplasm; b. elementary body; c. initial body;

   d. binary fission; e. inclusions; f. chlamydiae;

   g. elementary bodies.

6. a. Inclusion conjunctivitis; b. Rickettsialpox;

   c. Q fever; d. Scrub typhus (tsutsugamushi); e. Gonorrhea.

Concept Exercises

1. Berton Roueché observed in his book Eleven Blue Men that "Although medical authorities are of the uneasy opinion that thousands of new diseases would afflict mankind if all the microorganisms potentially capable of causing illness were to become sufficiently virulent to break down the body's resistance to them, the outbreak of just one such disease is happily an unusual occurrence." Yet it does happen on occasion, and there are many reasons for this. Environmental change is an important one. For instance, trench fever appeared during World War I because men were living in close contact in unsanitary conditions, which allowed the spread of in-fected lice. The use of antibiotics may cause the appearance of new diseases by selecting for more virulent forms of an organism or by destroying the natural flora of the body, allowing the establishment of a new disease-causing organism. Also, an unusual event such as the outbreak of Legionnaire's disease at an American Legion convention may call to the attention of the medical com-munity a "new" disease, which in fact has has existed unrecognized for a long time.

2. Rickettsialpox differs from the viral disease in that it is <u>not</u> infective but must be transmitted by the bite of a mite. In addi-ticn, an eschar will appear at the site of the bite. This symptom is not known in the viral diseases. As a bacterial disease, rickettsialpox can be treated with antibiotics. Viral diseases cannot!

3. You might ask whether the patient has been in a position to come in contact with any of the known vectors of the various rickettsial diseases or their reservoirs in nature. You should look for the presence of an eschar. You might decide to order a Weil-Felix test, a guinea pig test, and/or a xenodiagnosis.

Post-Test

1. a	6. d	11. a
2. b	7. c	12. c

3. c	8. c	13. a
4. d	9. a	14. c
5. b	10. c	15. c

8   The Viruses

The isolation of the anti-Shiga dysentery microbe is simple: one ino-
culates a broth tube with four or five drops of stool, incubates the
tube at 37° for 18 hours, and then filters the fluid through a
Chamberland candle. A small quantity of this filtrate added . . . to
a growing broth culture of Shiga bacilli . . . provokes the arrest of
the culture, the death of the bacilli, and then their lysis. . . . In
the absence of dysentery bacilli the antimicrobe does not grow in any
media. It does not attack heat-killed dysentery bacilli, whereas it
does grow perfectly well on a suspension of washed bacilli in physiological saline: it follows from these facts that the antidysentery
microbe is an obligatory bacteriophage.

> F. d'Hérelle, Sur un microbe invisible antagoniste des bacilles
> dysentériques. C. R. Acad. Sci. Paris, 167:373, 1917.

CHAPTER OUTLINE

   I.   Foundations of Virology

        A.   The transition period

  II.   Viral Structure and Replication

        A.   Viral morphology

        B.   Viral components

        C.   Viral replication

 III.   Other Aspects of Virology

        A.   Viral classification

        B.   Detection of viral diseases

        C.   Viral inhibition

        D.   Viral inactivation

  IV.   Viruses and Cancer

OVERVIEW AND OBJECTIVES

The above quotation is from the first paper published that described
the bacterial viruses. It identified all of the characteristics that
describe viruses in general. Viruses are obligate intracellular parasites. They are filterable, and they require a living host capable of
metabolism. Originally the word virus referred to any biological agent

that caused disease, but today the word is reserved for agents with the above characteristics. They are separated from other microbial obligate intracellular parasites, the chlamydiae and rickettsiae, by their small size and their inability to metabolize organic compounds. In addition, they contain either DNA or RNA but never both. This chapter discusses the general characteristics of the viruses and sets the stage for the next two chapters, which will discuss viral diseases of humans.

Viruses are made up of a genome composed of DNA or RNA (but never both), a protein coat or capsid, and in some cases a membrane envelope. Together these components constitute the extracellular form of the virus, the virion. During replication, only the nucleic acid genome enters the host cell and directs the cellular metabolic machinery to produce new virions. After several to many virions are produced the cell is lysed, releasing a burst of virions.

Because viruses have no cell wall or metabolism, antibiotics are not effective against viral diseases. There are, however, several body defenses that act to inhibit viruses. These include the immune system and interferon. Vaccination is effective in preventing many viral diseases.

Animal viruses are classified either by the type of nucleic acid contained in their virion or by the body tissues they infect. In the first classification, there are 18 families of viruses. The second classification divides the viruses into four groups.

No matter what group of organisms viruses infect, they cannot be detected unless they cause disease. Viruses are known to cause diseases of every group of organism (bacteria, plants, animals). They have been shown to cause several forms of cancer in animals and have been implicated in several human cancers.

After you have read Chapter 8 of your textbook, you should be able to:

1. Define or identify the following terms: virus, bacteriophage, sarcoma, icosahedron, helix, genome, capsid, capsomere, nucleo-capsid, envelope, virion, spides, neuraminidase, hemagglutinin, repressor protein, Negri body, Councilman body, Lipshutz body, Downey cell, Koplik spot, plaque, isotin-B-semithiocarbazone (IBT) amantadine, iodo-deoxyuridine (IDU), interferon, inactivated virus, attenuated virus, tumor, neoplasm, metastasized, oncology, fibroma, papilloma, sarcoma, leukemia, reverse transcriptase, and oncogene.

2. Outline the history of virology from the discoveries of Dmitri Iwanowski to those of Howard Temin and David Baltimore

3. Discuss the various viral components and describe how they inter-act to produce a virion.

4. Outline the two classifications of animal viruses in use today.

5. Discuss the various systems that are effective and inneffective in inhibiting viral growth.

6. Explain the possible role of viruses in cancer and explain the oncogene theory.

PRE-TEST

1. Bacteriophage can be detected in the laboratory because they form:
   a. plaques.
   b. Negri bodies.
   c. Downey cells.
   d. Lipshutz bodies.

2. Because viruses have neither a cell wall nor metabolism, they are
   not susceptible to:
   a. antibodies.
   b. interferon.
   c. antibiotics.
   d. attenuation.

3. Frederick Twort and Felis d'Hérrelle were the first to describe:
   a. animal viruses.
   b. bacteriophage.
   c. plant viruses.
   d. cancer viruses.

4. Virus capsids can usually be classified as to one of the following
   shapes, except:
   a. icosahedron.
   b. helix.
   c. icosahedron head with tail.
   d. spherical.

5. Hershey and Chase's experiments demonstrated that the component(s)
   of the virion which enter the host bacterium's cell was (were) the:
   a. nucleic acid.
   b. protein capsid.
   c. envelope.
   d. nucleic acid and the protein capsid.

6. The Rous sarcoma genome codes for an enzyme that carries out which
   of the following reactions?
   a. DNA $\longrightarrow$ RNA
   b. RNA $\longrightarrow$ Protein
   c. RNA $\longrightarrow$ DNA
   d. Protein $\longrightarrow$ DNA

7. From a wart you have isolated a virus that has an icosahedral
   symmetry and no envelope. You would expect this virus to have a
   genome made up of:
   a. DNA.
   b. RNA.
   c. protein.
   d. a nucleic acid with one strand of DNA and one strand of RNA.

8. Animal viruses that affect the respiratory system are grouped into

91

the:
a. pneumotropic group.
b. dermotropic group.
c. viscerotropic group.
d. neurotropic group.

9. Tumors of the lymph nodes and connective tissues are called:
a. fibroma.
b. papilloma.
c. sarcoma.
d. leukemia.

10. An effective vaccine against several viral diseases can be made using viruses that have been treated with either a physical agent such as ultraviolet light or a chemical agent such as formaldehyde. Such a virus is referred to as:
a. viable.
b. inactivated.
c. temperate.
d. attenuated.

11. A protein which retards viral replication by triggering a reaction that neutralizes not only the virus that induced its formation but also many other viruses is referred to as:
a. iodo-deoxyuridine.
b. interferon.
c. isotin-B-semithiocarbazone.
d. amantadine.

12. A veterinarian is called to examine a dog that bit a small girl. The dog subsequently dies. The veterinarian wants to determine whether the dog was rabid. He sends a sample of the dog's brain to a virologist who examines the brain cells for:
a. Koplik spots.
b. Negri bodies.
c. Councilman bodies.
d. Lipshutz bodies.

13. Viruses containing the genetic information for the enzyme reverse transcriptase are classified as:
a. rhabdoviruses.
b. reoviruses.
c. retroviruses.
d. poxviruses.

14. In the classification system that divides animal viruses into groups based on the tissue affected, rabies virus is classified as a:
a. pneumotropic virus.
b. dermotropic virus.
c. viscerotropic virus.
d. neurotropic virus.

15. The first person to crystalize tobacco mosaic virus won the Nobel

Prize in 1946. He was:
a. Ernest W. Goodpasture.
b. Francis Peyton Rous.
c. Wendel M. Stanley.
d. Dmitri Iwanowski.

PRACTICE EXERCISES

1. Matching. Match each person in the left-hand column with his or
   her discovery in the right-hand column by placing the appropriate
   number on the line provided. (All entries in the right-hand column
   will not be used.)

   6 a. Stanley
   7 b. Salk
   9 c. Baltimore
   3 d. Reed
   1 e. Huebner

   1. Developed the oncogene
       theory

   2. Showed that viruses could
       be dried

   3. Discovered the yellow fever
       virus

   4. Discovered tobacco mosaic
       virus

   5. Discovered interferon

   6. First to crystalize virus

   7. Developed polio vaccine

   8. Showed that viral nucleic
       acid entered host cell

   9. Discovered reverse trans-
       criptase

   10. Discovered bacteriophage

2. Identify the viral component described by each of the following
   phrases.

   a. The viral genome plus the capsid. nucleocapsid

   b. Projections of the envelope of certain virions that often
       contain neuraminidase. spikes

   c. Subunits of the capsid. capsomere

   d. A membrane component of some viruses which is similar to the
       host cellular membrane, except that it contains viral-specific
       components. envelope

   e. The viral DNA or RNA. genome

f. A layer of protein surrounding the viral DNA or RNA. _____
   Capsid

g. An enzyme sometimes found on spikes that allows the virus to
   agglutinate red blood cells. *hemagglutinin*

h. The term applied to the enveloped nucleocapsid. _____
   Virion

3. Complete the following table, which concerns the classification of
   animal viruses. (Refer to Table 8.1, if necessary.)

Nucleic Acid	Family	Symmetry	Envelope	Important Disease
a. DNA	*Poxviridae*	complex	(-)	smallpox
b. ___	papovaviridae	_____	_____	_____
c. RNA	retroviridae	_____	_____	_____
d. ___	_____	_____	_____	Herpes simplex
e. DNA	_____	_____	(-)	No human disease

4. True or False. Decide whether each of the following statements is
   true or false; then place a T for true or an F for false on the
   line provided.

__T__ a. If the viral genome becomes associated with the chromosome
         without the lytic cycle taking place, the host cell is said to
         be lysogenized and the phenomenon is referred to as lysogeny.

__T__ b. In viral diseases the normal body defenses cannot be supplemented
         by antibiotics because the viruses have no cell wall or meta-
         bolism.

__T__ c. The mechanics of cell transformation in cancer is still a matter
         for conjecture. It may resemble lysogeny in bacteria.

__T__ d. The oncogene theory states that all cells contain a region of
         DNA that can induce uncontrolled growth. The oncogene is
         normally repressed, but certain viruses may inactivate the
         repressor protein and cause transformation of the host cell.

__F__ e. A virus with reduced virulence, which can be used to produce a
         vaccine, is referred to as inactivated.

__F__ f. Detergent antiseptics inactivate viruses by dissolving the
         viral genome.

__T__ g. Formaldehyde is particularly effective against viruses because
         it penetrates the capsid and alters the genome by reacting with
         free amino groups on the nitrogenous bases.

   F   h. The term <u>virion</u> is applied to the enveloped nucleocapsid, but it is never used to refer to the naked nucleocapsid in cases where no envelope exists.

   T   i. In some cases, a bacteriophage codes for a <u>repressor</u> <u>protein</u> that prevents the lytic cycle from taking place.

5. In one or two sentences explain how each of the following substances <u>inhibit</u> or <u>inactivate</u> viruses.

   a. Amantadine:

_____

_____

   b. Formaldehyde:

_____

_____

   c. Silver:

_____

_____

   d. Interferon:

_____

_____

   e. Heat:

_____

_____

   f. Ultraviolet light:

_____

_____

6. Diagram the budding process by which certain animal viruses acquire their envelopes.

CONCEPT EXERCISES

1. In Chapter 4 of this Study Guide, you were asked to draw a
   typical bacterial growth curve. As your study of Chapter 8 has
   indicated to you, a "typical growth curve" for a bacteriophage and
   other lytic viruses looks quite different. Draw a bacterial virus
   growth curve.

2. A scientist has identified a new disease. When she applies Koch's postulates to the disease, she finds that she cannot grow a pure culture of the causative agent in defined medium. When she infects tissue cultures with serum from diseased individuals, however, the tissue cultures show signs of disease and cell death. How can she decide whether the disease is caused by rickettsial, chlamydial, or a viral parasite?

_____

_____

_____

_____

_____

3. You want to make a vaccine to a viral disease. What alterations would you make in your viral preparation in order to make it "safe" for use as a vaccine?

_____

_____

_____

_____

_____

_____

_____

_____

POST-TEST

1. An agent that inactivates viruses by dissolving the lipids of the viral envelope is:
   a. detergent antiseptic.
   b. formaldehyde.
   c. heat.
   d. silver.

2. Enveloped viruses derive their envelopes from:
   a. viral-specific components.
   b. host cell membranes.

c. host nuclear membranes.
d. host cell membranes modified with viral-specific components.

3. Enveloped viruses are released from the host cell by:
   a. lysing their host.
   b. budding through the host membrane.
   c. lysogenizing their host.
   d. use of reverse transcriptase.

4. Rabies virus is a(n) _____ virus, which is classified in the _____ group.
   a. DNA, herpesviridae
   b. RNA, herpesviridae
   c. DNA, rhabdoviridae
   d. RNA, rhabdoviridae

5. A microbiologist has isolated a brick-shaped virus that contains DNA and has no envelope. The virus is approximately 250 nm in diameter. He should classify this virus in the:
   a. poxviridae.
   b. herpesviridae.
   c. papovaviridae.
   d. parvoviridae.

6. The 1954 Noble Prize was given for the development of tissue culture techniques that allowed the cultivation of animal cells in laboratory flasks. This prize was shared by:
   a. Salk and Sabin.
   b. Iwanowski and Stanley.
   c. Enders, Weller, and Robbins.
   d. Ellerman and Bang.

7. Rous sarcoma virus causes a cancer in chickens. This is a(n) _____ virus, which is classified in the _____ because it contains reverse transcriptase.
   a. DNA, papovaviridae
   b. RNA, papovaviridae
   c. DNA, retroviridae
   d. RNA, retroviridae

8. You have isolated an animal virus whose capsid is a tightly wound coil resembling a corkscrew or spring. Such a capsid is referred to as a(n):
   a. icosahedron.
   b. helix.
   c. complex virion.
   d. capsomere.

9. Unless the virus described in exercise 8 is in a completely new group, its genome is composed of:
   a. DNA.
   b. RNA.
   c. protein.
   d. segmented DNA molecules.

10. The nucleic acid of an enveloped virus encased in its protein coat
    is often referred to as the:
    a. genome.
    b. nucleocapsid.
    c. virion.
    d. capsid.

11. Research has generated several drugs that interrupt the viral
    replication cycle. One such drug reacts with the mRNA of poxviruses
    and prevents the formation of capsid proteins. This drug is:
    a. isotin-β-semithiocarbazone.
    b. amantadine.
    c. iodo-deoxyuridine.
    d. interferon.

12. The togaviridae cause equine encephalitis and other diseases.
    These RNA viruses have a symmetrical capsid with 20 equilateral
    triangles with 20 edges and 12 points. Such a capsid is an example
    of a(n):
    a. helical capsid.
    b. icosahedral capsid.
    c. complex capsid.
    d. ovoid capsid.

13. Yellow fever is a viral disease of the liver. As such, the yellow
    fever virus is classified as a:
    a. pneumotropic virus.
    b. dermotropic virus.
    c. viscerotropic virus.
    d. neurotropic virus.

14. The best treatment of viral disease is provided by:
    a. interferon.
    b. antibiotics.
    c. antiviral drugs.
    d. prevention through vaccination.

15. For many years it was not understood how an RNA virus could trans-
    form its host cell, causing a tumor to develop. This dilemma was
    solved with the discovery of:
    a. chromosomal-hound RNA.
    b. RNA polymerase.
    c. reverse transcriptase.
    d. DNA polymerase.

ANSWERS TO EXERCISES

Pre-Test

1. a	6. c	11. b
2. c	7. a	12. b
3. b	8. a	13. c

4. d   9. c   14. d

5. a   10. b   15. c

Practice Exercises

1. a. 6   b. 7   c. 9 (Box 8.2); d. 3

   e. 1

2. a. nucleocapsid;   b. spikes;   c. capsomere;

   d. envelope;   e. genome;   f. capsid;

   g. hemagglutinin;   h. virion.

3. a. Poxviridae; b. DNA, icosahedral, no envelope, warts;

   c. icosahedral, capsid present, tumors; d. DNA, herpesviridae,

   icosahedral, envelope present; e. iridoviridae, icosahedral.

   (All answers to this exercise can be found in Table 8.1.)

4. a. T;   b. T;   c. T;   d. T;   e. F;

   f. F;   g. T;   h. F;   i. T.

5. a. Amantadine is thought to prevent the attachment of the in-
       fluenza virion to the host cell surface.

   b. Formaldehyde penetrates the capsid and alters the genome by
       reacting with free amino groups on the nitrogenous bases.

   c. Silver reacts strongly with protein and alters the configuration
       of the viral capsid.

   d. Interferon retards viral replication by a complex mechanism.
       It induces chromosome 21 to produce a protein that bonds to
       mRNA specified by the virus.

   e. Heat inactivates viruses by destroying the intergrity of the
       protein capsid.

   f. Ultraviolet light binds together adjacent thymines in the
       viral genome, thus destroying the core of DNA viruses.

6. The answer to this exercise can be found in Figure 8.6.

Concept Exercises

1. Viral growth curves are called "one-step" growth curves because a
   single burst of viruses is produced. Growth is not a smooth expon-
   ential process as in a bacterial population, but is characterized

by long periods when the number of virions does not increase during replication in the host cell. This is followed by lysis of the in- fected bacterial population with the release of a <u>burst</u> of virus particles. A typical one-step curve looks like this:

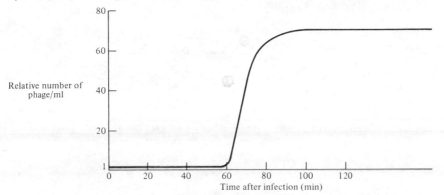

2. The quickest way would be to see whether the infecting agent is filterable through a 0.2 um filter. Most, but not all, virus particles will pass through such a filter, whereas rickettsia and chlamydia will not. Second, you should look in the electron micro- scope to see whether the agent has the characteristics of a prokaryotic cell or a virion.

3. Two methods are used to alter viruses so that they can be used as vaccines. The first, attenuation, involves passage of the viruses from culture to culture until a variant evolves with greatly re- duced virulence. The second, inactivation, uses viruses that have been treated with either a physical or chemical agent. Two of the best agents are formaldehyde and ultraviolet light because they inactivate the viral genome without altering the protein capsid. An unaltered capsid is necessary to ensure an active and specific immune response to the vaccine.

Post Test

1. a	6. c	11. a
2. d	7. d	12. b
3. b	8. b	13. c
4. d	9. b	14. d
5. a	10. b	15. c

9   The Viral Diseases of Humans I

The smallpox was always present, filling the churchyards with corpses, tormenting with constant fears all whom it had stricken, leaving on those whose lives it spared the hideous traces of its power, turning the babe into a changeling at which the mother shuddered, and making the eyes and cheeks of the bethrothed maiden objects of horror to the lover.

> T. B. Macaulay, *The History of England from the Accession of James II,* vol. iv. London: Longmans, 1849.

CHAPTER OUTLINE

I.   The Pneumotropic Viral Diseases

    A.   Influenza

    B.   Respiratory syncytial disease

    C.   Adenovirus infections

    D.   Rhinovirus infections

II.   The Dermotropic Viral Diseases

    A.   Chicken pox (varicella)

    B.   Herpes simplex

    C.   Measles (rubeola)

    D.   Mumps

    E.   Smallpox (variola)

    F.   Molluscum contagiosum

    G.   German Measles (rubella)

    H.   Kawasaki disease

OVERVIEW AND OBJECTIVES

Some of the oldest diseases known to man are viral in origin, yet an understanding of their nature has lagged well behind the understanding of bacterial infections. Although many bacterial diseases have been controlled or, in a practical sense, eliminated, most viral diseases do not yet have cures. The best method of treating a viral disease is through its prevention. The validity of this approach was demonstrated on October 26, 1979, when the World Health Organization announced that smallpox, a disease that has plagued man for centuries, had been eliminated from the earth. Smallpox is (was) a dermotropic viral disease. This chapter includes a discussion of the symptoms, modes of transmission, immunization, and treatment of the dermotropic and pneumotropic viral diseases of humans.

A pneumotropic viral disease is one in which the primary symptoms appear in the respiratory tract of the affected individual. They include the common cold (adenovirus and rhinovirus infections) and the flu (influenza), which are so common that many people consider them to be part of everyday life. Respiratory syncytial disease most often affects young children; adults rarely show severe symptoms. These diseases are often transmitted by droplets of saliva and respiratory mucus and in some cases by fomites, which are inanimate objects that harbor the disease on their surfaces.

Since the first pandemic of influenza in 1918, it has been one of the most troublesome and potentially devestating diseases of humans. It is estimated that more people died of influenza in 1918 than were killed during World War I. It has several characteristics that make its elimination both important and virtually impossible. First, no effective long-term vaccine can be produced because of the high mutation rate in the viral capsid proteins. This leads to high levels of antigenic variation, requiring development of new vaccines every few years. Second, several of the complications of influenza have high mortality levels. Pneumonia kills many older victims of influenza, while Guillain-Barre syndrome (GBS) leads to nerve damage and polio-like paralysis. Another complication of influenza (as well as the dermotropic disease chicken pox) is Reye's syndrome, which involves liver and brain damage in children recovering from these diseases.

Many dermotropic (or pox) viral diseases result in pocks (pitted scars) including chicken pox, smallpox, cowpox. These diseases have the skin as their primary site of infection. Other dermotropic diseases are herpes simplex, measles, mumps, molluscum contagiosum, German Measles, and Kawasaki disease. No viral agent has been isolated for Kawasaki disease, but its etiology suggests a viral infection. Many dermotropic viral diseases are common childhood diseases and are now being controlled with effective vaccination of children. Others such as herpes simplex lead to chronic infections, which recur throughout the life of the affected individual. Shingles (herpes zoster) is now considered to be a chronic form of chicken pox (varicella), and German measles has been linked to diabetes. A number of drugs are potentially useful in the treatment of certain dermotropic diseases. These include 5-iodo-2-deoxyuridine (IUDR), adenine arabinoside-A (ara-A), and vidarabine (vira-A).

After you have read Chapter 9 of your textbook, you should be able to:

1. Define or identify the following terms: influenza, spikes, hemagglutinin, neuraminidase, pandemic, antigenic variation, droplets, titer, amantadine, Guillain-Barre syndrome (GBS), Reye's syndrome,

respiratory syncytial disease, syncytium, maternal antibody, adenovirus, inclusions, anorexia, common cold, croup, keratoconjunctivitis, rhinovirus, acute coryza, fomites, chicken pox, varicella, herpes zoster, shingles, vesicles, crop of lesions, adenine arabinoside-A (ara-A), zoster immune globulin (ZIG), V-Z virus, herpes simplex, HSV-1, HSV-2, Lipshutz bodies, cold sore, gingivostomatitis, genital herpes, TORCH, 5-iodo-2-deoxyuridine (IUDR), vidarabine (vira-A), measles, rubeola, Koplik spots, subacute sclerosing panencephalitis (SSPE), mumps, epidemic parotitis, orchitis, oophoritis, smallpox, variola, macules, papules, vesicles, Guarnieri bodies, pustules, pock, variolation, vaccination, surveillance containment, alastrim, molluscum contagiosum, molluscum body, German measles, rubella, Kawasaki disease, and desquamation.

2. Outline the symptoms of each of the viral diseases discussed.

3. Compare and contrast the modes of transmission of the viral diseases described.

4. List the complications and chronic disorders associated with each of the pneumotropic and dermotropic viral diseases.

5. Discuss the effectiveness and ineffectiveness of vaccination against the viral diseases.

PRE-TEST

1. While a young girl is recovering from chicken pox she begins to vomit, becomes disoriented, has convulsions, and finally lapses into a coma. The child is displaying the symptoms of:
   a. Guillain-Barre syndrome.
   b. Parkinson's disease.
   c. Reye's syndrome.
   d. keratoconjunctivitis.

2. A new strain of influenza virus has been isolated. It is a type B virus and originated in swine. The first infection occurred in 1981 in California, and this was the fourth strain isolated from the outbreak. The proper nomenclature for this strain is:
   a. B:swine:California:4:81.
   b. B:California:4:81.
   c. B:swine:California:81:4.
   d. B:California:4:81:swine.

3. A major reason why an effective vaccine cannot be produced against influenza virus is the:
   a. low level of antigenicity of the capsid.
   b. high level of antigenic variation.
   c. interference of maternal antigens.
   d. association of Guillain-Barre syndrome with vaccination.

4. The type of herpes simplex that most often causes genital herpies is:

a. HSV-1.
b. HSV-2.
c. herpes zoster.
d. shingles.

5. The scientific name for measles is:
   a. rubella.
   b. variola.
   c. varicella.
   d. rubeola.

6. Viruses that have spikes on their envelopes and contain both hemagglutinin and neuraminidase cause, among other diseases:
   a. chicken pox.
   b. influenza.
   c. smallpox.
   d. the common cold.

7. A respiratory disease which affects young children takes its name
   from the giant cells that form from the fusion of infected culture
   cells. These cells are called:
   a. syncytia.
   b. Lipshutz bodies.
   c. Koplik spots.
   d. zoster cells.

8. Even though a virus that causes this disease has not yet been
   isolated, the course of the disease is suggestive of a viral agent.
   This disease is:
   a. rubella.
   b. rubeola.
   c. molluscum contagiosum.
   d. Kawasaki disease.

9. Guarnieri bodies are characteristic of:
   a. smallpox.
   b. chicken pox.
   c. mumps.
   d. rubella.

10. In adults, mumps virus represents a threat to the reproductive
    organs. In males, infection of the testes with mumps virus is
    called:
    a. oophoritis.
    b. papules.
    c. orchitis.
    d. pustules.

11. When adenovirus multiplies in the nucleus of an infected cell, it:
    a. produces skin lesions called vesicles.
    b. causes visible nuclear granules called inclusions.
    c. induces nuclear changes called fomites.
    d. forms Koplik spots.

12. A synthetic drug thought to act by blocking the penetration of influenza virus into the host cell is:
    a. amantadine.
    b. adenine arabinoside-A.
    c. 5-iodo-2-deoxyuridine.
    d. vidarabine.

13. Desquamation can be a symptom of:
    a. measles.
    b. German measles.
    c. mumps.
    d. Kawasaki disease.

14. When a large number of cases of a disease occur worldwide, the outbreak of the disease is referred to as a(n):
    a. epidemic.
    b. global outbreak.
    c. global epidemic.
    d. pandemic.

15. An inanimate object that transmits disease is a(n):
    a. fomite.
    b. inanimate object.
    c. contact epidemiology.
    d. anorexia.

PRACTICE EXERCISES

1. Matching. Many viral diseases have both common and scientific names. For each of the viral diseases below match the common name in the left-hand column with the scientific name in the right-hand column by placing the appropriate number on the line provided.

6	a. Chicken pox	1.	Rubella
3	b. Shingles	2.	Acute coryza
4	c. Measles	3.	Herpes zoster
1	d. German measles	4.	Rubeola
10	e. Smallpox	5.	Adenovirus infection
2	f. Head cold	6.	Varicella
8	g. Mumps	7.	Vaccinia
5	h. Croup	8.	Epidemic parotitis
9	i. Cold sores	9.	Herpes simplex
7	j. Cowpox	10.	Variola

2. Identify the family in which the viral agent of each of the

following diseases is classified.

a. Measles: _PARAmyxovieidae_

b. German measles: _Togavanidae_

c. Mumps: _paramyxovaxidae_

d. Influenza: _Orthomyxovasidae_

e. Smallpox: _poxvaridae_

3. Many viral diseases lead to a number of complications. Some of these complications are listed below. Identify which of the viral diseases are associated with each of these complications.

a. Encephalitis:

_____

b. Herpes zoster:

_____

c. Meningitis:

_____

d. Pneumonia:

_____

e. Reye's syndrome:

_____

f. Heart attack:

_____

g. Guillain-Barre syndrome:

_____

h. Congenital infections:

_____

4. Fill in the blanks. There are (a) _____ types of influenza virus: Types (b) _____ and (c) _____, which cause worldwide epidemics called (d) _____, and type (e) _____, which occurs sporadically. Each type is known for its (f) _____ _____, a process in

which changes occur in the protein structure of the (g) _____
_____ _____ as well as in the (h) _____ and
(i) _____. This results in a myriad of variants
that are unrecognized by the (j) _____ produced in
a previous infection. A person therefore can suffer innumerable
cases of influenza. Also, this phenomenon prevents the development
of an effective (k) _____.

5. <u>True</u> or <u>False</u>. Decide whether each of the following statements is
true or false; then place a T for true or an F for false on the
line provided.

____ a. TORCH is a term that was coined to focus attention on diseases
with congenital significance. (T for Toxoplasmosis; R for
Rubella; C for Cytomegalovirus infection; and H for Herpes
simplex. The 0 represents "Other diseases".)

____ b. Alastrim is a minor form of smallpox that was eradicated at
the same time as the major form was eliminated.

____ c. Molluscum bodies are associated with molluscum contagiosum.
These bodies compact the cells' nuclei and push them to one
side. The disease is diagnosed on the presence of these bodies.

____ d. Keratoconjunctivitis is an inflammation of the eye associated
with Type 8 adenovirus infection.

____ e. Shingles and chicken pox are caused by the same virus, which
is often referred to as <u>V-Z virus</u> to reflect this relationship.

____ f. Lipshutz bodies aid in the diagnosis of herpes simplex Type 1
but not in the diagnosis of Type 2.

____ g. Mumps represents a threat to the reproductive organs of adults.
When the mumps virus infects the female ovaries the condition
is referred to as <u>oophoritis</u>. It is relatively rare.

____ h. Kawasaki disease first appeared in the United States in 1971
but is named for the town in Japan where the second case was
reported.

____ i. Both herpes zoster and herpes simplex are recurring diseases.
New attacks are sometimes triggered by emotional or physical
upsets.

6. Vaccination is probably the most effective "treatment" for viral
diseases. Place an X in the space provided to identify those
diseases listed for which effective vaccines are available.

_____ a. Influenza

_____ b. Respiratory syncytial disease

_____ c. Mumps

3. Each of the following diseases is caused by a member of the herpes-viridae, <u>except</u>:
   a. chicken pox.
   b. shingles.
   c. smallpox.
   d. cold sores.

4. An infection of the brain is referred to as:
   a. pneumonia.
   b. encephalitis.
   c. meningitis.
   d. orchitis.

5. The <u>HI</u> test depends on the presence of _____ in the virion of the infecting virus.
   a. spikes
   b. herpes antigen
   c. hemagglutinin
   d. neuraminidase

6. Loss of appetite associated with a disease is called:
   a. amantadine.
   b. fomite.
   c. anorexia.
   d. syncytium.

7. All of the following are viral diseases, <u>except</u>:
   a. smallpox.
   b. great pox.
   c. chicken pox.
   d. cowpox.

8. A drug thought to inhibit viral disease because it is a nucleic acid substitute is:
   a. ara-A.
   b. ZIG.
   c. amantadine.
   d. TORCH.

9. A virus closely related to the smallpox virus causes:
   a. chicken pox.
   b. cold sores.
   c. molluscum contagiosum.
   d. mumps.

10. All of the following diseases can be transmitted by droplets, <u>except</u>:
    a. influenza.
    b. herpes simplex (Type II).
    c. chicken pox.
    d. adenovirus infections.

11. A viral disease characterized by formation of crops of lesions is:
    a. chicken pox.

111

b. herpes simplex.
c. shingles.
d. smallpox.

12. An adult male who has never had German measles wants to be vac-
    cinated against the disease. He should be advised against the im-
    munization because:
    a. the vaccine has not been tested in adults.
    b. antigenic variation is so great that vaccines are not effective.
    c. the vaccine is known to initiate arthritis in adults.
    d. diabetes is linked to vaccination of adults.

13. If the patient in exercise 12 were female, your advice might be:
    a. not to have the vaccination for the same reason you gave the
       male patient.
    b. to definitely have the vaccination because adult women may get
       oophoritis from rubella infections.
    c. to have the vaccination if the woman plans to or thinks she
       may become pregnant in the future.
    d. to have the vaccination only if she is currently pregnant.

14. A herpes virus that can cause a type of nonepidemic encephalitis
    in children is:
    a. herpes simplex (Type I).
    b. herpes simplex (Type II).
    c. herpes zoster.
    d. varicella.

15. Acute coryza is caused by a virus classified in the:
    a. orthomyxoviridae.
    b. paramyxoviridae.
    c. adenoviridae.
    d. picornaviridae.

ANSWERS TO EXERCISES

Pre-Test

1. c   6. b   11. b

2. a   7. a   12. a

3. b   8. d   13. d

4. b   9. a   14. d

5. d   10. c   15. a

Practice Exercises

1. a. 6; b. 3; c. 4; d. 1; e. 10; f. 2; g. 8; h. 5;

   i. 9; j. 7.

2. a. paramyxoviridae; b. togavirida; c. paramyxoviridae;
   d. orthomyxoviridae; e. poxviridae.

3. a. measles, herpes simplex, mumps; b. chicken pox; c. mumps;
   d. measles, respiratory syncytial disease, adenovirus infections;
   e. influenza, chicken pox; f. Kawasaki; g. influenza;
   h. chicken pox, German measles.

4. a. three; b. A; c. B; d. pandemics; e. C;
   f. antigenic variation; g. capsid; h. hemagglutinin;
   i. neuraminidase; j. antibodies; k. vaccine.

5. a. T; b. F; c. F; d. T; e. T; f. F; g. T; h. F;
   i. T.

6. a. Those diseases for which vaccines are available are: a, c, d,
   g, and j.

7. a. Chicken pox, herpes simplex; b. Rhinovirus infections;
   c. Molluscum contagiosum; d. Smallpox; e. Kawasaki disease;
   f. chicken pox; g. measles; h. Respiratory syncytial disease.

Concept Exercises

1. Obtain a number of volunteers. Divide them into two groups. Let
   one group sit in a draft, protect the other group from drafts.
   Calculate the frequency of colds in the two groups and determine
   whether there is a significantly higher frequency of colds in the
   "draft" group than in the "nondraft" group. (This type of experiment has disproven the assumption that getting chilled leads to
   catching colds.)

2. Since chicken pox and shingles are caused by the same virus, antibodies developed against chicken pox are capable of inactivating
   herpes zoster virus.

3. German measles is a dangerous congenital disease, which can lead
   to stillbirth and birth defects if a woman contracts the disease
   during pregnancy. Therefore it is important to assess the sus-
   ceptiability of the pregnant woman. As pointed out in the textbook, the greatest danger is during the first trimester of preg-
   nancy--a time when most women do not realize that they are pregnant and most likely have not yet visited their physician.

Post-test

1. d	6. c	11. a
2. a	7. b	12. c
3. c	8. a	13. c
4. b	9. c	14. a
5. c	10. b	15. d

10   The Viral Diseases of Humans II

<u>Then one day a little idea came to Pasteur, and he hurried to tell it</u>
<u>to Roux.</u>

   <u>"This rabies virus that gets into people by bites, it settles in</u>
<u>their brains and spinal cords. . . . All the symptoms of hydrophobia</u>
<u>show that it's the nervous system that this virus--this bug we can't</u>
<u>find--attacks. . . . That's where we have to look for the unknown</u>
<u>microbe. . ."</u>

          Paul De Kruif, "Pasteur and the Mad Dog," in <u>Microbe</u> <u>Hunters</u>.
          New York: Harcourt, Brace and World, 1953.

CHAPTER OUTLINE

   I.   The Viscerotropic Viral Diseases

        A.   Yellow fever

        B.   Dengue fever

        C.   Infectious mononucleosis

        D.   Cytomegalovirus disease

        E.   Lassa fever

        F.   Coxsackie virus diseases

        G.   ECHO virus diseases

        H.   Infectious hepatitis

        I.   Serum hepatitis

        J.   NANB hepatitis

        K.   Colorado tick fever

        L.   Sandfly fever

        M.   Lyme arthritis

  II.   The Neurotropic Viral Diseases

        A.   Rabies

        B.   Lymphocytic choriomeningitis

C. Polio

D. Arthropodborne encephalitis

E. Slow virus disease

OVERVIEW AND OBJECTIVES

In the 19th century, rabies was one of the most feared of diseases. It
is known in most mammalian species and was, at that time, always fatal.
While many other diseases have killed many more people, rabies has
always held a special horror for humans. In the late 1700s, France was
forced to pass laws against poisoning, strangling, or shooting of
people who were suspected of having hydrophobia (rabies). Pasteur was
determined to find the cause of the disease and its cure. Development
of the rabies vaccine was considered by Pasteur himself as one of the
crowining glories of a most glorious life of science. Pasteur never
saw the microbe that causes rabies, but today we know that it is caused
by one of the neurotropic viruses. In this chapter, we will continue
to examine the viral diseases of humans with the study of the
viscerotropic and neurotropic viruses.

Viscerotropic viruses are those that infect the internal organs.
Some are unfamiliar, whereas others have changed the course of history. In the 1800s, many nations had attempted to dig a canal across
the Isthmus of Panama, but each had failed because so many workers
died from yellow fever. The United States succeded mainly because of
the efforts of Walter Reed, who identified the vector of the disease--
the mosquito. Hence, the United States controlled this strategically
important canal from before World War I until recently. Few accomplishments have had such an effect on U. S. foreign policy as did Walter
Reed's discovery. Other viscerotropic diseases are less well known but
potentially as hazardous. Many of these diseases are, like yellow
fever, fairly benign in the indigenous populations but very severe to
exogenous populations. Yellow fever is one of the few viscerotropic
diseases for which there is a vaccine.

Neotropic diseases are those that affect mainly the central nervous
system. They include rabies, lymphocytic choriomeningitis, poliomyelitis, and arthropodborne encephalitis. Like rabies, poliomyelitis
(polio) was long a feared disease: each summer it killed and paralyzed
thousands of individuals, including many children. With the introduction
of the Salk and Sabin vaccines in the late 50s and early 60s, the number of cases of polio was reduced dramatically until the mid-70s, when
many parents failed to have their children vaccinated. An outbreak of
Type I polio in Pennsylvania in 1978 demonstrated that a disease is
not dead so long as any cases exist, and the failure to vaccinate
against such a disease can lead to the recurrence of the disease in
epidemic proportions.

After you have read Chapter 10 of your textbook, you should be
able to:

1. Define or identify each of the following: yellow fever, jaundice,

scarification, Councilman bodies, dengue fever, breakbone fever, saddleback fever, dengue hemorrhagic fever (DHF), infectious mononucleosis, lymphocytes, Epstein-Barr virus, Downey cells, Paul-Bunnell test, cytomegalovirus disease, Lipshutz bodies, Lassa fever, hemorrhagic fevers, arenavirus, Marburg disease, Ebola virus, Ebola hemorrhagic fever, coxsackie virus diseases, picornaviruses, herpangina, aseptic meningitis, pleurodynia, myocarditis, 24-hour cold virus, ECHO virus diseases, enteroviruses, exanthems, summer diarrhea, infectious hepatitis, short-incubation hepatitis (Type A), anicteric, serum hepatitis (Type B), Dane particle, Australia antigen, long-incubation hepatitis, NANB hepatitis, Colorado tick fever, leukopenia, sandfly fever, 3-day fever, pappataci fever, Lyme arthritis, rabies, hydrophobia, Merieux human diploid cell vaccine, Negri body, lymphocytic choriomeningitis (LCM), poliomyelitis, medulla, bulbar polio, Drinker respirometer, arthropod-borne encephalitis, and slow virus disease.

2. Identify the families of the causative viruses of the diseases described.

3. Describe the transmission patterns of these diseases.

4. Distinguish among the various forms of hepatitis.

5. Outline the complications to the diseases discussed.

PRE-TEST

1. Negri bodies are diagnostic for:
   a. polio.
   b. yellow fever.
   c. rabies.
   d. sandfly fever.

2. The Dane particle is a DNA virus and is the causative agent of:
   a. infectious hepatitis.
   b. NANB hepatitis.
   c. Virus A hepatitis.
   d. Serum hepatitis.

3. A physician has a patient with jaundice. He has not had a blood transfusion but has just returned from a visit to Central America. Of the following diseases, he would be most likely to have:
   a. dengue fever.
   b. yellow fever.
   c. infectious mononucleosis.
   d. serum hepatitis.

4. "Short-incubation hepatitis" is another name for:
   a. serum hepatitis.
   b. virus B hepatitis.
   c. NANB hepatitis.
   d. infectious hepatitis.

5. A fever that rises, then falls, and rises again is referred to as:
   a. sandfly fever.
   b. saddleback fever.
   c. tick fever.
   d. dengue fever.

6. Lyme arthritis is a rare form of joint disease, apparently trans-mitted by infected ticks. It is caused by a virus classified as a(n):
   a. togavirus.
   b. arenavirus.
   c. picornavirus.
   d. unclassified virus.

7. One name for the disease transmitted by the members of the Phlebotomus genus is:
   a. pappataci fever.
   b. saddleback fever.
   c. Colorado tick fever.
   d. arthropodborne encephalitis.

8. Kuru and senility may both be forms off:
   a. slow virus disease.
   b. arthropodborne encephalitis.
   c. lymphocytic choriomeningitis.
   d. poliomyelitis.

9. In the most serious form of polio, the virus infects the stem of the brain. The nerves of the upper body torso are affected and paralysis can result. This form of polio is known as:
   a. Brunhilde polio.
   b. bulbar polio.
   c. Lansing polio.
   d. Leon polio.

10. The arenaviruses are characterized as:
    a. RNA viruses that possess sandy internal granules.
    b. DNA viruses with complex virions.
    c. viruses with single-stranded DNA.
    d. icosahedral RNA viruses.

11. Vaccines are available for all of the following diseases, except:
    a. yellow fever.
    b. rabies.
    c. infectious hepatitis
    d. poliomyelitis.

12. A woman with a fluctuating fever comes to a physician. She says that every bone in her body feels like it's breaking. Of the following, the patient is likely to be suffering from:
    a. dengue fever.
    b. poliomyelitis.
    c. ECHO virus disease.
    d. Lyme arthritis.

13. Infectious mononucleosis is caused by Epstein-Barr virus. Another
    condition caused by this virus is:
    a. cytomegalovirus disease.
    b. Lyme arthritis.
    c. serum hepatitis.
    d. Burkitt's lymphoma.

14. In the Paul-Bunnell test, a sample of the patient's serum is mixed
    with sheep or horse erythrocytes. If the latter show an obvious
    clumping reaction, it indicates the presence of:
    a. Downey cells.
    b. antibodies against mononucleosis virus.
    c. Councilman bodies.
    d. Negri bodies.

15. Some RNA viruses that show uncertain symmetry of their virions ap-
    pear to have sandy, internal granules when seen in the electron
    microscope. One disease caused by such viruses is:
    a. Lassa fever.
    b. dengue fever.
    c. Lyme arthritis.
    d. Marburg disease.

PRACTICE EXERCISES

1. Identify the family in which the virus that causes each of the
   following diseases is classified.

   a. Rabies: _____

   b. Poliomyelitis: _____

   c. Yellow fever: _____

   d. Coxsackie virus disease: _____

   e. Infectious hepatitis: _____

2. True or False: Determine whether each of the following statements
   is true or false; then place a T for true or an F for false on the
   line provided.

   _____ a. Dengue fever is accompanied by extreme pain in the muscles and
            limbs, giving the impression that the bones are breaking.

   _____ b. Group A coxsackie viruses have been isolated from cases of
            aseptic meningitis in children.

   _____ c. Because its incubation period is longer than for other forms
            of hepatitis, infectious hepatitis is sometimes called "long-
            incubation hepatitis."

   _____ d. NANB hepatitis gets its name from the fact that it is caused
            by neither Type A nor Type B virus.

_____ e. One of the symptoms of Colorado tick fever is a fluctuating
fever. Because of this fever, the disease is sometimes called
"saddleback fever."

_____ f. No agent has been isolated for Lyme arthritis, but studies
point to the involvement of a virus. (The disease is named for
a town in Connecticut where Yale University researchers studied
a large number of cases.)

_____ g. People with rabies develop difficulty in swallowing, which leads
to saliva dripping from the mouth because it cannot be
swallowed. This symptom together with brain degeneration increases a person's reactions to the sight, sound or thought of
water and gives the disease its other name--hydrophobia.

_____ h. Coxsackie viruses of group B cause a common disease of children
in which vesicles with a punched-out appearance form on the
tonsils and soft palate. This disease is called herpangina.

3. Several viral diseases discussed in this chapter can be classified
by specific symptoms, some of which are:

1. jaundice   3. saddleback fever

2. hemorrhagic fever   4. Lipshutz bodies

Classify each of the diseases listed below according to one of
these symptoms by placing the corresponding number on the line provided.

_____ a. Yellow fever

_____ b. Serum hepatitis

_____ c. Sandfly fever

_____ d. Lassa fever

_____ e. Colorado tick fever

_____ f. Cytomegalovirus disease

_____ g. Dengue fever--primary infection

_____ h. Infectious hepatitis

5. Fill in the blanks. Serum hepatitis, or (a) _____
_____ hepatitis, is caused by a small virus
named the (b) _____ _____. The
virus is composed of an icosahedral core of (c) _____
surrounded by a protein that contains an antigen called the (d)
_____ _____ _____
antigen or (e) _____. The protein is then surrounded by a lipoprotein envelope containing a different protein

120

antigen, the (f) _____ _____
_____ antigen or (g) _____.
This is the (h) _____ antigen described in 1965
by the Nobel laureat Baruch Blumberg. Because of its incubation
period, serum hepatitis is sometimes called (i) _____
incubation hepatitis.

Infectious hepatitis, or (j) _____ _____
_____ hepatitis, is caused by a small (k) _____ _____
virion. The symmetry of this virion is (1) _____. The
virus is still classified with the (m) __ _____ _____
_____ by many virologists. Because of its incubation
period, infectious hepatitis is sometimes called (n) _____
_____ incubation hepatitis.

5. Many viscerotropic and neurotropic viral diseases discussed in
this chapter are transmitted by an arthropod vector. Place an X
in the space provided to identify the diseases listed that have an
arthropod vector.

_____ a. Arthropodborne encephalitis

_____ b. Dengue fever

_____ c. ECHO virus disease

_____ d. Colorado tick fever

_____ e. Yellow fever

_____ f. Rabies

_____ g. Lyme arthritis

_____ h. Poliomyelitis

_____ i. Sandfly fever

_____ j. Lassa fever

6. Virus particles contain either DNA or RNA but never both forms of
nucleic acid. Indicate whether the causative agent of each of the
following diseases is an RNA or DNA virus by placing an R for RNA
or a D for DNA on the line provided.

_____ a. Poliomyelitis

_____ b. Lymphocytic choriomeningitis

_____ c. Yellow fever

_____ d. Serum hepatitis

_____ e. Lassa fever

_____ f. Infectious hepatitis

_____ g. Colorado tick fever

_____ h. Rabies

_____ i. Cytomegalovirus disease

_____ j. Infectious mononucleosis

CONCEPT EXERCISES

1. Natives of the Caribbean islands are affected only mildly by yellow fever, but the mortality rate for outsiders is unusually high. Why should this be so?

_____

_____

_____

_____

_____

_____

_____

_____

_____

2. Many virologists believe that some forms of senility may be the result of an infection caused by a slow virus. What characteristics of senility would lead these scientists to such a conclusion?

_____

_____

_____

_____

_____

_____

_____

_____

3. Pasteur's vaccine for rabies consisted of pieces of spinal cord of rabbits dead of rabies which had been dried for various periods of time. On the first day, the patient is given spinal cord dried for fourteen days, on the second, cord dried for thirteen days, and so on until on the fourteenth day when cord dried for only one day is used. Explain why this process provides an effective vaccine for the prevention of rabies.

_____

_____

_____

_____

_____

_____

POST-TEST

1. The process of introducing vaccines into the patient by scratching them into the skin is called:
   a. scratching.
   b. skin testing.
   c. subcutaneous inoculation.
   d. scarification.

2. Yellow fever can be distinguished from all other diseases discussed in this chapter by the presence of:
   a. jaundice.
   b. Councilman bodies.
   c. Negri bodies.
   d. saddleback fever.

3. Sandfly fever is caused by a virus classified in the:
   a. picornaviridae.
   b. bunyaviridae.
   c. rhabdoviridae.
   d. togaviridae.

4. Viral diseases affecting the liver are classified as:
   a. pneumotropic.
   b. neurotropic.
   c. dermotropic.
   d. viscerotropic.

5. In congenital infection, this virus passes across the placenta and umbilical cord and damages the fetus by multiplying in its tissue. Problems arise from destruction of the placental tissues, and mental retardation is common. This condition is caused by:
   a. cytomegalovirus.
   b. ECHO virus.

123

c. lymphocytic choriomeningitis virus.
d. hepatitis virus B.

6. All of the following may be slow virus diseases, <u>except</u>:
   a. Creutzfeldt-Jakob syndrome.
   b. kuru.
   c. Lyme arthritis.
   d. senility.

7. The type of polio virus <u>most likely</u> to cause paralytic disease is:
   a. Type I, Brunhilde strain.
   b. Type II, Lansing strain.
   c. Type III, Leon strain.
   d. Type B, Dane strain.

8. Saddleback fever is a symptom of all the following diseases,
   <u>except</u>:
   a. Sandfly fever.
   b. Colorado tick fever.
   c. Lassa fever.
   d. dengue fever.

9. An adult female comes to her physician with jaundice. About three
   months ago she had been in an automobile accident and had received
   emergency blood transfusions. The physician believes that the
   woman has serum hepatitis. If this is true, which of the following
   types of virus will be present?
   a. an RNA picornavirus
   b. an RNA virus of unclassified symmetry
   c. a DNA herpesviridae
   d. a DNA virus of unclassified symmetry

10. The mosquito <u>Aedes aegypti</u> transmits to humans the virus that
    causes:
    a. yellow fever.
    b. Colorado tick fever.
    c. sandfly fever.
    d. Lyme arthritis.

11. The TORCH group of diseases are all congenital infections. One of
    the letters stands for a viscerotropic viral disease. The letter
    and disease are:
    a. "C" for Colorado tick fever.
    b. "C" for cytomegalovirus disease.
    c. "C" for coxsackie virus disease.
    d. "H" for hepatitis.

12. A viscerotropic viral disease that may be transmitted by droplets
    is:
    a. infectious mononucleosis.
    b. dengue fever.
    c. coxsackie virus disease.
    d. ECHO virus disease.

13. All of the following diseases are transmitted by ticks, except:
    a. poliomyelitis.
    b. Colorado tick fever.
    c. Lyme arthritis.
    d. arthropodborne encephalitis.

14. Liver inflammation is a principal symptom of a disease transmitted
    by contaminated food and water as well as by contact, arthropods,
    and sexual intercourse. This disease is:
    a. infectious hepatitis.
    b. Colorado tick fever.
    c. cytomegalovirus disease.
    d. ECHO virus disease.

15. A patient comes to her physician with swollen glands, high lymph-
    ocyte counts, and general discomfort. The physician orders a
    Paul-Bunnel test, which is positive. This patient has a disease
    caused by a virus that also causes:
    a. shingles.
    b. cold sores.
    c. Burkitt's lymphoma.
    d. cytomegalovirus disease.

ANSWERS TO EXERCISES

Pre-Test

1. c   6. d   11. c

2. d   7. a   12. a

3. b   8. a   13. d

4. d   9. b   14. b

5. b   10. a   15. a

Practice Exercises

1. a. rhabdoviridae; b. picornaviridae; c. togaviridae;

   d. picornaviridae; e. picornaviridae.

2. a. T; b. T; c. F; d. T; e. F; f. T; g. T; h. F.

3. a. 1; b. 1; c. 3; d. 2; e. 3; f. 4; g. 3; h. 1.

4. a. Virus B; b. Dane particle; c. DNA; d. hepatitis B core;

   e. HBcAg; f. hepatitis B surface; g. HBsAg;

   h. Australia; i. long; j. Virus A; k. RNA; l. uncertain;

   m. picornaviridae; n. short.

5. The arthropod-transmitted diseases are a, b, d, e, g, and i.

6. a. R; b. R; c. R; d. D; e. R; f. R; g. R; h. R; i. D; j. D.

Concept Exercises

1. Natives of the Caribbean islands have been exposed to yellow fever for generations. Natural selection has most likely selected for those individuals in the population with higher "natural" immunity. Natives of other parts of the world who are not normally exposed to the disease have had no selective pressure applied. Also, through constant exposure since birth, individuals native to the islands have most likely developed antibodies to the virus through "subclinical" infections.

2. Senility is a progressive degenerative neural "disease," which develops slowly late in life. All slow viruses including Kuru, scrapie, multiple sclerosis, Parkinson's disease, and Creutzfeldt-Jakob syndrome are progressively degenerative neural diseases that develop slowly over a long period of time after infection. In fact, Creutzfeldt-Jakob syndrome is often described as a "presenile dementia of humans" and shares all of the symptoms of true senility, except that it develops early in life--often in the forties or fifties.

3. As we learned in Chapter 8, many viruses are inactivated by drying. By drying rabbit spinal cord for fourteen days, Pasteur and his co-workers used an inoculum with a low viral titer. By reducing the drying time day by day, they slowly increased the titer of the inoculum and therefore challenged the immune system with progressively more virulent vaccines.

Post-Test

1. d	6. c	11. b
2. b	7. b	12. a
3. b	8. c	13. a
4. d	9. d	14. a
5. a	10. a	15. c

11 The Fungi

The deep or systemic mycoses are serious diseases caused by various fungi that can invade the subcutaneous tissues and become systemic. There is growing concern about the rising incidence of these infections. This increase may in part be because improved diagnostic methods are bringing them to light, but in southwestern United States coccidio-idomycosis is endemic in an expanding area and the number of primary infections is estimated to be about 10 million based on skin tests with coccidioidin. Histoplasmosis, considered to be relatively rare 25 years ago, is known on the basis of positive skin tests with histo-plasmin to be present or to have occurred in up to 90% of the popu-lation in our central states usually in the benign form. Based on the best estimates, approximately 30 million cases have occurred in the United States. The chronic pulmonary disease usually results in ap-proximately a 30% mortality.

> Everett Smith Beneke, Scope Monograph on Human Mycoses. Kalamazoo, Michigan: The Upjohn Co., 1970.

CHAPTER OUTLINE

I. Characteristics of the Fungi

    A. Structure

    B. Asexual reproduction in fungi

    C. Sexual reproduction in fungi

    D. Oomycetes

    E. Zygomycetes

    F. Ascomycetes

    G. Basidiomycetes

    H. Deuteromycetes

    I. Growth of the fungi

II. The Yeasts

III. Fungal Diseases of Humans

    A. Cryptococcosis

    B. Candidiasis

C. Sporotrichosis

D. Aspergillosis

E. Coccidioidomycosis

F. North American blastomycosis

G. Histoplasmosis

H. Dermatomycosis

OVERVIEW AND OBJECTIVES

Since before the beginning of recorded history, fungi have been the
servants of humans. In a 4000-year-old Egyptian tomb at Thebes on the
Nile, models of a brewery and bakery can be seen. Both processes depend on yeast to ferment raw materials to produce the final products.
In addition, yeasts are used to make foods palatable and nutritious,
and to synthesize economically important vitamins, fats, and proteins.
Fungi produce a number of antibiotics (see Chapter 23). They also
return important chemicals to the earth by decaying plant and animal
remains. Perhaps it is a small price to pay that some fungi produce
diseases in humans, animals, and plants. Fungal infections are difficult to treat, however, because--like their hosts--fungi are eukaryotic, and many of the antibiotics effective against prokaryotes (i.e.,
bacteria) are not effective against fungi. In addition, because all
eukaryotic cells are similar in their structure and metabolism, it is
difficult to identify a chemical agent that is more toxic to the fungal
pathogen than to the human host.

Fungi are a unique group of organisms, which are classified in
their own kingdom in modern systems of taxonomy. Fungi that do not
produce hyphae are termed yeasts. Some fungi have both yeastlike and
hyphael stages. These organisms are referred to as dimorphic. Fungi
can be either septate (divided into individual cells) or coenocytic
(septa between cells are absent or incomplete). They contain chitin
and/or cellulose in their cell walls. These organisms are saprobes
that utilize organic materials as a source of energy and building
blocks. Most fungi have complex life cycles, including both haploid
and diploid stages. Most reproduce both sexually and asexually.

There are five groups of fungi, which are divided according to the
type of sexual cycle they undergo. These five groups are the Oomycetes,
Zygomycetes, Ascomycetes, Basidiomycetes, and Deuteromycetes. In this
chapter many of the fungal diseases are discussed.

Many fungal diseases pose life-threatening situations to individual
patients. Cryptococcosis is considered the most dangerous fungal
disorder in humans. The disease affects the lungs and the coverings
of the spinal cord. It is caused by Cryptococcus neoformans.
Candidiasis is caused by Candida albicans, an organism normally found
in the intestine and vagina. Sporotrichosis is a disease that causes
pulmonary lesions and is caused by Sporothrix shenckii. Aspergillosis

128

is caused by members of the genus Aspergillus. Aspergillus flavus produces aflatoxins, which may be carcinogenic. Coccidioides immitis causes a disease endemic to the southwestern United States called Coccidioidomycosis. It has symptoms similar to influenza. Histoplasmosis is also a respiratory disease. It is caused by Emmonsiella capsulata. The causative agent of North American blastomycosis, Ajellomyces dermatitidis, is associated with pigeon droppings and dusty soil. The progressive form of this disease may involve many of the internal organs and may be fatal. Dermatomycosis is an infection of the skin, hair, and nails that is caused by a number of different fungi.

After you have read Chapter 11 of your textbook, you should be able to:

1. Define or identify the following terms: fungus, yeast, cellulose, septum, septate, aseptate, coenocytic, hypha, fruiting body, mycelium, mycology, sporangium, sporangiospores, conidia, conidiosphores, arthrospores, budding, diploid, haploid, slime molds, lichen, Oomycetes, oospore, zoospore, Zygomycetes zygospore, Ascomycetes, ascus, ascospores, Basidiomycetes, basidium, Deuteromycetes, dimorphic, cryptococcosis, meninges, Cryptococcus neoformans, T-lymphocyte, amphotericin B, candidiasis, Candida albicans, pseudohyphae, vulvovaginitis, pruritis, nystatin, candicidin, thrush, gentian violet, moniliasis, onychia, sporotrichosis, Sporothrix schenckii, edema, aspergillosis, Aspergillus fumigatus, aspergilloma, otomycosis, Aspergillus flavus, aflatoxin, coccidioidomycosis, Coccidioides immitis, spherule, North American blastomycosis, Ajellomyces dermatitidis, histoplasmosis, Emmonsiella capsulata, summer flu, Darling's disease, dermatomycosis, Trichophyton, Epidermophyton, Microsporum, and griseofulvin.

2. Describe the structure and sexual cycles of the fungi.

3. Describe the asexual and sexual reproduction structures and spores of the various groups of fungi.

4. List the symptoms and causative agents of the fungal diseases discussed.

PRE-TEST

1. Thrush is a disease of newborns and older people. It is caused by:
   a. Candida albicans.
   b. Sporothrix schenkii.
   c. Emmonsiella capsulata.
   d. Cryptococcus neoformans.

2. Mushrooms are classified as:
   a. Ascomycetes.
   b. Deuteromycetes.
   c. Basidiomycetes.
   d. Zygomycetes.

3. In your laboratory course in mycology, you have isolated a fungus

that forms hyphae in which the cytoplasm of the various cells can mix freely. An organism with this characteristic is called:
a. septate.
b. yeastlike.
c. photosynthetic.
d. coenocytic.

4. Zoospores are the asexual spores of the:
a. Oomycetes.
b. Zygomycetes.
c. Ascomycetes.
d. Basidiomycetes.

5. The sexual cycle of some fungi have not been identified. These fungi are classified as:
a. Oomycetes.
b. Ascomycetes.
c. Deuteromycetes.
d. Basidiomycetes.

6. Yeasts reproduce mainly by:
a. conidia.
b. budding.
c. sporangia.
d. basidia.

7. The phyla of the kingdom Fungi include all of the following, except:
a. Eumycophyta.
b. Myxobacteria.
c. Mysomycophyta.
d. Mycophycophyta.

8. A mixture of benzoic acid and salicylic acid is called Whitfield's ointment. It is used in the treatment of:
a. dermatomycosis.
b. histoplasmosis.
c. aspergillosis.
d. coccidioidomycosis.

9. Darling's disease is caused by:
a. Histoplasma capsulata.
b. Ajellomyces dermatitidis.
c. Emmonsiella capsulata.
d. Aspergillus flavus.

10. Many grains, peanuts, and hay can become contaminated with fungi that produce powerful toxins called aflatoxins. These toxins are produced by:
a. Aspergillus flavus.
b. Aspergillus fumigatus.
c. Sporothrix schenckii.
d. Candida albicans.

11. Besides causing human disease, fungi cause agricultural problems
    by producing diseases in plants. Two of these diseases are wheat
    rust and corn smut disease. They are both caused by fungi classi-
    fied as:
    a. Oomycetes.
    b. Ascomycetes.
    c. Basidiomycetes.
    d. Deuteromycetes.

12. Aspergillus fumigatus causes several diseases. If the spores of
    this organism become localized in ear wax, hyphae may invade the
    auditory canal. This condition is referred to as:
    a. otomycosis.
    b. aspergilloma.
    c. coccidioidomycosis.
    d. sporotrichosis.

13. A blockage of the lymph vessels leading to a swelling in the joints
    is called:
    a. onychia.
    b. moniliasis.
    c. edema.
    d. pruritis.

14. Septate fungi are found in all of the following classes, except:
    a. Oomycetes.
    b. Ascomycetes.
    c. Basidiomycetes.
    d. Deuteromycetes.

15. Some fungal diseases are caused by an organism that is normally
    found in the human intestine. This "opportunistic" pathogen is:
    a. Cryptococcus neoformans.
    b. Sporothrix schenkii.
    c. Candida albicans.
    d. Ajellomyces dermatitidis.

PRACTICE EXERCISES

1. Identify each of the sexual and asexual fruiting bodies and spores
   pictured.

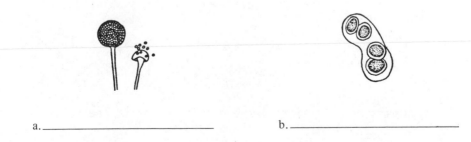

a._____   b._____

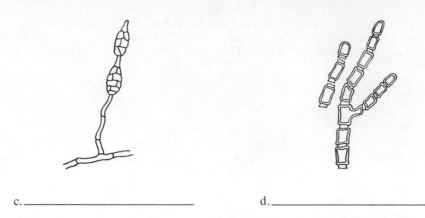

c._____   d._____

2. <u>True or False</u>. Indicate whether each of the following statements
   is true or false by placing a T for true or an F for false on the
   line provided.

   _____ a. The sexual spores of the <u>Oomycetes</u> are oospores and the asexual
            spores are called zoospores.

   _____ b. Besides the fungi, the kingdom Fungi includes the slime
            bacteria and the lichens.

   _____ c. Because the sexual cycle for the fungi classified in the
            <u>Deuteromycetes</u> is unknown, they are said to be "imperfect."

   _____ d. Because they both have a diploid and a haploid form, fungi
            are said to be biphasic.

   _____ e. The organism used to ferment grapes to wine and to leaven bread
            is <u>Saccharomyces cerevisiae</u>. This fungus is a yeast.

   _____ f. The organism that causes candidiasis is a small yeastlike oval
            which forms filaments called <u>pseudohyphae</u> when cultivated in
            the laboratory.

   _____ g. Aflatoxins are produced when <u>Aspergillus flavus</u> contaminates
            grains and hay. There is evidence that aflatoxins cause
            tumors in animals.

   _____ h. A mild form of histoplasmosis of the upper respiratory tract
            is called summer flu.

   _____ i. Darling's disease is another name for dermatomycosis.

   _____ h. In some fungi the septa between adjacent cells are fully
            closed. These fungi are called septic.

3. Identify the causative agent of each of the following diseases.

   a. Candidiasis: _____ _____

   b. North American blastomycosis: _____ _____

   _____

   c. Vaginitis: _____ _____

   d. Thrush: _____ _____

   e. Coccidioidomycosis: _____ _____

4. Fill in the blanks. With the notable exception of yeasts, the
   fungi consist of masses of intertwined filaments called (a) _____
   _____. These are composed of basic morphological units
   called (b) _____. The fungi are surrounded by cell
   walls composed of (c) _____ or (d) _____
   ____, or both. The fungi are (e) _____ with nuclei
   separated from the (f) _____ by a nuclear membrane
   and membrane-enclosed organelles. The fungi are not photosynthetic
   and do not contain (g) _____. They must consume
   preformed carbon molecules and are therefore (h) _____
   ___. In many fungi, the individual cells are separated from one
   another by cross walls, or (i) _____. These fungi
   are called (j) _____. Other fungi have pores in
   the wall separating the individual cells, and the cytoplasm and
   organelles mingle freely among adjacent cells. These fungi are
   called (k) _____ or (l) _____/

5. Fill in the spaces below. (Refer to Table 11.2.)

Class name	Cross walls	Sexual spore	Common name
a. Oomycetes	_____	_____	_____
b. Zygomycetes	_____	_____	_____
c. _____	(+)	unknown	_____
d. Basidiomycetes	_____	_____	_____
e. _____	(+)	_____	sac fungi

6. Besides causing disease in humans, fungi cause many plant diseases
   of economic importance. Indicate the class of fungi in which each
   of the organisms that cause the following plant diseases is classified.

                                          Class

   a. Late blight of potatoes   _____

b. Ergot rye disease   _____

c. Wheat rust   _____

d. Downy mildew of grapes   _____

e. Spear rot of asparagus   _____

CONCEPT EXERCISES

1. Many fungi produce antibiotics that inhibit the growth of bacteria.
   These antibiotics are very important in modern chemotherapy, as
   will be discussed in Chapter 23. It is unlikely, however, that
   fungi produce these compounds simply to aid humans in combatting
   bacterial infections. Why do so many fungi produce antibiotics?

   _____

   _____

   _____

   _____

   _____

   _____

2. There are five classes of fungi. Someday one of these classes may
   no longer exist. Which class of true fungi is this and why may it
   be eradicated?

   _____

   _____

   _____

   _____

   _____

   _____

POST-TEST

1. Fungi of this class are terrestrial organisms that form a characteristic zygospore when two hyphae of opposite sexes fuse. This class
   is:
   a. Oomycetes.
   b. Zygomycetes.
   c. Ascomycetes.
   d. Basidiomycetes.

2. Members of the Basidiomycetes produce clublike structures called basidia. All of the following are classified in this group, except:
   a. rusts.
   b. mushrooms.
   c. slime molds.
   d. smuts.

3. Organisms that have a motile amoeboid stage in their life cycle are classified as:
   a. Eumycophyta.
   b. Myxomycophyta.
   c. Mycophycophyta.
   d. Basidiomycophyta.

4. The "water molds" is the common name of the:
   a. Oomycetes.
   b. Basidiomycetes.
   c. Deuteromycetes.
   d. Zygomycetes.

5. The drug often used to treat cryptococcosis is:
   a. amphotericin B.
   b. gentian violet.
   c. griseofulvin.
   d. nystatin.

6. A patient with an ear infection consults his physician. The physician is informed by her clinical laboratory that the infection is fungal in origin. The fungus is most likely:
   a. Aspergillus fumigatus.
   b. Coccidioides immitis.
   c. Trichophyton species.
   d. Emmonsiella capsulata.

7. A basidiomycete that causes disease in humans is:
   a. Candida albicans.
   b. Emmonsiella capsulata.
   c. Coccidioides immitis.
   d. Cryptococcus neoformans.

8. A patient with a venereal disease goes to her gynecologist. She has pruritis, a whitish "cheesy" discharge, and burning internal pain. The physician's diagnosis probably is:
   a. nystatin.
   b. vulvovaginitis.
   c. meningovaginitis.
   d. Darling's disease.

9. Tinea are dermatomycosis diseases caused by several different genera of fungi. Each of the following is identified in this chapter as causing tinea, except:
   a. Microsporum.
   b. Trichophyton.
   c. Emmonsiella.
   d. Epidermophyton.

10. One of the compounds used to treat dermatomycosis is undecyclenic acid, which is commonly called:
    a. Desenex.
    b. Whitfield's ointment
    c. griseofulvin.
    d. candidacin.

11. A patient comes to his physician with wartlike blisters. The physician sends a culture to a clinical microbiologist. She isolates a fungus with cells that appear as a figure 8. She also is able to determine that this fungus produces asci. The patient is probably suffering from:
    a. North American blastomycosis.
    b. aspergillosis.
    c. tina pedis.
    d. tina barbae.

12. A polymer of acetylglucosamine found in the cell walls of fungi is:
    a. cellulose.
    b. sucrose.
    c. chitin.
    d. peptidoglycan.

13. Each of the following is an asexual spore, except a(n):
    a. conidiospore.
    b. zoospore.
    c. oospore.
    d. sporangiospore.

14. Fungi classified in the Deuteromycetes are known to produce which kind of sexual spores?
    a. Zygospores
    b. Ascospores
    c. None
    d. Basidiospores

15. A farmer brings some grapes covered with mildew to her USDA agent. This disease is caused by a:
    a. water mold.
    b. sac fungus.
    c. club fungus.
    d. terrestrial mold.

ANSWERS TO EXERCISES

Pre-Test

1. a	6. b	11. c
2. c	7. b	12. a
3. d	8. a	13. c
4. a	9. c	14. a

5. c   10. a   15. c

Practice Exercises

1. a. sporangium; b. ascus; c. conidium; d. arthrospore.

2. a. T; b. F; c. T; d. F; e. T; f. T; g. T; h. T;
   i. F; j. F.

3. a. <u>Candida</u> <u>albicans</u>; b. <u>Ajellomyces</u> <u>dermatitidis</u>;
   c. <u>Candida</u> <u>albicans</u>; d. <u>Candida</u> <u>albicans</u>; e. <u>Coccidioides</u>
   <u>immitis</u>.

4. a. mycelia; b. hyphae; c. cellulose; d. chitin;
   e. eukaryotic; f. cytoplasm; g. chlorophyll; h. heterotrophic;
   i. septa; j. septate; k. aseptate; l. coenocytic.

5. a. cross walls: (-), oospore, water molds; b. cross walls:
   (-), zygospore, terrestrial molds; c. <u>Deuteromycetes</u>, imperfect
   fungi; d. cross walls: (+), basidiospores, club fungi;
   e. <u>Ascomycetes</u>, ascospores.

6. a. <u>Oomycetes</u>; b. <u>Ascomycetes</u>; c. <u>Basidiomycetes</u>; d. <u>Oomycetes</u>;
   e. <u>Deuteromycetes</u>.

Concept Exercises

1. Most fungi are soil and water organisms. They are eukaryotic with
   generation times that are often slower than those of bacteria, yet
   they must compete with bacteria for the relatively small amounts
   of organic materials in the soil. By producing antibiotics, they
   are able to inhibit the bacteria around them and, hence, to gain a
   selective advantage over the bacteria.

2. The <u>Deuteromycetes</u> are classified because they have no <u>identified</u>
   sexual stage. When a sexual stage is found, the organisms are
   placed in the appropriate class. Thus, it is possible with the
   continuing improvements in scientific technology that sexual forms
   of all fungi will be found and that the class <u>Deuteromycetes</u> will
   cease to exist.

Post-Test

1. b   6. a   11. a

137

2. c	7. d	12. c
3. b	8. b	13. c
4. a	9. c	14. c
5. a	10. a	15. a

12   The Protozoa

Grassi said to Robert Koch: "There are places in Italy where mosquitoes are absolutely pestiferous-- but there is no malaria at all in those places!"

"Well--what of it?"

"This of that!" Shouted Battista Grassi.   "Either malaria is carried by one special particular bloodsucking mosquito, out of the twenty or forty kinds of mosquitoes in Italy--or it isn't carried by mosquitoes at all!"

"Mosquitoes--without malaria . . . but never malaria--without mosquitoes! That means one special kind of mosquito! I must discover the suspect. . . ."

Paul De Kruif, "Ross vs. Grassi," in Microbe Hunters. New York: Harcourt, Brace and World, 1953.

CHAPTER OUTLINE

   I.   Characteristics of the Protozoa

        A.   Sarcodina (amoebae)

        B.   Mastigophora (flagellates)

        C.   Ciliophora (ciliates)

        D.   Sporozoa (nonmotile forms)

  II.   Protozoan Diseases of Humans

        A.   Amoebiasis

        B.   Primary amoebic meningoencephalitis (PAM)

        C.   Giardiasis

        D.   Trichomoniasis

        E.   African trypanosomiasis (sleeping sickness)

        F.   American tryponosomiasis (Chagas' disease)

        G.   Leishmaniasis (kala-azar)

        H.   Balantidiasis

I.   Toxoplasmosis

J.   Malaria

K.   Babesiasis

L.   Pneumocytosis

OVERVIEW AND OBJECTIVES

Like the fungal diseases, illness caused by protozoa are difficult to treat because the organisms are eukaryotic and close to their hosts in biochemistry and metabolism. Also, like fungal diseases, protozoan diseases have had a significant effect on human history. Malaria has been known since at least the fifth century BC. It is believed that Alexander the Great died of malaria. His untimely death at age 33 changed the history of Western Civilization. Three hundred million new cases are reported annually, and it is considered by the World Health Organization to be the most important health problem in medicine today.

Another protozoan disease, African trypanosomiasis, effectively inhibited the colonization of eastern and central Africa until David Bruce identified the tsetse fly as the vector of the disease in 1898. Several thousand cases of the disease are still reported yearly in Africa.

Protozoa are eukaryotic microorganisms that have the ability to be motile, at least during part of their life cycle. These organisms are classified, along with some of the eukaryotic algae, in the kingdom Protista. Because of their motility, they were classified for many years as animals, and their name comes from the Greek meaning "first animals." They are heterotrophic and saprobic.

There are four major classes of protozoa, which are divided according to their means of locomotion. Sarcodina, or the amoebae, move by means of pseudopodia. This movement is referred to as amoeboid motion. Many members of the class, the foraminifera, have hard shell-like coverings composed of calcium carbonate. Protozoa that move by flagella are classified as Mastigophora. This group includes the photosynthetic protozoan Euglena gracillis. The Ciliophora move by means of extracellular organelles called cilia. The fourth class of protozoa, the Sporozoa are nonmotile forms. They may have short-lived juvenile forms that are motile.

There are several protozoan diseases of humans. Many of these are common only in tropical zones, but several occur worldwide and can become extremely important social as well as medical issues. Organisms classified in the Sarcodina cause amoebiasis and primary amoebic meningoencephalitis. Giardiasis, trichomoniasis, African trypanosomiasis, American trypanosomiasis, and leishmaniasis (kala-azar) are all caused by members of the class Mastigophora. Balantidiasis is caused by a ciliate (ciliophora), while toxoplasmosis, malaria, babesiasis, and pneumocytosis are caused by members of the Sporozoa.

140

After you have read Chapter 12 of your textbook, you should be able to:

1. Define or identify the following terms: pellicle, flagella, cilia, lysosome, heterotrophic, saprobic, Protista, Sarcodina, amoebae, pseudopodia, amoeboid motion, foraminifera, Mastigophora, flagel-lates, Euglena gracilis, Astasia longa, Ciliophora, ciliates, Paramecium, kappa factors, trichocysts, contractile vacuole, Sporozoa, amoebiasis, cyst, trophozoite, parasitemia, paromomycin, metronidazole, tetracycline, primary amoebic meningoencephalitis (PAM). Entamoeba histolytica, Naegleria, giardiasis, Giardia lamblia, bilateral symmetry, dysentery, trichomoniasis, Trichomonas vaginalis, pruritis, tinidazole, micronazole, African trypanosomiasis, sleeping sickness, Trypanosoma brucei, Glossina palpalis, American tryponosomiasis, Chagas' disease, Trypanosoma cruzi, Triatoma, Rhodnius, chagoma, leishmaniasis, kala-azar, Leishmania donovani, amastigote, promastigote, Phlebotomus, visceral leishmaniasis, leukopenia, radiorespirometry, cutaneous leishmaniasis, Oriental sore, balantidiasis, Balantidium coli, toxoplasmosis, zoonosis, Toxoplasma gondii, Sabin-Feldman dye test, malaria, Plasmodium species, sporozoite, merozoite, tertian malaria, quartan malaria, estivoautumnal malaria, blackwater fever, quinine, chloroquine, primaquine, mefloquine, Duffy blood factors, babesiasis, Babesia microti, pneumocytosis, and Pneumocystis carinii.

2. Describe the four major phyla of protozoa and explain the characteristics that differentiate them.

3. List the various protozoans that cause the diseases discussed in this chapter, and identify both the disease caused by each organism and the class to which each organism is assigned.

4. Discuss the modes of transmission of the several protozoan diseases discussed.

5. Describe the organelles and modes of locomotion of the various types of protozoa.

PRE-TEST

1. Trichomoniasis is caused by Trichomonas vaginalis. This organism is classified in the Mastigophora. Therefore the organism moves by means of an organelle called a:
   a. pseudopodium.
   b. flagellum.
   c. cilium.
   d. These organisms are nonmotile.

2. Many protozoa are surrounded by a chitin-like shell called a:
   a. contractile vacuole.
   b. cell membrane.
   c. pellicle.
   d. pseudopodium.

3. A member of the Sarcodina produces a disease of the intestines that begins with watery stools but, if untreated, will cause bloody stools to develop as digestion of the tissue by the organism reaches the underlying blood vessels. This disease is:
   a. PAM.
   b. giardiasis.
   c. amoebiasis.
   d. African trypanosomiasis.

4. Pseudopodia are the organs of movement of organisms classified as:
   a. Sarcodina.
   b. Mastigophora.
   c. Ciliophora.
   d. Sporozoa.

5. A woman comes to her physician complaining of drowsiness and a desire to sleep. She is suffering from tremors. She has just returned from Central Africa. Her physician believes that she may be suffering from a disease caused by Trypanosoma brucei, variety gambiense. If so, she has been bitten by a:
   a. mosquito.
   b. tick.
   c. triatomid bug.
   d. tsetse fly.

6. Members of the Sporozoa cause each of the following diseases, except:
   a. babesiasis.
   b. balantidiasis.
   c. malaria.
   d. toxoplasmosis.

7. Quinine is effective in the treatment of disease caused by members of the genus:
   a. Plasmodium.
   b. Toxoplasma.
   c. Pneumocytis.
   d. Leishmania.

8. The "world's most urgent public health problem" is:
   a. sleeping sickness.
   b. trichomoniasis.
   c. malaria.
   d. influenza.

9. A sexually transmitted protozoan disease is:
   a. African trypanosomiasis.
   b. trichomoniasis.
   c. American trypanosomiasis.
   d. toxoplasmosis.

10. A disease caused by a protozoan that contains chitin, and may therefore be a fungus, is:
    a. toxoplasmosis.

b. PAM.
c. pneumocytosis.
d. balantidiasis.

11. You have isolated a strain of ciliate that has the capacity to kill other strains of paramecia. This strain is probably producing:
a. kappa factors.
b. contractile vacuoles.
c. trichocysts.
d. foraminifera.

12. Each of the following is a general characteristic of protozoa, except:
a. heterotrophic.
b. saprobic.
c. photosynthetic.
d. eukaryotic.

13. The organs of locomotion of members of the class Sporozoa are:
a. pseudopodia.
b. flagella.
c. cilia.
d. These organisms are nonmotile.

14. A new technique for the diagnosis of one protozoan disease requires the patient to swallow a gelatin capsule tied to a string. The capsule is retrieved after four hours and examined for organisms. This disease is:
a. trichomoniasis.
b. giardiasis.
c. toxoplasmosis.
d. malaria.

15. Sandflys transmit several diseases. One of these is protozoan in origin and is caused by:
a. Leishmania donovani.
b. Babesia microti.
c. Trypanosoma brucei.
d. Toxoplasma gondii.

PRACTICE EXERCISES

1. Identify the organ of locomotion of each pathogenic organism listed.

a. Entamoeba histolytica: _____

b. Toxoplasma gondii: _____

c. Naegleria species: _____

d. Trichomonas vaginalis: _____

e. Leishmania donovani: _____

f. Giardia lamblia: _____

g. Balantidium coli: _____

h. Babesia microti: _____

i. Plasmodium species: _____

j. Trypanosoma cruzi: _____

2. True or False. Determine whether each of the following statements is true or false; then place a T for true or an F for false on the line provided.

____ a. The protozoa are a group of single-celled prokaryotic organisms.

____ b. Protozoan cells are enclosed by a membrane that in certain cases is surrounded by a pellicle containing chitin-like material for rigidity.

____ c. Movement in the Sarcodina is by pseudopodia, meaning "false feet."

____ d. Paramecium species possess unusual features, including the trichocysts which are nucleic acid particles that appear to be responsible for the production of toxins that destroy other ciliates.

____ e. The salient feature of the Sporozoa is the absence of motility. They are never motile during any part of their life cycle.

____ f. Paramecium contains both a macronucleus and one or more micronuclei.

____ g. The species Astasia longa is a photosynthetic form, which is otherwise indistinguishable from the nonphotosynthetic species Euglena gracilis.

____ h. Cilia and flagella are structurally similar.

____ i. The protozoa obtain nutrients by engulfing food particles by phagocytosis or through special organs of ingestion.

____ j. While most members of Ciliophora are free living, most members of Sporozoa are parasitic.

3. A number of different treatments are employed against protozoan diseases. These drugs tend to be used specifically against only one or a few diseases. For each drug listed, name one disease against which the drug is used.

a. Paromomycin: _____

b. Quinine: _____

c. Sulfonamides: _____

d. Antimony: _____

e. Metronidazole: _____

4. Fill in the blanks. The malaria parasite has a very complex life cycle that takes place partly in the (a) _____ and partly in the (b) _____. The parasite enters the bloodstream in (c) _____ form and immediately invades the (d) _____, where it is very difficult to treat. After several hours many (e) _____ form, emerge, and penetrate the (f) _____. Following a complex series of transformations, thousands of (g) _____ rupture simultaneously and release tens of thousands of new parasites. At this point, the victim suffers a (h) _____: first the patient is intensely cold, then hot--with a temperature rising rapidly to 104°F-106°F--accompanied by intense headache and mild delirium. After two to three hours, massive perspiration ends the (i) _____. The patient falls asleep and awaits the next attack.

   In infections with Plasmodium vivas and Plasmodium ovale there is a 48-hour interval between attacks. This malaria is called (j) _____ malaria. Plasmodium malariae spends about 72 hours in the red blood cells, and this form of malaria is called (k) _____ malaria. The cycle of Plasmodium falciparum is not defined, and attacks may occur at widely scattered intervals. This type of malaria is known as (l) _____ malaria referring to the summer/fall seasons when mosquitos breed heavily.

5. Matching. Each disease in the left-hand column has a corresponding vector of transmission in the right-hand column. Match them by placing the appropriate number on the line provided.

_____ a. Balantidiasis   1. Triatomid bug

_____ b. Malaria   2. Mosquito

_____ c. Babesiasis   3. None

_____ d. Trichomoniasis   4. Sexual contact

_____ e. Kala-azar   5. Sandfly

_____ f. Toxoplasmosis   6. Tsetse fly

_____ g. American trypanosomiasis 7. Cats

_____ h. African trypanosomiasis 8. Tick

_____ i. Pneumocytosis   9. Food, water

6. Distinguish between the two terms or objects in each pair below. Your answer should be only one or two sentences or phrases.

   a. Flagella/cilia:

   _____

   _____

   b. Sporozoa/Sarcodina:

   _____

   _____

   c. Sleeping sickness/Chagas' disease:

   _____

   _____

   d. Quartan malaria/tertian malaria:

   _____

   _____

   e. Balantidiasis/babesiasis:

   _____

   _____

CONCEPT EXERCISES

1. Smallpox has been eliminated as a medical problem from the earth. Malaria has been described by the World Health Organization as "the most important health problem that medicine must confront." Why has it been so difficult to eliminate malaria?

   _____

   _____

   _____

2. The classes of protozoa are identified separately according to their means of locomotion. Members of the Sporozoa are nonmotile. Do you think this is a cause or a consequence of their parasitic nature? Why?

   _____

   _____

146

3. Sickle-cell anemia is characterized by erythrocytes (red blood cells) that change their normal shape to a sickle or crescent shape when oxygen tension is low. This is due to an altered form of hemoglobin in the cells. The gene for this disorder is found in high frequencies in individuals from areas in which malaria is prevalent. The homozygous state of the disease can lead to severe anemia, but the heterozygous form is usually mild. It appears that the heterozygous form lends protection against malaria. What characteristics of the disease suggest a possible mechanism for this protection?

POST-TEST

1. PAM is a serious disease resembling viral meningitis. It is caused by the protozoan:
   a. Entamoeba histolytica.
   b. Naegleria species.
   c. Giardia lamblia.
   d. Trichomonas vaginalis.

2. A physician believes that her patient has infectious mononucleosis. The tests for "mono" are negative. She then learns that her patient loves cats and has several at home. The physician should consider that her patient may have:
   a. toxoplasmosis.
   b. trichomoniasis.
   c. trypanosomiasis.
   d. amoebiasis.

3. You are in charge of a cancer ward. One of your patients who has been immunosuppressed as part of her antineoplastic therapy has developed an infection of the alveolar sacs of the lungs. She has fever, cough, and substantial respiratory distress. Among other diseases, you should consider:
   a. babesiasis.
   b. malaria.
   c. toxoplasmosis.
   d. pneumocytosis.

4. Protozoa that move by pseudopodia are classified as:
   a. Sarcodina.
   b. Mastigophora.
   c. Ciliophora.
   d. Sporozoa.

5. The genus _Paramecium_ possesses organelles that discharge filaments and trap the organism's prey. These organelles are called:
   a. kappa factors.
   b. trichocysts.
   c. contractile vacuoles.
   d. foraminifera.

6. Organelles found in protozoa that enclose food particles and contain digestive enzymes are _best_ called:
   a. contractile vacuoles.
   b. foraminifera.
   c. lysosomes.
   d. pellicles.

7. Cilia are made up of:
   a. nine fibers surrounding a single filament.
   b. a hollow core surrounded by nine fibers.
   c. two fibers wrapped around each other.
   d. nine fibers surrounding two additional fibers.

8. The form of malaria known as _estivoautumnal malaria_ is caused by:
   a. Plasmodium falciparum.
   b. Plasmodium ovale.
   c. Plasmodium malariae.
   d. Plasmodium vivax.

9. Persons with malaria may pass hemoglobin in the urine. This gives the disease the alternative name of:
   a. red flow disease.
   b. tertian malaria.
   c. bloody urine disease.
   d. blackwater disease.

10. This protozoan can cause serious problems if a pregnant woman becomes infected. The fetus may become infected because the parasites pass across the placenta. They may cause brain and eye damage, lesions of the visceral organs, or spontaneous abortion. This organism is:
    a. Toxoplasma gondii.
    b. Trypanosoma brucei.
    c. Trypanosoma cruzi.
    d. Trichomonas vaginalis.

11. Only a few members of the _Ciliophora_ are associated with human disease. One of the few diseases caused by this group of organisms is:
    a. trichomoniasis.
    b. babesiasis.
    c. balantidiasis.
    d. toxoplasmosis.

12. Many members of the _Sarcodina_ live in hard shell-like coverings composed of calcium carbonate. These organisms are _most accurately_ called:

a. amoebae.
b. flagellates.
c. foraminifera.
d. trichocysts.

13. One class of protozoa (the Sporozoa) contains many pathogens. The members of this class are:
a. never motile.
b. only motile in the adult form.
c. always motile in the juvenile form.
d. motile in the juvenile form in some species only.

14. Organelles composed of an arrangement of 9 + 2 fibrils and which best synchronously are a characteristic of the:
a. Sarcodina.
b. Mastigophora.
c. Ciliophora.
d. Sporozoa.

15. A patient comes to you with pruritis, internal stinging pain, and a burning sensation during urination. Urine samples reveal the presence of a flagellated protozoan. You would prescribe which of the following drugs to treat this disorder:
a. penicillin.
b. metronidazole.
c. sulfonamides.
d. tetracycline.

ANSWERS TO EXERCISES

Pre-Test

1. b   6. b   11. a

2. c   7. a   12. c

3. c   8. c   13. d

4. a   9. b   14. b

5. d   10. c   15. a

Practice Exercises

1. a. pseudopodia; b. none; c. pseudopodia; d. flagella;

   e. flagella; f. flagella; g. cilia; h. none; i. none;

   j. flagella.

2. a. F; b. T; c. T; d. F; e. F; f. T; g. F; h. T;

   i. T; j. T.

149

3. a.   amoebiasis, balantidiasis; b.   malaria; c.   pneumocytosis;

   d.   leishmaniasis (kala-azar); e.   giardiasis, trichomoniasis,

   and balantidiasis.

4. a.   mosquito; b.   human blood; c.   sporozoite; d.   liver;

   e.   merozoites; f.   red blood cells; g.   red blood cells;

   h.   malaria attack; i.   hot stage; j.   tertian; k.   quartan;

   l.   estivoautumnal.

5. a.   9; b.   2; c.   8; d.   4; e.   5; f.   7; g.   1; h.   6;

   i.   3.

6. a.   Both are similar in structure but flagella "lash about" while
   cilia beat synchronously.   b.   Sporozoa are nonmotile protozoa,
   whereas Sarcodina move by pseudopodia.   c.   Sleeping sickness is
   African trypanosomiasis caused by Trypanosoma brucei; Chagas'
   disease is American trypanosomiasis caused by Trypanosoma cruzi.
   d.   Quartan malaria has 72 hours between attacks and is caused by
   Plasmodium falciparum; tertian malaria has 48 hours between attacks
   and is caused by either Plasmodium vivax or Plasmodium ovale.
   e.   Balantidiasis is a disease of the intestine caused by a
   ciliate, but babesiasis is a disease of the red blood cells caused
   by a nonmotile protozoan.

Concept Exercises

1. Unlike smallpox, malaria has a nonhuman reservoir in the form of
   its other host, the mosquito. To eliminate the disease, the
   reservoir must be eliminated. This has proved impossible to date.

2. While we cannot be certain, it is likely that nonmotility is a
   result of the parasitic relationship of these organisms to their
   host. In this niche, movement is not necessary and evolution has
   probably eliminated motility organs as unnecessary.

3. Malaria is essentially a disease of the blood. Plasmodium species
   replicates in the red blood cell. It appears that the mixture of
   normal and abnormal hemoglobins in the heterozygote leads to
   microcytic anemia, which impedes the development of the malarial
   parasite.

Post-Test

1. b	6. c	11. c
2. a	7. d	12. c
3. d	8. a	13. d

4. a	9. d	14. c
5. b	10. a	15. b

13   Infection and Disease

The human body is a galaxy to a microbe, yet without microbes the body
would not live an hour. If we feel awe, let us address it not to
dimension but to being--and we share being with the galaxies themselves.

Timothy Ferris, Galaxies. San Francisco:
Sierra Club Books, 1980.

CHAPTER OUTLINE

    I. The Host-Parasite Relationship

        A. The progress of disease

        B. Communicable diseases

        C. Other types of diseases

   II. Establishment of Disease

        A. Portal of entry

        B. Dose

        C. Tissue penetration

        D. Virulence factors

        E. Toxins

        F. The normal flora

OVERVIEW AND OBJECTIVES

Bacteria and other microorganisms exist on and in the body from birth,
and the relationship between humans and microorganisms can take many
forms. Many microorganisms are beneficial or, at least, are commensal.
They help us digest our food and "protect" us from more harmful organisms
by inhibiting the establishment of pathogenic forms. Other microorganisms are harmful, and the relationships described in the next several
chapters will be concerned mainly with interactions that cause disease
in the human host. In this chapter, we will examine the various types
of host-parasite relationships and discuss some of the general parameters of the establishment of disease.

    Pathogenicity is the ability of a parasite to cause disease.
Various pathogens have different levels of pathogenicity. The degree
of pathogenicity is referred to as its level of virulence. The level
of virulence ranges from that of organisms which invariably cause

disease when they come into contact with the human host to that of opportunistic pathogens which only cause disease in a compromised host. One of the important side effects of some antibiotics such as chloramphenicol is that they destroy the normal flora and allow the establishment of potentially pathogenic forms. Diseases can also be clinical, when the symptoms are apparent, or subclinical, when the parasite is present but few (if any) symptoms are present.

Disease can take several general forms. It can be communicable, which means that the disease is transmissible among hosts. Diseases that pass with particular ease from host to host are classified as contagious; other diseases are classified as noncommunicable because the agent must be acquired from the environment and is not acquired from an infected person. Still other diseases are not infectious at all; they are not caused by pathogenic organisms but by other factors. These include nutritional, physiological, and genetic diseases. The study of microbiology is primarily concerned with infectious disease and this textbook discusses directly only that aspect of disease.

Several different factors contribute to whether a disease will become established in a particular situation. An important one is the dose, or number of organisms that initially enter the host, which varies from disease to disease. Another is the portal of entry, which is the place where an organism enters the body. Ability of the organism to penetrate tissue is also a factor. The number and types of virulence factors produced by the organism contribute to the tissue penetration of the organism. They include enzymes, which destroy proteins and other macromolecules. Other virulence factors protect the organism from host defense mechanisms such as phagocytosis. Toxins are produced by many organisms. These include exotoxins, which are microbial poisons produced during the metabolism of the bacteria, and endotoxins, which are part of the cell wall of gram(-) bacteria.

After you have read Chapter 13 of your textbook, you should be able to:

1. Define and identify the following terms: pathogen, commensal, opportunist, virulence, period of decline, defervescence, period of convalescence, clinical, subclinical, communicable disease, droplets, fomites, mechanical vectors, biological vectors, contagious, noncommunicable, endemic, epidemic, pandemic, acute, chronic, carrier, reservoir, primary disease, secondary disease, local infection, systemic disease, bacteremia, septicemia, fungemia, viremia, parasitemia, physiological disease, nutritional disease, genetic disease, infectious disease, portal of entry, dose, tissue penetration, virulence factors, aggressins, procoagulase, coagulase, streptokinase, hyaluronidase, spreading factor, leucocidin, hemolysin, toxin, exotoxin, antitoxin, toxoid, lockjaw, endotoxin, endotoxin shock, and normal flora.

2. Distinguish between infection and pathogenicity.

3. Describe the different types of infectious diseases by the degree to which they are transmitted, the various frequencies with which

they occur, and the various courses the disease can take.

4. Explain why all disease is not infectious and what disorders other types of disease can inflict an individual.

5. List and explain the various factors that can affect the establishment and severity of disease.

PRE-TEST

1. Pseudomonas aeruginosa is a soil organism. Every time we eat a fresh salad, we consume millions of these organisms. They usually do us no harm. However, these same organisms can cause serious infection in persons who have been severely burned. Such a pathogen is called:
   a. communicable.
   b. commensal.
   c. opportunistic.
   d. noncommunicable.

2. A disease such as sickle-cell anemia, which is caused by an alteration in DNA, is referred to as a(n):
   a. genetic disease.
   b. nutritional disease.
   c. infectious disease.
   d. physiological disease.

3. A disease that develops rapidly, shows substantial symptoms, comes to a climax, and then fades, is a(n):
   a. acute disease.
   b. endemic disease.
   c. epidemic disease.
   d. chronic disease.

4. You have a patient come to you with a disorder, which you determine to be thrush (see Chapter 11). This disease can be described as a(n):
   a. bacteremia.
   b. parasitemia.
   c. viremia.
   d. fungemia.

5. The degree to which an organism is able to cause disease is referred to as its:
   a. virulence.
   b. pathogenicity.
   c. communicability.
   d. defervescence.

6. A microbial poison produced during the metabolism of a bacterium and immediately released into the environment is a(n):
   a. antitoxin.
   b. exotoxin.
   c. endotoxin.
   d. toxoid.

7. You have a patient suffering from continuous muscle contractions and a general breakdown of her nervous system. She received a puncture wound while visiting her grandmother's farm approximately two weeks earlier. This patient is likely suffering from the effects of a toxin produced by:
   a. Clostridium tetani.
   b. Clostridium botulinium.
   c. Vibrio cholerae.
   d. Corynebacterium diphtheriae.

8. Hemolysin is a virulence factor that dissolves red blood cells. Each of the following pathogens produces hemolysin, except:
   a. pneumococci.
   b. clostridia.
   c. straphylococci.
   d. streptococci.

9. A scientist who studies the pattern of disease in a community and attempts to locate it source is called a(n):
   a. pathologist.
   b. epidemiologist.
   c. microbiologist.
   d. infectiologist.

10. A person who is a long term carrier of a pathogen and a source of infection to the next person is best referred to as a(n):
    a. acute source.
    b. chronic source.
    c. subclinical source.
    d. carrier.

11. A disease that is usually present at a low level in a certain geographic area is said to be:
    a. epidemic.
    b. pandemic.
    c. endemic.
    d. ubiquitous.

12. Members of the normal flora of the mouth include all of the following genera, except:
    a. Neisseri.
    b. Leptotrichia.
    c. Bacteroides.
    d. Pseudomonas.

13. Endotoxins are produced by:
    a. fungi.
    b. gram(+) bacteria.
    c. gram(-) bacteria.
    d. the genus Bacillus.

14. One of the effects of endotoxins is to increase body temperature. Hence, they can be referred to as:
    a. virulence factors.

155

b. pyrogenic.
c. shock factors.
d. temperate.

15. A <u>disease</u> that develops in a weakened individual is referred to as a(n):
a. opportunistic infection.
b. primary infection.
c. chronic infection.
d. secondary infection.

PRACTICE EXERCISES

1. In one or two sentences distinguish between the two members of each pair of terms below.

a. Acute/chronic:

_____

_____

_____

b. Primary disease/secondary disease:

_____

_____

_____

c. Infectious disease/physiological disease:

_____

_____

_____

d. Local infection/systemic infection:

_____

_____

_____

e. Endemic/epidemic:

_____

_____

_____

f. Exotoxin/endotoxin:

_____

_____

_____

g. Pathogenicity/virulence:

_____

_____

_____

h. Communicable disease/noncommunicable disease:

_____

_____

_____

2. True or False. Indicate whether each of the following statements
   is true or false by placing a T for true or an F for false on the
   line provided.

_____ a. Arthropids may be important as biological vectors when they
         carry parasites on their body parts, or as mechanical vectors
         when they are heavily infected by the parasites.

_____ b. A person who harbors an organism but shows no sign of the
         disease is said to be a reservoir.

_____ c. When an outbreak of a disease above normal levels occurs on
         a worldwide scale, the disease is said to be epidemic.

_____ d. Systemic diseases are those that have disseminated to the
         deeper organs and systems.

_____ e. The portal of entry is important in determining the establish-
         ment of disease. (For example, tetanus will occur if the
         spores are introduced to wound tissue from soil but will not
         if they are consumed in food.)

_____ f. The dose required to cause disease is constant for all diseases,
         and is 10^9 organisms.

_____ g. An antitoxin is a specific kind of antibody the host elicits
         against an exotoxin.

_____ h. The most virulent forms of exotoxins are referred to as toxoids.

_____ i. Procoagulase is a virulence factor produced by staphylococci. It is converted coagulase and induces a fibrin clot allowing the organism to resist phagocytosis.

_____ j. Subclinical cases of a disease may lead to immunity to the disease and, hence, increases resistance.

3. Fill in the blanks. (a) _____ is defined as the ability of a parasite to gain entrance to a host and bring about a physiological or anatomical change called (b) _____. The term (c) _____ refers to an organism capable of producing such a condition. Parasites vary greatly in their (d) _____. Some parasites will infect the tissues and derive beneficial nutrition but fail to overcome the body's defenses. These parasites are called (e) _____. Another class of parasites are the (f) _____. These organisms often come into contact with the host but will only cause disease in a host whose defenses have become compromised. The degree to which a parasite is capable of causing disease is called its (g) _____. This word is derived from the Latin word meaning "full of poison."

4. Below is a list of characteristics of bacterial toxins. Some are characteristic of <u>exotoxins</u>; others are characteristic of <u>endotoxins</u>. Indicate the type of toxin of which each is characteristic by placing an X for exotoxin or a D for endotoxin on the line provided.

_____ a. Usual source is gram(+) bacteria.

_____ b. Chemical composition is protein.

_____ c. Antibodies are elicited by the host.

_____ d. May increase body temperature.

_____ e. Chemical composition is lipopolysaccharide-peptide.

_____ f. May be converted to a toxoid.

_____ g. Not possible to convert to a toxoid.

_____ h. May increase water elimination.

_____ i. May increase hemorrhaging.

_____ j. May interrupt protein synthesis.

5. Transmission of communicable diseases may be direct or indirect. These can take several forms. For each situation described select the type of transmission from the list below, and place the corresponding number on the line provided.

1. indirect transmission by <u>droplets</u>.

2. Indirect transmission by <u>fomites</u>.

3. Indirect transmission by a <u>mechanical</u> <u>vector</u>.

4. Indirect transmission by a <u>biological</u> <u>vector</u>.

5. <u>Direct</u> <u>transmission</u>.

_____ a. An infected tick transmits Rocky Mountain spotted fever.

_____ b. Transmission of influenza by a sneeze.

_____ c. Transfer of disease when a fly carrying parasites on its feet walks across a cut on the hand.

_____ d. Obtaining syphilis through sexual intercourse.

_____ e. Borrowing and using a comb from a person having a scalp tinea.

_____ f. Getting "mono" by kissing your boy friend.

_____ g. Obtaining a dermatological infection by occupying a hospital bed that had not been properly disinfected after use by a patient with the same dermatological infection.

_____ h. Getting malaria from the bite of an infected mosquito.

_____ i. Obtaining a venereal disease from a toilet seat.

_____ j. Getting lockjaw after being scratched by a rose thorn.

6. <u>Matching</u>. Match each term in the left-hand column with its definition in the right-hand column by placing the appropriate number on the line provided.

_____ a. Fungemia

_____ b. Pandemic

_____ c. Toxoid

_____ d. Septicemia

_____ e. Genetic disease

_____ f. Opportunist

_____ g. Pathogen

_____ h. Bacteremia

_____ i. Endemic

1. Spreading in the blood

2. Mutation in DNA

3. World-wide outbreak of a disease

4. Presence of fungi

5. Capable of causing disease

6. Presence of viruses

7. Bacteria in the blood

8. Causing disease in a compromised host

_____ j. Viremia

9. Present at low levels in environment

10. Heat inactivated protein from gram(+) bacteria

CONCEPT EXERCISES

1. Many pathogens are so virulent that they are able to overcome their host's defense mechanisms and establish themselves, causing severe disease and even death. Yet it has often been said that the best pathogens do not kill or even severely weaken their hosts. Explain this statement.

_____

_____

_____

_____

_____

_____

2. A professor of bacteriology once wrote to a leading soap manu-facturer protesting that its deodorant soap was too powerful a disinfectant and that it had given him a case of boils. Explain how a soap could be _too_ effective and how this might lead to disease.

_____

_____

_____

_____

_____

_____

3. Pseudomonas aeruginosa is a soil organism with which we often come in contact. This organism usually does not cause disease but can cause severe lung infections in children born with the genetic disease cystic fibrosis. This organism produces a substance (A), which degrades elastin, a major protein of connective tissue. P. aeruginosa also produces a substance (B), which acts to inhibit protein synthesis in eukaryotic cells while not affecting protein synthesis in prokaryotic cells.

a. In which class of pathogens would you place P. aeruginosa?

b. What is the most likely portal of entry in cystic-fibrosis-
    associated infections?

_____

_____

c. Describe substance A in one or two sentences.

_____

_____

d. Describe substance B in one or two sentences.

_____

_____

POST-TEST

1. Leucocidin, a substance produced by certain bacteria, has the
   ability to disintegrate white blood cells. This substance is
   classified as a(n):
   a. virulence factor.
   b. endotoxin.
   c. exotoxin.
   d. antitoxin.

2. The symptoms of tetanus are caused by a protein produced by
   Clostridium tetani. Protection against tetanus can be obtained
   by injecting a nonimmune person with heat-inactivated protein.
   Such a protein is referred to as a(n):
   a. antitoxin.
   b. endotoxin.
   c. exotoxin.
   d. toxoid.

3. Some parasites are normal residents of the human flora that do not
   cause disease. Such parasites are called:
   a. pathogens.
   b. avirulent.
   c. commensals.
   d. opportunists.

4. The presence of protozoa in the blood is most often referred to
   as:
   a. bacteremia.
   b. septicemia.
   c. protozoemia.
   d. parasitemia.

161

5. A disease that lingers for long periods of time is called a(n):
   a. acute disease.
   b. chronic disease.
   c. primary disease.
   d. secondary disease.

6. Certain microorganisms inhabit parts of the body without causing symptoms of disease. These organisms are collectively referred to as:
   a. normal flora.
   b. opportunists.
   c. avirulent.
   d. symbiotes.

7. As you may remember from Chapter 6, the phenomenon of "transforma-tion" in bacteria was discovered by Griffith. He was studying forms of pneumococci that were incapable of causing disease. These forms had lost their extracellular polysaccharide capsule, which protects them from phagocytosis. This capsule could correctly be referred to as a(n):
   a. toxin.
   b. virulence factor.
   c. avirulence factor.
   d. procoagulase.

8. All of the following are characteristics of endotoxins, except:
   a. usual source is gram(-) bacteria.
   b. lipo-polysaccharide-peptide.
   c. cannot be converted to toxoid.
   d. can elicit antibody production.

9. A disease that disseminates throughout the body, including the deeper organs and systems, is called:
   a. local.
   b. chronic.
   c. secondary.
   d. systemic.

10. A patient comes to you suffering from rapid weight loss, muscle wasting, marked peripheral neuritis, and muscular weakness. The person is from an area where polished rice is a dietary staple. You diagnose the "dry" form of beriberi. This disease is classi-fied as a(n):
   a. physiological disease.
   b. nutritional disease.
   c. genetic disease.
   d. infectious disease.

11. Diseases caused by agents that pass with particular ease from host to host are termed:
   a. communicable.
   b. contagious.
   c. noncummunicable.
   d. epidemic.

12. The nonencapsulated pneumococci described in exercise 7 can be referred to as:
    a. virulent.
    b. commensal.
    c. opportunistic.
    d. avirulent.

13. The period of a disease during which the symptoms subside is often referred to as the period of:
    a. defervescence.
    b. convalescence.
    c. avirulence.
    d. subclinical infection.

14. One effect of exotoxins is to increase:
    a. body temperature.
    b. hemorrhaging.
    c. capillary permeability.
    d. swelling in tissues.

15. Changes in the permeability of the blood vessels accompanies diseases caused by gram(-) bacteria. This permits leakage of blood fluid to the intercellular spaces, and the patient may lapse into a coma. This condition is referred to as:
    a. endotoxin shock.
    b. exotoxin shock.
    c. toxoid shock.
    d. gram(-) shock.

ANSWERS TO EXERCISES

Pre-Test

1. c	6. b	11. c
2. a	7. a	12. d
3. a	8. a	13. c
4. d	9. b	14. b
5. a	10. d	15. d

Practice Exercises

1. a. Acute disease develops rapidly, comes to a climax, and fades. Chronic disease tends to linger for long periods of time.

2. b. Primary disease occurs in an apparently healthy body, while a secondary disease develops in a weakened individual.

    c. Infectious disease is caused by a pathogen, but physiological disease results from a malfunction of a body organ or system.

163

d. Local infection is restricted to a single area of the body, whereas systemic infection is disseminated to the deeper organs and systems.

e. An endemic disease is one that is usually present at a low level in a certain geographic area; an epidemic is the outbreak in explosive proportions of a disease in a certain geographical area.

f. Exotoxins are microbial poisons produced during the metabolism of bacteria and immediately released to the external environment. Endotoxins are part of the cell wall of gram(-) bacteria and are released at cell death.

g. Pathogenicity is the ability of a parasite to cause disease, while virulence is an expression of the _degree_ of pathogenicity.

h. A communicable disease is one in which the causative agent is transmissible among hosts. A noncommunicable disease is one in which the causative agent must be acquired from the environment and is usually not transmitted from host to host.

2. a. F; b. T; c. F; d. T; e. T f. F; g. T; h. F;

   i. T; j. T.

3. a. Pathogenicity; b. disease; c. pathogen; d. pathogenicity;

   e. commensals; f. opportunists; g. virulence.

4. a. X; b. X; c. X; d. D; e. D; f. X; g. D; h. X;

   i. D; j. X.

5. a. 4; b. 1; c. 3; d. 5; e. 2; f. 5; g. 2; h. 4;

   i. 2; j. 2.

6. a. 4; b. 3; c. 10; d. 1; e. 2; f. 8; g. 5; h. 7;

   i. 9; j. 6.

Concept Exercises

1. If a pathogen severely weakens, and particularly if it kills, its host, the parasite has destroyed its niche. It must therefore find a new host or die itself. Thus the best pathogens cause mild disease or no disease at all and, hence, ensure a long relationship with their host. The study of evolution of disease throughout history leads to the discovery that many diseases have become less severe with time. This is generally true of syphilis and tuberculosis.

2. A disinfectant such as soap may be too effective and destroy the normal flora of the skin. This allows the establishment of

organisms that can cause disease and which would otherwise be excluded from gaining a foothold by the normal flora of the skin.

3. a. <u>P. aeruginosa</u> should be classified as an opportunistic pathogen.

    b. The most likely portal of entry for <u>P. aeruginosa</u> in cystic-fibrosis-associated infections of the lung is the respiratory system.

    c. Substance A is a virulence factor that increases the tissue penetration of the organism.

    d. Substance B is an exotoxin that inhibits protein synthesis. This exotoxin acts by the same mechanism as the exotoxin produced by <u>Corynebacterium diphtheriae</u>, described in Table 13.3.

<u>Post-Test</u>

1. a	6. a	11. b
2. d	7. b	12. d
3. c	8. d	13. a
4. d	9. d	14. c
5. b	10. b	15. a

14 Resistance to Disease

Metchnikoff hurried to Vienna to proclaim his theory that we are immune to germs because our bodies have wandering cells to gobble germs up; he made a bee-line for the laboratory of his friend Professor Claus. . . .

"I would be greatly honored to have you publish your theory in my journal," said Claus.

"But I must have a scientific name for these cells that devour microbes--a Greek name--what would be a Greek name for such cells?" cried Metchnikoff.

Claus and his learned colleagues scratched their heads and peered into their dictionaries and at last they told him: "Phagocyte is Greek for devouring cell--phagocytes is what you must call them!"

> Paul De Kruif, "Metchnikoff: The Nice Phagocytes," in Microbe Hunters. New York: Harcourt, Brace and World, 1953.

CHAPTER OUTLINE

I. Nonspecific Resistance

  A. Mechanical and chemical barriers

  B. The human circulatory system

  C. Phagocytosis

  D. Inflammation

II. Specific Resistance

  A. Antigens

  B. Types of antigens

  C. The immune system

  D. Operation of the immune system

  E. Cellular immunity

  F. Humoral immunity

  G. Types of antibodies

  H. Origin of antibodies

OVERVIEW AND OBJECTIVES

Disease is much like a war, and the human host has developed several
defensive weapons against attack. The body is protected from the environment by a physical barrier to attack; the skin and mucous membranes. Not only do these tissues cover the external surface of the
body, but they also line the gastrointestinal tract so that materials
passing through it do not come into direct contact with the internal
organs of the body. If an organism penetrates this mechanical barrier,
the organism must still escape several types of chemical barriers,
including extremes in pH, degredative enzymes, and other inactivating
proteins. Escaping these barriers, the pathogen must still deal with
the complicated and highly aggressive immune system. In this chapter,
we will outline the various mechanical and chemical barriers to infection provided by our bodies and introduce you to components of the
immune system. These defense mechanisms can be classified as either
nonspecific or specific. We will discuss each classification in turn.

Nonspecific resistance to disease takes several forms. These include the mechanical barriers of the skin and mucous membranes and of
the cilia, which help to remove invading organisms for the respiratory
tract. Chemical barriers are also nonspecific in their action although
they may be more effective against one group of organisms than another.
Chemical barriers include lysozyme, an enzyme that destroys the cell
walls of microorganisms, and interferon, which promotes resistance to
viral infections.

The human circulatory system includes many nonspecific resistance
factors, as well as the more specific ones of the immune system. Among
the most important of the nonspecific barriers are the phagocytes.
These cells carry out the process of phagocytosis, in which they engulf
a foreign body and digest it. Phagocytes are chemotactic, which means
that they are attracted to foreign cells. They will then migrate toward the invading cell and engulf it. The circulatory system is important also because it contributes to the process of inflammation.

Specific resistance is provided by the immune system. This system
reacts to the presence of foreign substances called antigens. A person's
own proteins are usually not antigenic, but sometimes self-tolerance
breaks down and an autoimmune disease results.

The immune system contains two general components: cellular immunity and humoral immunity. Cellular immunity is brought about when
certain antigens, such as fungi and protozoa, stimulate the T-lymphocytes. These sensitized T-lymphocytes enter the circulation and migrate to the site where the antigen is present. There they release
lymphokines, which act to attract and stimulate macrophages. Lymphokines disappear quickly after the antigen has been eliminated and long-
term immunity is acquired through colonies of sensitized T-lymphocytes
which remain in the tissues.

Humoral immunity is derived from the B-lymphocytes. These cells
do not enter the circulatory system, but are stimulated by phagocytosed
antigens to produce soluble proteins called antibodies. Long-term im-

167

munity is conferred by the development of <u>memory cells</u>, which are B-lymphocytes that are quickly stimulated to produce specific antibodies if the antigen is encountered in the future.

After you have read Chapter 14 of your textbook, you should be able to:

1. Define or identify each of the following terms: species immunity, mechanical barrier, chemical barrier, mucous membranes, lysozyme, complement interferon, serum, plasma, erythrocyte, bilirubin, jaundice, leukocyte, polymorphonuclear cell (PMN), neutrophil, eosinophil, basophil, monocyte, macrophage, lymphocyte, interstitial fluid, lymphatic fluid, lymph nodes, phagocytosis, phagocytes, reticuloendothelial system (RES), pinocytosis, endocytosis, chemo-taxis, complement system, antibody, opsonization, opsonis, opsonic index, surface phagocytosis, inflammation, rubor, tumor, calor, dolor, pus, abscess, boil, carbuncle, antigen, hapten, antigenic determinant site, specific immunologic tolerance, autoantigens, autoimmune disease, alloantigens, heterophile antigens, erythro-poietic cells, thymus, B-lymphocytes, T-lymphocytes, gut-associated lymphoid tissue (GALT), bursa of Fabricius, immune respônse (Ir) genes, cellular immunity, transfer factor, lymphoblast, lymphokine, cell-mediated immunity, tissue immunity, humoral immunity, plasma cell, antibody, circulating immunity, memory cell, immunoglobulin (Ig), light chain, heavy chain, constant domain, variable domain, Fab fragment, Fc fragment, primary antibody response, secondary antibody response, congenital immunity, secretory antibody, colo-strum, template theory, clonal selection hypothesis, helper T-lymphocytes, and suppressor T-lymphocytes.

2. Distinguish between nonspecific and specific resistance.

3. List the various mechanical and chemical barriers the human body provides against infection and indicate how each helps to inhibit infection.

4. Outline the various components of the circulatory system and ex-plain the function of each.

5. Distinguish between antigens and antibodies.

6. Explain the differences between the cellular and humoral immune systems, and describe how each functions in its role in specific resistance.

7. Describe the structure and function of each of the immunoglobulins.

PRE-TEST

1. The erythrocyte:
   a. carries oxygen to the body tissues.
   b. has a multilobed nucleus.
   c. contains granules, which stain with basic dyes.
   d. are the white blood cells.

2. A nonspecific resistance factor effective against viral infection is:
   a. lysozyme.
   b. bile.
   c. interferon.
   d. complement.

3. When Metchnikoff put a sliver into the body of a starfish larva, he saw that it was soon surrounded by wandering cells. He was observing a process which is today best described as:
   a. pinocytosis.
   b. chemotaxis.
   c. endocytosis.
   d. opsonization.

4. Rubor is:
   a. a red color from blood accumulation.
   b. pain from an injury to local nerves.
   c. a swelling from the accumulation of fluid.
   d. a warmth from the heat of the accumulation of blood.

5. A person's own proteins, which elicit an immune response when self-tolerance breaks down, are called:
   a. alloantigens.
   b. heterophile antigens.
   c. autoantigens.
   d. cellular antigens.

6. The secretory antibody is:
   a. IgG.
   b. IgM.
   c. IgD.
   d. IgA.

7. The portion of the immunoglobulin molecule that contains the antigen binding site can be described as all of the following, except the:
   a. light chain.
   b. Fab fragment.
   c. variable domain.
   d. Fc fragment.

8. The uptake of dissolved material is best described as:
   a. phagocytosis.
   b. endocytosis.
   c. pinocytosis.
   d. chemotaxis.

9. Humans do not contract hog cholera, and hogs do not contract polio. These are examples of:
   a. racial immunity.
   b. autoimmunity.
   c. heterophilic immunity.
   d. species immunity.

10. Bilirubin is:
   a. a degradation product of hemoglobin.
   b. the yellow color to the skin that is a symptom of hepatitis.
   c. a compound that carries oxygen to the tissues.
   d. a substance that acts to stimulate chemotaxis.

11. Lysozyme is most effective against:
   a. gram(-) bacteria.
   b. fungi.
   c. gram(+) bacteria.
   d. viruses.

12. Platelets are:
   a. cells that have no nuclei and function chiefly in the blood-clotting mechanism.
   b. red blood cells.
   c. PMNs which have granules that stain with acidic dyes.
   d. cells that have multilobed nuclei.

13. Cells primarily responsible for cell-mediated immunity are the:
   a. B-lymphocytes.
   b. memory cells.
   c. erythrocytes.
   d. T-lymphocytes.

14. Plasma cells are best described as:
   a. part of the plasma.
   b. part of the cellular immunity system.
   c. antibody releasing cells.
   d. red blood cells.

15. The process by which complement components bind to antibody-parasite complexes and enhance phagocytosis is termed:
   a. chemotaxis.
   b. opsonization.
   c. activation.
   d. macrophage aggregation.

PRACTICE EXERCISES

1. The human circulatory system contains many different types of cells and macromolecules that are important to both nonspecific and specific resistance. Each of the statements below describes one of these components. Identify the cell or macromolecule by writing its name on the line provided.

   a. A cell containing a multilobed nucleus and many cytoplasmic lysosome granules. _____

   b. A PMN that functions chiefly as a phagocyte and can pass through pores into vessels of the circulatory system.

   _____

   c. A cell having no nucleus, which functions chiefly in the

blood-clotting mechanism. _____

d. A leukocyte with a single large nucleus and granules. It makes up 33 percent of the leukocytes and functions in the immune system. _____

e. The blood cell that carries oxygen to the tissues bound loosely to hemoglobin. _____

f. A cell with a multilobed nucleus and granules that stain with basic dyes. _____

g. A cell with a single bean-shaped nucleus that takes up most of the cytoplasm. The cell lacks granules and forms a type of phagocyte in the tissues. _____

h. The fluid that surrounds the tissue cells and fills the inter-cellular spaces. It is sometimes called tissue fluid. _____ _____

i. A general term for the white blood cells. _____

j. The fluid part of blood containing the clotting agents. _____ _____

2. On the diagram depicting an immunoglobulin molecule, label the areas corresponding to each of the following:

a. light chains

e. constant domain

b. heavy chains

f. variable domain

c. Fab fragment

g. antigen-binding site

d. Fc fragment

h. the phagocyte-binding site

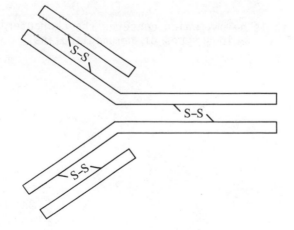

3. <u>True</u> or <u>False</u>. Decide whether each of the following statements is true or false; then place a T for true or an F for false on the line provided.

_____ a. Cellular immunity occurs when certain antigens stimulate the B-lymphocytes.

_____ b. The major characteristics of inflammation are rubor, calor, tumor, and dolor.

_____ c. The first antibody type to appear after the invasion of an infectious agent is IgM.

_____ d. Immunities can vary between species (species immunity) or between groups of a species (racial immunity). In either case, they are nonspecific and act against <u>all</u> pathogens.

_____ e. The intact skin and its extensions into the body cavity mucous membranes are the most important of the nonspecific resistance factors.

_____ f. The rates of phagocytosis can be modified by a number of factors. For example, a rough environmental surface such as the wall of a blood vessel can hinder the trapping of a particle.

_____ g. A common product of phagocytosis is a mixture of serum, dead tissue cells, leukocytes, and dead bacteria known as pus.

_____ h. Certain molecules are not of themselves antigenic, but they will combine with tissue proteins or polysaccharides to form antigens. These molecules are called <u>haptens</u>.

_____ i. Hemolytic disease of the newborn is an autoimmune disease.

_____ j. Production of the surface antigens of T-lymphocytes but <u>not</u> of B-lymphocytes is under the control of immune response (Ir) genes.

4. Fill in the table below, which concerns the characteristics and functions of the various types of immunoglobulins.

Type	Location	Number of 4-Chain Units	Appearance in Body
IgG	_____ _____	_____	_____ _____
IgM	_____ _____	_____	_____ _____
IgA	_____ _____	_____	_____ _____
IgE	_____ _____	_____	_____ _____
IgD	_____ _____	_____	_____ _____

5. Matching. The human body has several nonspecific resistance barriers to disease. Match each mechanical or chemical barrier in the left-hand column with the correct description of its action in the right-hand column by placing the corresponding number on the line provided.

_____ a. Lysozyme

_____ b. Skin

_____ c. Bile

_____ d. Duodenal enzymes

_____ e. Mucous membranes

_____ f. Acidity of the vagina

_____ g. Interferon

1. Digest structural components of microorganisms

2. Protective covering

3. Trap airborne particles

4. Inhibits replication of viruses

5. pH toxic to microorganisms

6. Digests cell wall of gram(+) bacteria

7. Inhibitory to most microorganisms

6. Fill in the blanks. When certain antigens stimulate the T-lymphocytes, (a) _____ immunity is initiated. The pool of T-cells is increased and sensitized by (b) _____ factors released by the original cells. The lymphocytes now revert to young cells called (c) _____, which produce a series of low molecular weight proteins known as (d) _____. These compounds have important activities, the overall effect of which is to increase the efficiency of (e) _____ of the antigen. (f) _____ disappear rapidly from the site after the antigen has been eliminated, and long-term immunity is supplied by colonies of sensitized (g)

_____-_____ that remain in the tissues. This type of
immunity is also called (h) _____-_____ _____
or (i) _____ _____.

A second type of immunity, called (j) _____ immunity, derives from the stimulation of (k) ____-lymphocytes by
antigens contained in the macrophages. These lymphocytes do not
enter the circulation. Rather, they remain in the lymphoid tissue
and multiply to form a clone of cells, called (1) _____
_____ cells. The prinicpal products of these cells are proteins
known as (m) _____, which are synthesized according
to direction in the Ir genes and released into the circulation.
(n) _____ cells will continue to produce these proteins for two or three days or until the antigenic stimulation comes
to an end. At this point they die off and are replaced by a second
clone of (o) ____-lymphocytes, called (p) _____ cells.
The latter remain in the lymphoid tissue for many years and are
activated when the antigen is reintroduced. Because of these
characteristics, this type of immunity is alternatively called (r)
_____ immunity.

CONCEPT EXERCISES

1. When Griffith discovered transformation (see Chapter 6) in 1928,
   he was studying two forms of pneumococci. One form was virulent
   and produced an extracellular polysaccharide capsule. The other
   strain was avirulent and did not produce the capsule. How might
   this virulence factor affect the bacterium's ability to overcome
   the host's resistance barriers?

   _____

   _____

   _____

   _____

   _____

   _____

2. We have discussed the process of inflammation in this chapter because it is a mechanism of defense. How can this seemingly patho-
   logical condition be protective?

   _____

   _____

   _____

   _____

_____

_____

_____

_____

_____

3. We learned in Chapter 2 that heating a protein can inactivate its biological activity. Heating a protein also destroys or alters its antigenicity so that vaccines made with heat-inactivated proteins often are not protective.

   a. Why does heat inactivation alter the antigenicity of a protein?

_____

_____

_____

   b. What does this tell you about the nature of <u>antigenic determinant sites</u>?

_____

_____

_____

_____

_____

POST-TEST

1. Molecules that are not themselves antigenic but become antigenic when they combine with tissue proteins or polysaccharides are called:
   a. antigens.
   b. coantigens.
   ⓒ. haptens.
   d. quasiantigens.

2. Lupus erythematosus is caused by the stimulation of the immune system by a(n):
   a. heterophile antigen.
   b. alloantigen.
   c. species antigen.
   ⓓ autoantigen.

3. Kupffer cells are components of the:
   a. circulatory system.
   b. reticuloendothelial system.
   c. humural immunity system.
   d. cellular immunity system.

4. T-lymphocyte stimulation leads to a type of immunity called all of the following, except:
   a. cell-mediated immunity.
   b. tissue immunity.
   c. circulating immunity.
   d. cellular immunity.

5. The phagocyte-binding site is part of the:
   a. Fab fragment.
   b. variable domain.
   c. light chain.
   d. Fc fragment.

6. The principal component of the primary antibody response is:
   a. IgG.
   b. IgM.
   c. IgA.
   d. IgD.

7. Colostrum contains:
   a. IgG.
   b. IgM.
   c. IgA.
   d. IgD.

8. Helper T-lymphocytes:
   a. stimulate the production of lymphokins.
   b. activate T-lymphocytes.
   c. encourage linkage between the macrophage and B-lymphocytes.
   d. opsonize macrophages.

9. The presence of antibodies _____ chemotaxis of the phagocyte to the parasite.
   a. does not affect
   b. greatly enhances
   c. inhibits
   d. delays

10. Specific immunologic tolerance is directed toward:
    a. autoantigens.
    b. alloantigens.
    c. heterophile antigens.
    d. racial antigens.

11. The thymus:
    a. modifies lymphopoietic cells into T-lymphocytes.
    b. produces plasma cells from B-lymphocytes.
    c. selectively destroys T-lymphocytes.
    d. is involved in the humoral immune response.

12. Unprocessed antigens, that is, those that have not been phagocytized, are _____ stimulants of the immune system.
    a. excellent
    b. equivalant to processed antigens as
    c. poor
    d. much more potent than processed antigens as

13. A compound that digests the cell wall of gram(+) bacteria is:
    a. bile.
    b. lysozyme.
    c. interferon.
    d. stomach acid.

14. The ABO blood group is an excellent example of a(n):
    a. alloantigen.
    b. autoantigen.
    c. heterophile antigen.
    d. racial antigen.

15. Macrophage activating factor:
    a. draws macrophages to the site of infection.
    b. prevents macrophages from moving away from the site of infection.
    c. causes the macrophages to clump together at the site of infection.
    d. appears to increase the motility of macrophages and the amount of lysosomal enzymes they contain.

ANSWERS TO EXERCISES

Pre-Test

1. a	6. d	11. c
2. c	7. d	12. a
3. c	8. c	13. d
4. a	9. d	14. c
5. c	10. a	15. b

Practice Exercises

1. a. polymorphonuclear cell; b. neutrophil; c. platelet;

   d. lymphocyte; e. erythrocyte; f. basophil; g. monocyte;

   h. interstitial fluid; i. leukocyte; j. plasma.

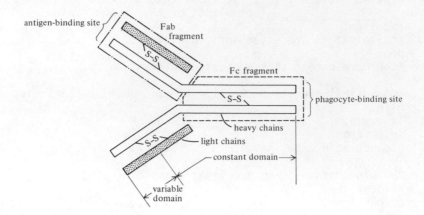

3. a. F; b. T; c. T; d. F; e. T; f. F; g. T; h. T;

   i. F; j. F.

4. IgG, Location: blood, lymph; Number: 1; Appearance: on stimulation by antigen.

   IgM, Location: blood, lymph; Number: 5; Appearance: on stimulation by antigen; principal component of primary response.

   IgA, Location: secretions, body cavities; Number: 2; Appearance: on stimulation by antigen.

   IgE, Location: blood, lymph; Number: 1; Appearance: on stimulation by allergen.

   IgD, Location: blood, lymph; Number: 1; Appearance: unknown.

5. a. 6; b. 2; c. 7; d. 1; e. 3; f. 5; g. 4.

6. a. cellular; b. transfer; c. lymphoblasts; d. lymphokins;

   e. phagocytosis; f. Lymphokines; g. T-lymphocytes;

   h. cell-mediated immunity; i. tissue immunity; j. humoral;

   k. B; l. plasma; m. antibodies; n. Plasma; o. B;

   p. memory; r. circulating.

Concept Exercises

1. The capsule of the virulent pneumococci protects the cell from several host defense systems. The most important is protection from phagocytosis. It may also help in establishing colonies in the host, as it may aid in attachment to internal surfaces of the

respiratory tract.

2. Inflammation is protective for several reasons. First, the tissues at the site of infection become richly supplied with phagocytes. Second, the supply of plasma to the tissues is increased, raising the local concentration of antibacterial serum factors and anti-bodies (if the individual is immune). Third, progressive inflam-mation leads to the accumulation of dead host cells, from which antimicrobial tissue substances are released. Fourth, the higher temperatures characteristic of fever have been shown to slow the multiplication of some viruses.

3. a. Heat inactivation, as we learned in Chapter 2, destroys the three-dimensional structure of the protein. It "unfolds" the protein.

   b. The antigenic determinant sites of proteins are made up of regions of the protein consisting of several amino acids. When the three-dimensional structure of the protein is destroyed by heat, the amino acids that make up the antigenic site may no longer be in contact and, hence, the site is destroyed as well.

Post-Test

1. c	6. b	11. a
2. d	7. c	12. c
3. b	8. c	13. b
4. c	9. b	14. a
5. d	10. a	15. d

Tests for the detection of antibodies resulting from infection with Treponema pallidum are of unique diagnostic importance. In few other conditions are serological tests as critical for diagnosis, the opportunity for misdiagnosis so great, and the potential consequences to the patient so drastic. It is paradoxical that the first-generation, and still the first-line, tests for syphilis are biologically non-specific. In these tests cardiolipin antigens, derived from beef heart, are used to detect antilipid antibodies traditionally termed reagin. It is not known whether the antibodies are produced in response to lipid antigens in T. pallidum or to antigens resulting from host-parasite interactions.

> E. Coffey, L. Bradford, and S. A. Larsen, Serological tests for syphilis, D. H. Lennette, A. Balows, W. J. Jausler, Jr., and J. P. Truant (eds.), Manual of Clinical Microbiology, 3rd. ed. Washington: American Society for Microbiology, 1980, pp. 509-520.

CHAPTER OUTLINE

   I. The Role of Antibodies in Resistance

      A. The complement system

      B. The classical pathway

      C. The alternative pathway

  II. Immunity to Disease

      A. Naturally acquired active immunity

      B. Artificially acquired active immunity

      C. Naturally acquired passive immunity

      D. Artificially acquired passive immunity

 III. Serology

      A. Radioimmunoassay

      B. Radioallergosorbent test

      C. Enzyme immunoassay

      D. Fluorescent antibody test

E. Neutralization

F. Precipitation

G. Agglutination

H. Flocculation

I. Complement fixation

OVERVIEW AND OBJECTIVES

Serological tests are important diagnostic tools in medicine. As we have already learned in our discussions of viral, fungal, and protozoan disease, a serological test is carried out for the ultimate diagnosis of many diseases. Such tests depend on the body's immunological response to the infection. In this chapter we will examine the role of the humoral immune system in resistance to disease, the mechanism of acquiring immunity to disease, and the various serological tests used in the diagnosis of disease.

Antibodies are important in resistance to many types of disease. They also can inactivate viruses by combining with viral capsids, but are relatively ineffective against many viruses that remain latent in the host cell. They are capable of inactivating toxins and increasing the ability of phagocytes to engulf bacteria. In most cases the inactivation of bacteria by antibodies involves a complex series of reactions of a group of proteins called the complement system. This system increases phagocytosis and often leads to lysis of the invading bacteria. The complement system can act through two different pathways: the classical pathway and the alternative pathway.

After exposure to an infectious agent, the body may acquire longterm resistance to the organism. This state is known as immunity. Immunity can be acquired through several means. Some are natural (acquired by infection with the agent) and some are artificial (acquired by deliberate inoculation using an immunizing agent). Active immunity, whether acquired naturally or artificially, results from the response of the immune system to exposure to the antigen. Naturally acquired passive immunity is acquired by the passage of antibodies from the mother's bloodstream to the fetus or by passage to the newborn through the mother's colostrum, or milk. Artificially acquired passive immunity results from injection of antibody-rich serum into the circulation. This is usually done only if a nonimmune individual has been exposed to the infectious agent. Antiserum must always be used with caution because the chances of a hypersensitive reaction are so great.

Antigen-antibody reactions are often used in the diagnostic laboratory for the identification of disease. Such tests are known collectively as serological reactions. Many measure the presence or the increase in titer of a specific antibody in the patient in response to infection. Many tests are available and used in specific cases. Radioimmunoassay and radioallergosorgent tests depend on radioactively labeled antibodies or antigens. Other tests utilize enzymes, fluorescent-labeled antibodies, electrophoresis, and complement fixation to assay the presence of antibody in a patient's serum. These tests are described and discussed in this chapter.

After you have read Chapter 15 of your textbook, you should be able to:

1. Define or identify the following terms: complement system, ana-phylatoxin, classical pathway, alternative pathway, histamine, im-mune adherence phenomenon, attack complex, complement cascade, properdin, initiating factor (IF), C3 proactivator, immune, active immunity, secondary anamnestic response, immunizing agent, booster shot, adjuvant, passive immunity, maternal antibodies, congenital immunity, antiserum, hyperimmune serum, prophylactic serum, thera-peutic serum, convalescent serum, gamma globulin, immune complexes, serum sickness, anaphylaxis, serology, serological reaction, titer, blocking antibody, radioimmunoassay (RIA), radioallergosorbent test (RAST), antiglobulin antibody, enzyme immunoassay (EIA), flu-orescent antibody test, fluorescein, rhodamine, direct fluorescent method, indirect fluorescent method, neutralization, precipitation, lattice, zone of equivalence, Dudin tube technique, double dif-fusion, Ouchterlony plate technique, immunoelectrophoresis (IEA), electrophoresis, radial immunodiffusion, agglutination, Widal test, polyvalent serum, passive agglutination, hemagglutination, hemag-glutination inhibition test, flocculation, cardiolipin, complement fixation, test system, indicator system, and hemolysin.

2. Describe the roles of antibodies in resistance to the various classes of diseases.

3. Compare and contrast the classical and alternative pathways of the complement system.

4. Distinguish among naturally and artificially acquired active and passive immunity.

5. List the various serological tests discussed and briefly describe each test's advantages and disadvantages.

PRE-TEST

1. An adjuvant is:
   a. a substance that increases the efficiency of a vaccine.
   b. part of the classical complement pathway.
   c. part of the alternative complement pathway.
   d. a substance used as a vaccine.

2. When an antibody-containing serum is used in the therapy of an established disease, the serum is classified as a(n):
   a. antiserum.
   b. prophylactic serum.
   c. therapeutic serum.
   d. convalescent serum.

3. When the immune system recognizes a foreign protein in a serum injection and complement is activated, a person may develop a type
   of allergy called:
   a. immune complex disease.
   b. anaphylaxis.
   c. hypersensitivity.
   d. serum sickness.

4. You are carrying out a serological test. You first mix a sample
   of diphtheria toxin with the patient's serum, inject it into a
   mouse, then watch to see whether the animal dies or survives. You
   have performed a(n):
   a. precipitation test.
   b. neutralization test.
   c. agglutination test.
   d. complement fixation test.

5. Antibodies inhibit _____ by binding near the active
   site.
   a. viruses
   b. bacteroa
   c. endotoxins
   d. exotoxins

6. The attack complex of the complement system contains all of the
   following, except:
   a. C6.
   b. C9.
   c. C4.
   d. C7.

7. Properdin is:
   a. part of the classical complement pathway.
   b. an adjuvant.
   c. part of the alternative complement pathway.
   d. part of the attack complex.

8. The intentional injection of an attenuated virus into a person will
   lead to:
   a. naturally acquired active immunity.
   b. artificially acquired active immunity.
   c. naturally acquired passive immunity.
   d. artificially acquired passive immunity.

9. Convalescent serum is an antiserum:
   a. used to protect against a condition.
   b. derived from the blood of a patient recovering from an illness.
   c. used to treat an established disease.
   d. made from a pool of sera from human donors.

10. A serological test utilizing a radioactively labeled antigen to
    measure the amount of an unknown antigen in a sample is called a(n):
    a. radioallergosorbent test.
    b. enzyme immunoassay.

c. radioimmunoassay.
d. radial immunodiffusion assay.

11. Antigen-antibody reactions studied under laboratory conditions are known collectively as:
    a. complement fixation reactions.
    b. artificial active immunity reactions.
    c. serological reactions.
    d. artificial passive immunity reactions

12. The formation of a lattice of thousands of antigen and antibody molecules results in a(n):
    a. agglutination reaction.
    b. flocculation reaction.
    c. neutralization reaction.
    d. precipitation reaction.

13. Gel-precipitation methods depend on the diffusion of antigens and antibodies through a semisolid medium. In one such test, a plug of gel is placed between the antigen and antibody solution in a thin tube. This test is known as the:
    a. Oudin technique.
    b. zone of equivalence test.
    c. Ouchterlony technique.
    d. agglutination test.

14. The C3a subunit of the classical pathway of the complement system is important because it acts as a(n):
    a. attack complex.
    b. properdin.
    c. anaphylatoxin.
    d. immune adherence complex.

15. The classical and alternative pathways of the complement system share all of the following components, except:
    a. C5.
    b. attack complex.
    c. C3a.
    d. C4.

PRACTICE EXERCISES

1. Indicate the age(s) of a person at which each of the following immunizations should be given.

    a. Diphtheria:

    _____

    _____

    b. Trivalent oral poliomyelitis:

    _____

c. Tetanus:

_____

d. Rubella:

_____

e. Pertussis:

_____

f. Measles:

_____

g. Mumps:

_____

2. Each of the following statements is true for one or more types of immunity. Indicate which type(s) by placing the appropriate number(s) on the line provided.

1. Naturally acquired active immunity.

2. Artificially acquired active immunity.

3. Naturally acquired passive immunity.

4. Artificially acquired passive immunity.

_____ a. Effective in newborns.

_____ b. Antibodies are immunizing agent.

_____ c. Self is source of antibody.

_____ d. A long time is necessary for the appearance of immunity.

_____ e. Used for prophylactic functions.

_____ f. Long-term immunity acquired.

_____ g. Effective dose required is small.

_____ h. Has low effectiveness in adults.

_____ i. Results from intentional exposure to immunizing agent.

_____ j. Serves a therapeutic function.

_____ k. Antigens serve as immunizing agent.

_____ l. Highly effective in the adult.

3. True or False. Indicate whether each of the following statements is true or false by placing a T for true or an F for false on the line provided.

_____ a. Antibodies combine directly with viral capsids and neutralize their receptor sites, thereby rendering the viruses incapable of penetrating a host cell and replicating.

_____ b. The radioallergosorbent test is performed with a known quantity of antigen labeled with a radioactive isotope (Ag*), an unknown quantity of the same antigen carrying no label (Ag), and a known amount of specific antibody (Ab).

_____ c. The titer of an antibody is the most dilute concentration of antibody that yields a detectable reaction with its specific antigen.

_____ d. The intentional exposure to antigens followed by a response by the immune system results in artificially acquired passive immunity.

_____ e. The memory cells in the lymphoid tissue are responsible for the production of antibodies in naturally acquired passive immunity. They will remain for years and will produce IgM immediately upon successive stimulation by antigens.

_____ f. Gamma globulin is derived from the fraction of blood protein of which antibodies are composed. It is usually a pool of sera from human donors, and thus it should contain a mixture of antibodies including those for the disease to be treated.

_____ g. Passive immunity must be used with caution because, in many individuals, the immune system may recognize foreign proteins in the serum and may form antibodies against them.

_____ h. The EIA serological reaction is similar to the RIA serological reaction, except that enzymes are utilized in place of radioisotopes.

_____ i. The zone of equilivalence is the ideal concentration for precipitation, and when it is reached a visible mass of particles will be seen at the interface or settling to the bottom of the tube.

_____ j. The complement system enhances phagocytosis of viral particles and may lead to their lysis.

4. Each of the following is a short description of a serological reaction. Identify the reaction by placing the name of the test on the line provided.

186

a. Serum is added to cardiolipin. If the patient has syphilis,
    particles will precipitate and cling together. An attempt to
    quantitate the test can be made by low-power microscopic observa-
    tion of the solution.

    _____

b. Antigen and antibody solutions are placed in wells cut into
    agarose in Petri dishes. The plates are incubated and precipi-
    tation lines form at the zones of equivalence.

    _____

c. Rhodamin or a similar dye is linked to antibody molecules.
    These antibodies are then combined with antigens, which generally
    occur on the surface of cells. In this way an unknown organism
    may be identified by its combination with known antibodies.

    _____

d. The test is performed in two parts. First, the patient's
    serum, specific antibodies, and complement derived from guinea
    pigs are reacted. Second, sheep red cells and hemolysins are
    added. The red blood cells will lyse if the patient's serum
    does not contain antigens to the original specific antibody.

    _____

e. This procedure is performed on a slide or in a tube. In the
    slide technique, emulsions of unknown bacteria are added to
    drops of specific known antibody, and the mixture is observed
    for clumping.

    _____

f. This text uses a known quantity of antigen labeled with radio-
    active isotope, an unknown quantity of the same antigen carrying
    no label, and a known amount of specific antibody. The object
    of the test is to determine the concentration of the unlabeled
    antigen by measuring the degree of competition between the
    labeled and unlabeled antigen for the antibody.

    _____

g. In this test an enzyme is coupled with the antigen to be tested,
    and known amounts of complex are combined with a standard amount
    of antibody and an unknown concentration of antigen. The three
    components are mixed and, after reaction has taken place, con-
    centration of both the bound antigen-enzyme and free antigen-
    enzyme are determined. Because competition for the active
    site on the antibody has occurred the bound-to-free ratio is
    equivalent to the bound-to-free ratio of the unknown antigen.

    _____

h. In this procedure two techniques are combined. A mixture of
    antigens is placed in a reservoir on an agarose slide and
    electrophoresis is carried out. Troughs are then cut into the
    agarose and known antibody solutions are added. The slide is
    then incubated, and precipitation lines occur where antigens
    and antibodies diffuse toward one another.

    _____

5. The complement system has two pathways. Some components and
   characteristics are common to both pathways; others are unique to
   one pathway or the other. Indicate whether each of the following
   is part of the classical pathway (C), the alternative pathway (A),
   or both (B), by placing the appropriate letter on the line provided.

   _____ a. The anaphylatoxin C3a

   _____ b. C1

   _____ c. The attack complex

   _____ d. Properdin

   _____ e. Antibodies

   _____ f. Most effective against gram(-) bacteria

   _____ g. C4

   _____ h. initiating factor (IF)

   _____ i. C3 proactivator

   _____ j. Lysis of the bacterial cell takes place

6. Fill in the blanks. Naturally acquired (a) _____
   immunity develops when antibodies pass into the fetal circulation
   from the mother's bloodstream via the (b) _____ and
   (c) _____ _____. These antibodies,
   called (d) _____ _____, will remain
   with the child for approximately (e) _____ months after birth
   and will fade as immunocompetence is acquired. Certain ones, such
   as measles antibodies, will remain as long as (f) _____ to
   (g) _____ months. The term (h) _____ _____
   _____ is synonymous with this type of immunity. The predominant type of antibody present is (i) _____.

       (j) _____ antibodies also may pass to the new-
   born through the first milk, or (k) _____, of the
   nursing mother. In this case (l) _____ is the predominant
   antibody, although (m) _____ and (n) _____ have also
   been found.

7. The following dilution series of an immune serum was prepared:

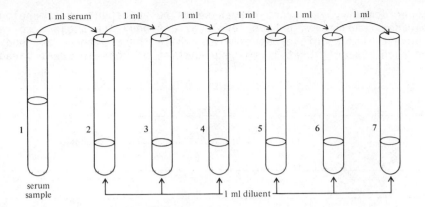

A precipitate was observed in several tubes. The most dilute tube containing a precipitate was tube 5. What is the titer of antibody in this serum sample? _____

CONCEPT EXERCISES

1. At the present time, the serology of <u>Legionella</u> <u>pneumophila</u> is still evolving. It has been ascertained that many healthy people have low titers of antibody directed against the legionnaires' disease organism. What are some possible explanations for this phenomenon?

_____

_____

_____

2. A young man comes into your office in March. He wants to be protected against tetanus because he plans to work on a farm the next summer.

   a. What type of immunization would you recommend?

   _____

   b. What type of immunity will this treatment produce?

   _____

   c. Suppose that the same young man had said that he was working on a farm at present and had just stepped on a rusty nail in the pigpen. He received a deep puncture wound from the nail. Would your recommendation change and, if so, in what way?

   _____

   _____

   _____

189

3. Superficially, recurrent herpes seems to represent an immunological paradox. Adults with high levels of antibody are subject to recurrent attacks of herpes simplex, while those with no antibody have no such attack. What is the explanation of this apparent paradox?

_____

_____

_____

_____

_____

_____

POST-TEST

1. The alternative pathway of the complement system contains all of the following components, except:
   a. properdin.
   b. antibodies.
   c. C3 proactivator.
   d. attack complex.

2. The type of immunity acquired through intentional inoculation of the antigen is termed:
   a. naturally acquired active immunity.
   b. artificially acquired active immunity.
   c. naturally acquired passive immunity.
   d. artificially acquired passive immunity.

3. The complement system is most effective in resistance to:
   a. viruses.
   b. toxins.
   c. gram(+) bacteria.
   d. gram(-) bacteria.

4. Initiating factor:
   a. is the first step in the classical complement pathway.
   b. begins the process of naturally acquired active immunity.
   c. is converted to an active form that binds a substance called C3 proactivator.
   d. acts to stimulate artificially acquired passive immunity.

5. The Sabin oral polio vaccine is an example of artificially acquired:
   a. active immunity acquired through an attenuated virus vaccine.
   b. active immunity acquired through an inactivated virus vaccine.
   c. passive immunity acquired through an attenuated virus vaccine.
   d. passive immunity acquired through an inactivated virus vaccine.

6. Secondary anamnestic response is a consequence of:
   a. the classical complement pathway.

b. the alternative complement pathway.
c. active immunity.
d. passive immunity.

7. The zone of <u>equivalence</u> is the:
   a. concentration of an antiserum, which is ideal for precipitation.
   b. titer of an antiserum.
   c. concentration of antigen, which leads to the flocculation of cardiolipin.
   d. time at which active and passive immunity are equally effective in protecting against disease.

8. Antibodies provide resistance to viruses by:
   a. binding directly to the capsid receptor sites.
   b. binding directly to the host cell receptor sites.
   c. activating the classical complement pathway leading to lysis of the infected host cell.
   d. activating the alternative complement pathway leading to lysis of the viral particle.

9. The immune adherence phenomenon describes:
   a. the binding of an antibody to its antigen.
   b. adhesion of a cell to a phagocyte mediated by the C4b, 2a, 3b complex.
   c. the activation of C3 by the initiating factor.
   d. attachment of a flocculant immune precipitate to the test tube surface during flocculation tests.

10. The series of events in the classical complement pathway are some-
    times called the:
    a. immune adherence phenomenon.
    b. attack complex.
    c. complement cascade.
    d. anaphylatoxin reaction.

11. The function of naturally acquired active immunity is:
    a. therapeutic.
    b. prophylactic.
    c. both therapeutic and prophylactic.
    d. neither therapeutic nor prophylactic.

12. An alcoholic extract of beef heart used in the VDRL test is known
    as:
    a. gamma globulin.
    b. antiserum.
    c. hemagglutinin.
    d. cardiolipin.

13. The function of naturally acquired passive immunity is:
    a. therapeutic.
    b. prophylactic.
    c. both therapeutic and prophylactic.
    d. neither therapeutic nor prophylactic.

14. Maternal antibodies will remain with a child for approximately:
    a. three months.
    b. six months.
    c. one year.
    d. his or her entire life.

15. In this serological test, commercially available bacteria are placed on a slide and the slide is flooded with the patient's serum. Tagged antiglobulin antibodies are then added. If the patient's serum contains antibacterial antibodies, the labeled antiglobulin will bind to the slide and can be observed in the microscope. This technique is known as the:
    a. direct method fluorescent antibody test.
    b. indirect method fluorescent antibody test.
    c. radioimmunoassay test.
    d. radioallergosorbent test.

ANSWERS TO EXERCISES

Pre-Test

1. a	6. c	11. c
2. c	7. c	12. d
3. d	8. b	13. a
4. b	9. b	14. c
5. d	10. c	15. d

Practice Exercises

1. a. At 2, 4, and 6 months; boosters at 1 1/2 years and 4-7 years, then at 14-16 years, and every 10 years thereafter.

   b. At 2, 4, and 6 months; boosters at 1 1/2 years and 4-7 years (optional at 6 months).

   c. Same as a.

   d. At 15 months.

   e. At 2, 4, and 6 months; boosters at 1 1/2 years and 4-7 years.

   f. Same as d.

   g. Same as d.

2. a. 3, 4; b. 3, 4; c. 1, 2; d. 1, 2; e. 1, 2, 3, 4;
   f. 1, 2; g. 1, 2; h. 3; i. 2, 4; j. 1, 4; k. 1, 2 1. 1, 2.

3. a. T; b. F; c. T; d. F; e. F; f. T; g. T; h. T;
   i. T; j. F.

4. a. flocculation; b. Ouchterlony plate precipitation technique;
   c. direct method fluorescent antibody test; d. complement fixation test; e. agglutination; f. radioimmunoassay; g. enzyme
   immunoassay; h. immunoelectrophoresis.

5. a. B; b. C; c. B; d. A; e. C; f. B; g. C; h. A;
   i. A; j. B.

6. a. passive; b. placenta; c. umbilical cord; d. maternal
   antibodies; e. six; f. 12; g. 15; h. congenital immunity;
   i. IgG; j. Maternal; k. colostrum; l. IgA; m. IgG;
   n. IgM.

7. 1:16.

Concept Exercises

1. Low titers could suggest natural exposure to L. pneumophila or to
   other microorganisms that share antigenic determinants, mild or
   subclinical infection, or perhaps a residual titer of considerable
   duration.

2. a. I would immunize him with a toxoid.

   b. This should produce an artificially acquired active immunity.

   c. I would give the young man an antitoxin antiserum to produce
      an artificially acquired passive immunity, which has the ad-
      vantage of developing fast but the disadvantage of perhaps
      causing a hyperimmune reaction.

3. This apparent paradox is due to the fact that antibody, though
   present in high titer in the serum, cannot penetrate cells to eliminate the latent virus from the body during remissions. By contrast, individuals without antibodies have never acquired the
   primary infection and probably never will, once they have reached
   adulthood, because for some reason those who get through childhood
   without contracting the infection rarely contract it later.

Post-Test

1. b 2. b 3. d 4. c 5. a 6. c 7. a 8. a 9. b 10. c
11. c 12. d 13. b 14. b 15. b

The transplantation of tissues from a healthy donor to a recipient who
has suffered irreparable damage to some tissue or organ or who has a
deformity of an arm or leg is such a logical experiment that it is not
surprising that it was attempted many times in ancient medical history.
In virtually every instance the grafted tissue failed to survive more
than a few days. There is no doubt that many of the early failures
resulted from lack of surgical expertise or from bacterial infections,
but the bulk of these medical adventures were doomed to fail because
the laws regulating tissue transplantation immunity were being trans-
gressed.

> James T. Barrett, _Textbook of Immunology_,
> 2nd ed. St. Louis: C. V. Mosby, 1974.

CHAPTER OUTLINE

I. Hypersensitivity

    A. Type I: Anaphylactic hypersensitivity

    B. Atopic diseases

    C. Type II: Cytotoxic hypersensitivity

    D. Type III: Immune complex hypersensitivity

    E. Type IV: Cellular hypersensitivity

    F. Immune deficiency diseases

II. Transplantation and Tumor Immunology

    A. The transplantation problem

    B. Tumor immunology

OVERVIEW AND OBJECTIVES

One beautiful spring afternoon in Knoxville, Tennessee, I was playing
golf when I heard the sound of an ambulance siren. Rushing over to
see what had happened, I discovered that a fellow golfer has been stung
by a bee. That evening I read in the paper that the man had died before the ambulance could arrive. This experience vividly demonstrated
the severe consequences of anaplylactic hypersensitivity and the speed
with which it appears. In this chapter we will discuss disorders of
the immune system, including (1) various forms of hypersensitivity,
(2) various immune deficiency diseases, (3) various problems with organ
transplants, and (4) tumor immunology.

Four types of hypersensitivity are recognized. Perhaps the most severe and life-threatening is anaphylactic hypersensitivity (Type I). This form is characterized by vigorous contractions of the body's smooth muscles and is known as anaphylaxis. Common allergies are a milder form of this type of hypersensitivity. Type II hypersensitivity can also be life-threatening. It is referred to as cytotoxic hypersensitivity and is best characterized by transfusion reactions. Serum sickness is a common manifestation of Type III hypersensitivity, which is known as immune complex hypersensitivity. Cellular hypersensitivity (Type IV) is a delayed reaction, which is characterized by erythema and a thickening and drying of the skin tissue, called induration. Contact dermatitis and infection allergy are two forms of this type of hypersensitivity.

There are several types of immune deficiency diseases. In each case one or more components of the immune system are impaired. These diseases are usually genetic in origin. They may also result from certain acute and chronic diseases.

In the last twenty years one of the greatest advances in medicine has been the development of procedures for organ transplantation. Perhaps the most difficult problem with these procedures is organ rejection. This is a consequence of the immune system, which recognizes the transplant as "foreign." Recent developments in the understanding of the major and minor histocompatibility complexes give hope that the problem of transplant rejection may someday be solved.

Tumor cells express many antigens not found on normal cells. These antigens should be recognized by the immune system as "foreign." It is not understood why an apparently healthy person's immune system does not attack these cancer cells. Several alternative hypotheses are currently being considered as possible explanations. At the same time immunotherapy for the management of cancer is being developed.

After you have read Chapter 16 of your textbook, you should be able to:

1. Define or identify the following terms: hypersensitivity, immediate hypersensitivity, delayed hypersensitivity, anaphylactic hypersensitivity (Type I), anaphylaxis, allergen, mast cells, basophils, adenyl cyclase, adenosine monophosphate (AMP), histamine, serotonin, bradykinin, slow-reacting substance of anaphylaxis (SRS-A), edema, desensitization, blocking antibodies, atopic disease, common allergy, hay fever, dander, asthma, food allergies, flare, wheal, urticaria, cytotoxic hypersensitivity (Type II), target cell, hemolytic disease of the newborn (Rh disease), erythroblastosis fetalis, thrombocytopenia, agranulocytosis, autoimmune disease, immune complex hypersensitivity (Type III), serum sickness, Arthus phenomenon, farmer's lung, pigeon fancier's disease, systemic lupus erythematosus (SLE), butterfly rash, rheumatoid arthritis, cellular hypersensitivity (Type IV), induration, infection allergy, tuberculin skin test, contact dermatitis, uroshiol, immune deficiency disease, Bruton's agammaglobulinemia, DiGeorge's syndrome, transplantation immunology, tumor immunology,

autograft, syngeneic graft, allogenic graft, xenogenic graft, necrosis, major histocompatibility complex, minor histocompatibility complex, tissue typing, cytotoxicity test, oncofetal antigen, killer cell, and monoclonal antibodies.

2. Distinguish between teh various types of hypersensitivity.

3. Give at least two examples of each type of hypersensitivity.

4. List the characteristics of the immune deficiency diseases described.

5. Explain the importance of transplantation immunology to the prognosis of an organ transplant.

6. Discuss the unique immunological properties of the tumor cell and how these may be important in the treatment of cancer.

PRE-TEST

1. IgE is the antibody involved in _____ hypersensitivity.
   a. anaphylactic
   b. cytotoxic
   c. immune complex
   d. cellular

2. At least four types of antigens have been identified in tumor cells. One type, oncofetal antigens, is:
   a. the consequence of the induction of DNA viruses.
   b. induced by chemical carcinogens.
   c. expressed during the differentiation of embryonic tissues.
   d. the consequence of the induction of RNA viruses.

3. Repeated exposure to allergenic shampoos may lead to drying and scaling of the scalp. This is an example of:
   a. infection allergy.
   b. contact dermatitis.
   c. common allergy.
   d. cytotoxic hypersensitivity.

4. T-lymphocytes are the origin of _____ hypersensitivity.
   a. anaphylactic
   b. cytotoxic
   c. immune complex
   d. cellular

5. The blood type that has no ABO-group serum antibodies is:
   a. O.
   b. A.
   c. B.
   d. AB.

6. All of the following are examples of Type I hypersensitivity, except:
   a. anaphylaxis.

b.   hay fever.
c.   Arthus phenomenon.
d.   asthma.

7. Grafts between members of the same species is __best__ described as
    a(n):
    a.   autograft.
    b.   allogeneic graft.
    c.   xenogenic graft.
    d.   syngeneic graft.

8. Hemolytic disease of the newborn may result when which of the
    following couples have children?
    a.   An Rh (+) man and an Rh (+) woman
    b.   An Rh (+) man and an Rh (-) woman
    c.   An Rh (-) man and an Rh (+) woman
    d.   An Rh (-) man and an Rh (-) woman

9. The type of transplant with the greatest chance of success is a(n):
    a.   autograft.
    b.   syngeneic graft.
    c.   allogeneic graft.
    d.   xenogenic graft.

10. A series of events in which mediators cause the body's smooth
    muscles to undergo vigorous contractions is called:
    a.   common allergy.
    b.   asthma.
    c.   anaphylaxis.
    d.   infection allergy.

11. Contact dermatitis and infection allergy can be classified as
    _____ hypersensitivity.
    a.   anaphylactic
    b.   immediate
    c.   delayed
    d.   immune complex

12. Skin reactions are characteristic of several types of hypersensiti-
    vity. Cellular hypersensitivity is characterized by:
    a.   wheal formation.
    b.   usually no skin reaction.
    c.   flare formation.
    d.   tissue neurosis.

13. Cytotoxic and immune complex hypersensitivities have a common
    mediator. This mediator is:
    a.   histamine.
    b.   complement.
    c.   lymphokines.
    d.   SRS-A.

14. Urticaria is a(n):
    a.   rash characterized by both wheal and flare formation.

197

b. autoimmune disease.
c. immune deficiency disease.
d. term used to describe particles of animal skin and hair.

15. Red blood cells, white blood cells, and platelets are target cells involved in _____ hypersensitivity.
    a. anaphylactic
    b. cytotoxic
    c. immune complex
    d. cellular

PRACTICE EXERCISES

1. Identify the term being described by writing it on the line provided.

    a. A series of events in which mediators cause the body's smooth muscles to undergo vigorous contractions.

    _____   _____

    b. A common manifestation of immune complex hypersensitivity, it occurs where high concentrations of antigen are used, such as in injections of serum against diphtheria and tetanus.

    _____

    c. This condition is demonstrated by injecting an extract of the microbial agent that causes a particular disease into the skin tissue. If the person has had the disease, an immune response takes place and the area reddens and thickens.

    _____

    d. This disorder is characterized by wheezing and stressed breathing and appears to be caused by the same allergens associated with hay fever.

    _____

    e. A graft between members of different species.

    _____

    f. A method that consists of combining the cells of the tissue donor separately with sera containing antibodies against each of the histocompatibility antigens.

    _____   _____

    g. An antigen associated with tumor cells, which is expressed during the differentiation of tissues in the embryonic stage but is found in very small numbers in normal adult cells.

    _____

h. A process in which excessive amounts of IgG form complexes with antigens near the site of the latter's portal of entry into the body or in the blood vessels.

_____

i. A characteristic of cellular hypersensitivity in which the skin drys and thickens.

_____

j. An autoimmune disease in which the B-lymphocytes produce IgG when stimulated by the nuclear components of disintegrating white blood cells.

_____

2. Several mediators of anaphylactic hypersensitivity are composed of amino acids or are derived from amino acids. Identify each of the mediator molecules pictured.

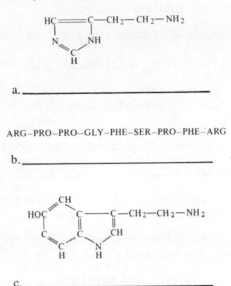

a. _____

ARG–PRO–PRO–GLY–PHE–SER–PRO–PHE–ARG

b. _____

c. _____

3. Each of the following statements is true for one or more types of hypersensitivity. Identify the type(s) characterized by each of the statements by placing the appropriate number(s) on the line provided.

1. Type I, anaphylactic   3. Type III, immune complex

2. Type II, cytotoxic   4. Type IV, cellular

_____ a. IgG is involved.

_____ b. Host tissues cells are involved.

_____ c. T-lymphocytes are origin of hypersensitivity.

_____ d. Histamine acts as a mediator.

_____ e. Hemolytic disease of newborns is one example.

_____ f. It is manifested in 30 minutes or less.

_____ g. There usually is no skin reaction.

_____ h. Lymphokines act as mediators.

_____ i. B-lymphocytes are the origin of hypersensitivity.

_____ j. Sensitivity is transferred by serum.

_____ k. Infection allergy is one example.

_____ l. Rheumatic fever is one example.

_____ m. IgE is the antibody involved.

_____ n. Common allergy is one example.

_____ o. Sensitivity is transferred by lymphoid cells.

4. <u>True or False</u>. Decide whether each of the following statements is true or false; then place a T for true or an F for false on the line provided.

_____ a. The symptoms of anaphylactic hypersensitivity are caused when IgE produced by the T-lymphocytes in response to the allergen fixes itself to the surface of mast cells and basophils.

_____ b. Blocking antibodies appear to be an effective device for protection of those sensitized to bee stings.

_____ c. Rheumatoid arthritis is an autoimmune disease in which immune complex formation takes place in the joints.

_____ d. When B-lymphocytes are unable to form plasma cells, the condition is called <u>DiGeorge's syndrome</u>.

_____ e. Tissue rejection will not take place in either an autograft or a syngeneic graft.

_____ f. The major histocompatibility complex is a set of antigens located on the surface of an organ cell. Unlike the minor histocompatibility complex, the major complex is capable of inducing the immune response.

_____ g. Host resistance to tumors is apparently dependent on a type of T-lymphocyte called the killer cell.

_____ h. It has recently been discovered that attenuated tubercle bacilli (BCG) greatly increase the phagocytosis of tumor cells in mice.

_____ i. A rare example of anaphylactic hypersensitivity is called thrombocytopenia. It results from antibodies produced against certain drugs.

_____ j. Farmer's lung disease is a form of immune complex hypersensitivity in which IgG forms complexes with antigens near the site of the latter's entry into the body.

5. Fill in the blanks. The method of rejection of transplated tissue involves both (a) _____-_____ and (b) _____
   _____. Skin and tumor grafts are rejected mainly by the (c)
   _____-_____ that enter the tissue and release (d)
   _____. (e) _____ are attracted to
   the site and the number of (f) _____ in each is increased. Digestion of the tissue leads to a drying and thickening
   of the skin as in (g) _____ hypersensitivity, and
   cell death, or (h) _____, soon follows.

      In organ transplants a different process takes place. Antigens
   stimulate host (i) _____-_____ to produce (j) _____
   _____. These enter the organ where they combine with
   antigens on the surface of the cells lining the blood vessel walls.
   The interaction activates (k) _____ and, as the
   cells are lysed, there is local inflammation. Debris soon fills
   the vessel and the blood supply to the organ is impeded.

CONCEPT EXERCISES

1. A patient who has suffered burns over much of his body and who will require skin grafts is brought to an emergency room. His wife is with him. In taking a medical history of the patient, the physician asks the wife whether the patient has any close relatives. She seems upset about all the questions and asks the physician why he wants to know about the patient's brothers and sisters. What explanation should he give her?

_____

_____

_____

2. Several examples of autoimmune disease are discussed in this chapter of your textbook. From the knowledge of the immune system you have gained from studying Chapters 14, 15, and 16, explain why these conditions are abnormal. What might explain the mechanism of these diseases?

_____

_____

_____

_____

_____

_____

_____

_____

_____

3. Before a doctor prescribes penicillin or other drugs as chemotherapy
   for an infectious disease, what should the doctor ask her patient
   and why?

_____

_____

_____

POST-TEST

1. No antibodies are involved in _____ hypersensitivity.
   a. anaphylactic
   b. cytotoxic
   c. immune complex
   d. cellular

2. An allergen is a(n):
   a. antibody produced in anaphylactic hypersensitivity.
   b. antigen that initiates anaphylaxis.
   c. antigen that induces cell-mediated immunity.
   d. antibody produced in response to autoantigen.

3. In a blood transfusion the:
   a. recipient should not contain antibodies to the donor's anti-
       gens.
   b. recipient should not contain antigens to the donor's anti-
       bodies.
   c. recipient should not contain antigens or antibodies cross-
       reactive to the donor's.
   d. donor should not contain antigens or antibodies cross-reactive
       to the recipient's.

4. The antibody involved in anaphylactic hypersensitivity is:
   a. IgG.
   b. IgM.
   c. IgE.
   d. IgA.

5. Serotonin is a derivative of the amino acid:
   a. histidine.
   b. serine.
   c. arginine.
   d. tryptophan.

6. Edema is a condition in which:
   a. a rash consisting of both wheals and flares is present.
   b. wheezing and stressed breathing are symptoms.
   c. the skin becomes swollen about the eyes, wrists, and ankles.
   d. IgG forms complexes with antigens near the site of the latter's entry into the body.

7. Systemic lupus erythematosus is an autoimmune disease that is an example of _____ hypersensitivity.
   a. anaphylactic
   b. cytotoxic
   c. immune complex
   d. cellular

8. The inability to produce plasma cells from B-lymphocytes is called:
   a. DiGeorge's syndrome.
   b. Bruton's agammaglobulinemia.
   c. Arthus phenomenon.
   d. erythroblastosis fetalis.

9. A patient comes to his physician several hours after being stung by a bee. He has been stung before and is worried that he may have become allergic to bee stings. What should his physician do?
   a. Tell him not to worry because the allergic reaction would already have developed.
   b. Administer antivenom because a hypersensitivity reaction would not develop for several hours to days.
   c. Administer antivenom because bee stings produce only delayed hypersensitivity.
   d. Tell him not to worry because if he were allergic, he would have had a reaction to the first bee sting.

10. Each of the following statements is true for immune complex hypersensitivity, except:
    a. It is manifested within hours to days.
    b. Complement is involved as a mediator.
    c. The origin of hypersensitivity is the T-lymphocytes.
    d. There is usually no skin reaction.

11. Food allergies are a form of _____ hypersensitivity.
    a. anaphylactic
    b. cytotoxic
    c. immune complex
    d. cellular

12. Each of the following is an example of immune complex hypersensitivity, except:
    a. serum sickness.

b. pigeon fancier's disease.
   c. rheumatic fever.
   d. agranulocytosis.

13. Mast cells and basophils are the cells involved in _____
    hypersensitivity.
    a. anaphylatic
    b. cytoxic
    c. immune complex
    d. cellular

14. When the immune system is depressed, _____ cells do not
    form and tumors develop rapidly.
    a. mast
    b. killer
    c. target
    d. cytotoxic

15. Sensitivity to all of the following types of hypersensitivity is
    transferable by serum, <u>except</u> _____.
    a. anaphylactic
    b. cytotoxic
    c. immune complex
    d. cellular

ANSWERS TO EXERCISES

1. a   6. c   11. c

2. c   7. b   12. d

3. b   8. b   13. b

4. d   9. a   14. a

5. d   10. c   15. b

Practice Exercises

1. a. anaphylaxis; b. serum sickness; c. infection allergy;

   d. asthma; e. xemogenic graft; f. cytotoxicity test;

   g. oncofetal antigen; h. Arthus phenomenon; i. induration;

   j. systemic lupus erythematosus.

2. a. serotonin; b. bradykinin; c. histamine.

3. a. 2, 3; b. 3, 4; c. 4; d. 1; e. 2; f. 1; g. 2, 3;

   h. 4; i. 1, 2, 3; j. 1, 2, 3; k. 4; l. 3; m. 1; n. 1;

   o. 4.

4. a. F; b. T; c. T; d. F; e. T; f. F; g. T; h. T;

   i. F; j. T.

5. a. T-lymphocytes; b. antibodies; c. T-lymphocytes;

   d. lymphokines; e. Phagocytes; f. lysosomes; g. Type IV;

   h. necrosis; i. B-lymphocytes; j. antibodies; k. complement.

Concept Exercises

1. He should explain to the wife that the best tissue match will be
   with the person genetically closest to her husband. A twin brother
   would be best.

2. During early development, the body classifies proteins as "self"
   and inactivates the immune response to them. In an autoimmune disease these proteins are recognized as "foreign" and an inappropriate
   immune response is developed. Several explanations might be suggested for the mechanism of an autoimmune response. One might be
   that the cells capable of producing the immune response escaped
   inactivation. Another might be that with age or disease the autoantigen may have altered in structure so that it is no longer recognized as self.

3. He should ask you whether you are allergic to the drug. Many drugs,
   such as penicillin, are capable of activating an anaphylactic
   hypersensitivity reaction in sensitive individuals.

Post-Test

1. d	6. c	11. a
2. b	7. c	12. d
3. a	8. b	13. a
4. c	9. a	14. b
5. d	10. c	15. d

17 Airborne Bacterial Diseases of Humans

It was to save babies that they killed so many guinea-pigs!

    Emile Roux, the fanatical helper of Pasteur, in 1888 took up the tools his master had laid down, and started on searches of his own. In a little while he discovered a strange poison seeping from the bacillus of diphtheria--one ounce of the pure essence of this stuff was enough to kill seventy-five thousand big dogs. A few years later, . . . Emil Behring, the poetical pupil of Koch, spied out a strange virus, an unknown something in the blood of guinea-pigs. It could make that powerful diphtheria poison completely harmless.

        Paul De Kruif, "Roux and Behring Massacre the Guinea-Pigs," in *Microbe Hunters*. New York: Harcourt, Brace and World, 1953.

CHAPTER OUTLINE

I.   Airborne Bacterial Diseases of Humans

    A.   Tuberculosis

    B.   Diphtheria

    C.   Meningococcal meningitis

    D.   Strep throat and scarlet fever

    E.   Pneumococcal pneumonia

    F.   Klebisella pneumonia

    G.   Whooping cough (pertussis)

    H.   Primary atypical pneumonia (PAP)

    I.   Haemophilus meningitis

    J.   Bacterial conjunctivitis (pinkeye)

    K.   Legionnaires' disease

OVERVIEW AND OBJECTIVES

This chapter begins a survey of the bacterial diseases of humans. These diseases will be grouped according to their mode of transmission. In this chapter we will discuss the airborne diseases and in following chapters, foodborne, waterborne, soilborne, arthropodborne, contact, and endogenous diseases will be explored. The discussion of each disease, the causative agent, symptoms, diagnostic methods, treatment, and availability of immunization will be outlined.

The airborne bacterial diseases are those that are spread through droplets and secretions. They are primarily diseases of the respiratory tract and are most common where people crowd together and live in crowded, substandard conditions. In these situations the diseases are easily passed from person to person. In addition, poor nutrition and other factors tend to reduce host resistance. Many of these organisms exist only in the human body and must be transmitted from one person to another. For this reason, immunization (where available), isolation of a patient, and prompt chemotherapy are important in controlling these diseases.

Tuberculosis, diphtheria, and whooping cough are historically important diseases. They have all caused significant numbers of deaths in the past. Today these diseases are under control in many developed countries, including the United States, but are still important health hazards in underdeveloped countries. Meningococcal meningitis and haemophilus meningitis are diseases of the spinal cord and brain and are often fatal if treatment is not initiated quickly. Strep throat and scarlet fever are both caused by the same organism, <u>Streptococcus</u> <u>pyogenes</u>. Scarlet fever may induce a hyperimmune disease called rheumatic fever, which may weaken the heart muscle. Pinkeye (bacterial conjunctivitis) is a disease of the eye caused by <u>Haemophilus</u> <u>aegypticus</u>.

Many airborne diseases can be classified as pneumonias. These are diseases of the bronchial tubes and lungs and include pneumococcal pneumonia, klebsiella pneumonia, primary atypical pneumonia, and Legionnaires' disease.

After reading Chapter 17 of your textbook, you should be able to:

1. Define or identify the following terms: tuberculosis, <u>Mycobacterium</u> <u>tuberculosis</u>, sputum, tubercle, miliary tuberculosis, consumption, Pott's disease, acid-fast, <u>Mycobacterium</u> <u>bovis</u>, bacillus Calmette-Guerin (BCG), diphtheria, <u>Corynebacterium</u> <u>diphtheriae</u>, metachromatic granules, pseudomembrane, phage conversion, meningococcal meningitis, <u>Neisseria</u> <u>meningitidis</u>, emningococcus, meningococcemia, meninges, oxidase, Waterhouse-Friderichsen syndrome, strep throat, scarlet fever, <u>Streptococcus</u> <u>pyogenes</u>, erythrogenic toxin, scarlatina, Aschoff bodies, beta-hemolytic streptococci, alpha-hemolytic streptococci, endocarditis, gamma-hemolytic streptococci, M protein puerperal fever, child-bed fever, septicemia, blood poisoning, erysipelas, glomerulonephritis, pneumococcal pneumonia, <u>Streptococcus</u> <u>pneumoniae</u>, lobar pneumonia, double pneumonia, bronchopneumonia, walking pneumonia, optochin, Klebsiella pneumonia, <u>Klebsiella</u> <u>pneumoniae</u>, nosocomial infections, whooping cough (pertussis), hypoxia, <u>Bordetella</u> <u>pertussis</u>, primary atypical pneumonia (PAP), Eaton agent, pleuropneumonia-like organism (PPLO), <u>Mycoplasma</u> <u>pneumoniae</u>, pleomorphic, cold agglutinin screening test (CAST), haemophilus meningitis, <u>Haemophilus</u> <u>influenzae</u>, bacterial conjunctivitis (pinkeye), <u>Haemophilus</u> <u>aegypticus</u>, conjunctiva, photophobia, X factor, Y factor, restriction enzymes, Legionnaires' disease and <u>Legionella</u> <u>pneumophila</u>.

2. List the major symptoms and causative organisms of the diseases discussed.

3. Explain why many airborne diseases are found most often in areas where people are crowded together and malnurished.

4. Discuss the forms of antimicrobial therapy and immune protection that can be used against these diseases.

5. Outline the steps leading to discovery of the organism that causes Legionnaires' disease and explain why it was difficult to identify.

PRE-TEST

1. Legionnaires' disease is caused by a:
   a. gram(+) coccus.
   b. gram(+) rod.
   c. gram(-) coccus.
   d. gram(-) rod.

2. Mycobacterium tuberculosis is unusual because it:
   a. must be lysogenized before it can cause disease.
   b. is acid-fast.
   c. forms a capsule.
   d. has no cell wall.

3. The organism that causes child-bed fever is:
   a. Corynebacterium diphtheriae.
   b. Streptococcus pyogenes.
   c. Streptococcus pneumoniae.
   d. Serratia marcescens.

4. A child suffering from repeated bouts of a violent, high-pitched cough is brought to her physician's office. The physician is likely to diagnose an infection of:
   a. Bordetella pertussis.
   b. Streptococcus pneumoniae.
   c. Mycobacterium tuberculosis.
   d. Naemophilus influenzae.

5. The toxin produced by virulent strains of Corynebacterium diphtheriae is the product of a viral gene, and the organism cannot produce disease unless it is lysogenized by this virus. This phenomenon is an example of:
   a. virus-induced disease.
   b. phage conversion.
   c. toxin induction.
   d. virus-mediated virulence.

6. Streptococcus pyogenes causes all of the following diseases, except:
   a. strep throat.
   b. scarlet fever.
   c. pneumococcal pneumonia.
   d. puerperal fever.

208

7. Several bacterial diseases have symptoms similar to those of viral, rickettsial, and chlamydial diseases. A bacterial disease similar to Q fever, psittacosis, and viral pneumonia is:
   a. Legionnaire's disease.
   b. pneumococcal pneumonia.
   c. klebsiella pneumonia.
   d. diphtheria.

8. Hypoxia is:
   a. a dry cough.
   b. excretions of the respiratory tract.
   c. a chemical compound that inhibits the growth of diplococci.
   d. oxygen starvation.

9. Neisseria meningitidis produces a characteristic enzyme called:
   a. neisseriase.
   b. kinase.
   c. oxidase.
   d. reductase.

10. A pleiomorphic organism with no cell wall which causes a type of pneumonia is:
    a. Mycoplasma pneumoniae.
    b. Corynebacterium diphtheriae.
    c. Mycobacterium tuberculosis.
    d. Streptococcus pneumoniae.

11. Swollen, red eyes are characteristic of a disease caused by:
    a. Mycoplasma pneumoniae.
    b. Haemophilus influenzae.
    c. Haemophilus aegypticus.
    d. Bordetella pertussis.

12. Erythrogenic toxin is:
    a. produced by Streptococcus pyogenes and damages the capillaries.
    b. a form of endotoxin produced by gram(-) bacteria.
    c. a product of phage conversion that inhibits protein synthesis.
    d. produced by Neisseria meningitidis and damages the meninges.

13. Aschoff bodies are a result of Type ____ hypersensitivity.
    a. I
    b. II
    c. III
    d. IV

14. In some cases of meningococcal meningitis, hemorrhagic lesions form in the adrenal glands, causing hormonal imbalance. This condition is called:
    a. Waterhouse-Friderichsen syndrome.
    b. Schick syndrome.
    c. adrenal imbalance syndrome.
    d. Aschoff bodies.

15. It has been hypothesized that an allergic reaction between strep-

tococcal antibodies and tissue antigens is responsible for all of
the following conditions, except:
a. erysipelas.
b. St. Anthony's fire.
c. glomerulonephritis.
d. septicemia.

PRACTICE EXERCISES

1. Many airborne bacterial diseases have characteristic signs, some
   of which are listed below. Determine which organism causes the
   characteristic described and write its scientific name on the line
   provided.

   a. Psuedomembrane present:

   _____ _____

   b. Spinal paralysis without skin spots:

   _____ _____

   c. Respiratory plug of mucus:

   _____ _____

   d. Spinal paralysis with skin spots and toxemia:

   _____ _____

   e. Tubercle:

   _____ _____

2. Matching. Match the bacterial species in the left-hand column with
   the best description of the species in the right-hand column by
   placing the corresponding number on the line provided. Descriptions
   may be used more than once or not at all. (You may wish to review
   Table 17.1 before answering this exercise.)

   _____ a. Mycobacterium   1. Gram(-) rod, which does
            tuberculosis   not produce an exotoxin or
                                      capsule

   _____ b. Corynebacterium
            diphtheriae   2. Gram(-) coccus, which pro-
                                     duces an exotoxin

   _____ c. Neisseria
            meningitidis   3. Gram(-) rod, which produces
                                     a capsule

   _____ d. Streptococcus
            pyogenes   4. Pleomorphic organism with
                                     no cell wall

   _____ e. Streptococcus
            pneumoniae   5. Acid-fast rod

210

_____ f. Klebsiella
pneumoniae

6. Gram(+) coccus, which produces a capsule

_____ g. Bordetella
pertussis

7. Gram(+) rod, which produces
an exotoxin

_____ h. Mycoplasma
pneumoniae

8. Gram(-) rod, which produces
an exotoxin

_____ i. Haemophilus
influenzae

9. Gram(+) rod, which does not
produce an exotoxin

_____ j. Haemophilus
aegypticus

10. Gram(-) coccus, which does
not produce an exotoxin

_____ k. Legionella
pneumophila

3. Each of the following phrases is descriptive of a condition associated with one or more airborne bacterial diseases. Identify
the condition being described by writing its name on the line provided.

a. Blood vessels in the kidney become inflamed, apparently as a
result of immune complex formation:

_____

b. An infection that is acquired in the hospital:

_____

c. Inability to see clearly in bright light:

_____

d. Infiltration of both sides of the lung by bacteria:

_____

e. The spread of bacteria to the blood:

_____

f. An inflammation of the skin about the face, scalp, eyes, and
trunk:

_____

g. The hard nodule caused by deposit of calcium salts and fibrous
materials in the lung:

_____

211

h. A disease of the thin mucous membrane that covers the cornea
    and forms the inner eyelid:

    _____

i. A condition associated with pertussis in which oxygen starva-
    tion takes place:

    _____

j. A disease of the heart muscle caused by streptococci:

    _____ _____

4. Immunization is available for many, but not all, airborne bacterial
   diseases. In the list below indicate the diseases for which vaccines are available by placing an X on the line to the left of the
   disease. For those you check, indicate the form of the immunization
   on the line to the right of the disease.

   _____ a. Tuberculosis _____

   _____ b. Diphtheria _____

   _____ c. Meningococcal meningitis _____

   _____ d. Scarlet fever _____

   _____ e. Pneumococcal pneumonia _____

   _____ f. Klebsiella pneumonia _____

   _____ g. Whooping cough _____

   _____ h. Primary atypical pneumonia _____

   _____ i. Haemophilus meningitis _____

   _____ j. Pinkeye _____

   _____ k. Legionnaires' disease _____

5. True or False. Indicate whether each of the following statements
   is true or false by placing a T for true or an F for false on the
   line provided.

   _____ a. Patient isolation is only minimally effective in the control
            of airborne diseases because the organisms are found in great
            numbers in the environment.

   _____ b. The organism that causes tuberculosis is resistant to decolori-
            zation with a 5% solution of acid alcohol.

   _____ c. Bacillus Calmette-Guerin is a preparation of an attenuated strain of <u>Mycobacterium</u> <u>bovis</u> used in immunization programs against tuberculosis.

_____ d. Many strains of <u>Streptococcus</u> <u>pyogenes</u> produce a toxin called erythrogenic toxin, which damages the capillaries and increases their permeability, allowing blood to leak into the skin tissues.

_____ e. Oxidase that causes haemophilus meningitis.

_____ f. Puerperal fever is a form of pneumonia caused by <u>Streptococcus pneumoniae</u>.

_____ g. Nosocomial infections are hospital acquired.

_____ h. The cold agglutinin screening test is used to test a patient's serum when PAP is suspected.

_____ i. <u>Legionella</u> <u>pneumophila</u> is a fastidious organism that requires both X factor and Y factor in its culture medium.

_____ j. <u>Corynebacterium</u> <u>diphtheriae</u>, when lysogenized by certain bacteriophages, produces a toxin that interferes with the protein metabolism of the host cells. This leads ultimately to the formation of a pseudomembrane, which may block the respiratory tract.

6. Many antibiotics are used in the treatment of airborne bacterial diseases. For each antibiotic listed below, identify one disease discussed in this chapter for which it is a recommended treatment. (You may wish to review Table 17.1 before answering this exercise.)

a. Sulfonamides:

_____

b. Penicillins:

_____

c. Aminoglycosides:

_____

d. Erythromycin:

_____

e. Streptomycin:

_____

f. Neomycin:

_____

CONCEPT EXERCISES

1. Prompt drug therapy is recommended for many of the airborne diseases discussed in this chapter. It is important not to overprescribe antibiotics and drugs, however. From the knowledge you have gained from your study of bacteriology so far, why do you think that it is not a good idea to administer antibiotics when they are not necessary or useful?

_____

_____

_____

_____

_____

2. Why was the identification of the organism that causes Legionnaires' disease difficult?

_____

_____

_____

_____

_____

3. The isolation of Mycobacterium tuberculosis is difficult. It is usually isolated from the sputum of a patient with tuberculosis, but very few organisms are usually present! Why does an infection that consists of so few organisms lead to such a severe morbidity, and why is it so difficult to cure?

_____

_____

_____

_____

_____

_____

1. The vaccine used against tuberculosis is an attenuated strain of:
   a. Mycobacterium tuberculosis.
   b. Corynebacterium diphtheriae.
   c. Mycobacterium bovis.
   d. Mycoplasma pneumoniae.

2. A woman with a chronic cough, chest pains, fever, and a flow of thick sputum comes to her physician. A chest x-ray indicates nodules in her lungs. She most likely has:
   a. diphtheria.
   b. tuberculosis.
   c. primary atypical pneumonia.
   d. pneumococcal pneumonia.

3. A patient has strep throat. The antibiotic of choice for treatment of this disease is:
   a. streptomycin.
   b. penicillin.
   c. aminoglycosides.
   d. erythromycin.

4. A clinical microbiologist has isolated an encapsulated gram(-) rod from a patient suffering from pneumonia. The patient most likely has:
   a. pneumococcal pneumonia.
   b. primary atypical pneumonia.
   c. klebsiella pneumonia.
   d. Legionnaires' disease.

5. PPLOs are distinctive because they:
   a. are acid-fast.
   b. are virulent only if a phage conversion has taken place.
   c. have no cell wall.
   d. produce a toxin that inhibits host protein synthesis.

6. A mild case of pneumococcal pneumonia is sometimes called:
   a. lobar pneumonia.
   b. double pneumonia.
   c. bronchopneumonia.
   d. walking pneumonia.

7. Immunization in the form of killed bacteria in DPT is used against which of the following diseases?
   a. diphtheria
   b. scarlet fever
   c. tuberculosis
   d. whooping cough

8. All of the following organisms produce a toxin that is involved in the disease they cause, except:
   a. Corynebaterium diphtheriae.
   b. Neisseria meningitidis.

c. Streptococcus pneumoniae.
d. Streptococcus pyogenes.

9. Streptococcus pyogenes produces a protein that is present in the pili and allows the bacterial cells to adhere firmly to the pharyngeal tissue. This protein is called:
   a. M protein.
   b. X factor.
   c. Y factor.
   d. S protein.

10. Each of the following is a name for the organism that causes primary atypical pneumonia, except:
    a. pneumococcus.
    b. Eaton agent.
    c. pleuropneumonia-like organism.
    d. Mycoplasma pneumoniae.

11. The causative organism of pinkeye has served modern science in a positive role as a source of:
    a. adjuvant.
    b. NAD.
    c. BCG.
    d. restriction enzymes.

12. Only one airborne disease of the eye is discussed in this chapter. The causative organism of this disease is a:
    a. gram(-) rod.
    b. gram(-) coccus.
    c. gram(+) rod.
    d. gram(+) coccus.

13. Streptococcus pyogenes is a(n):
    a. alpha-hemolytic streptococcus.
    b. beta-hemolytic streptococcus.
    c. gamma-hemolytic streptococcus.
    d. delta-hemolytic streptococcus.

14. A common form of nosocomial pneumonia is caused by:
    a. Streptococcus pneumoniae.
    b. Klebsiella pneumoniae.
    c. Mycoplasma pneumoniae.
    d. Legionella pneumophila.

15. Pott's disease is tuberculosis of the:
    a. spine.
    b. liver.
    c. bones.
    d. kidneys.

ANSWERS TO EXERCISES

Pre-Test

1. d   6. c   11. c

216

2. b	7. a	12. a
3. b	8. d	13. c
4. a	9. c	14. a
5. b	10. a	15. d

Practice Exercises

1. a. <u>Corynebacterium</u> <u>diphtheriae</u>; b. <u>Haemophilus</u> <u>influenzae</u>;

   c. <u>Bordetella</u> <u>pertussis</u>; d. <u>Neisseria</u> <u>meningitidus</u>;

   e. <u>Mycobacterium</u> <u>tuberculosis</u>.

2. a. 5; b. 7; c. 2; d. 6; e. 6; f. 3; g. 8; h. 4;

   i. 1; j. 1; k. 1.

3. a. glomerulonephritis; b. nosocomial infection; c. photophobia;

   d. double pneumonia; e. septicemia; f. erysipelas;

   g. tubercle; h. conjunctivitis; i. hypoxia; j. endocarditis.

4. The diseases for which immunization is available are: a. BCG:

   b. toxoid in DPT: d. toxoid; e. only to certain strains;

   g. killed bacteria in DPT.

5. a. F; b. T; c. T; d. T; e. F f. F; g. T; h. T;

   i. F; j. T.

6. a. tuberculosis; b. diphtheria, meningococcal meningitis,

   scarlet fever, pneumococcal pneumococcal pneumonia, and whooping

   cough; c. klebsiella pneumonia and haemophilus meningitis;

   d. whooping cough, primary atypical pneumonia, and Legionnaires'

   disease; e. tuberculosis; f. bacterial conjunctivitis.

Concept Exercises

1. As we learned in Chapter 6, bacteria have the ability to acquire
   resistance to drugs through mutation and the infection of drug-
   resistant plasmids (R factors). If drugs are used indiscriminately,
   they will, over time, act to select for resistant strains. The
   increase in the frequency of resistant bacteria will then reduce
   the usefulness of the drug in cases where it is truly needed.

217

2. Because the disease had many similarities to rickettsial, chlamydial, and viral diseases, epidemiologists were searching for these
   types of intracellular parasites instead of looking for bacteria.
   It was also thought that an environmental pollutant or poison might
   be the cause of the disease.

3. Because the immune response to the organism causes the formation
   of tubercles, the damage to the lung is greater than might be
   caused if the bacterium simply infected individual cells. The
   acid-fast nature of the organism makes the infection one of the
   most difficult to cure. The patient often stops treatment before
   the organism is completely eliminated. In addition, the organism
   is very resistant to environmental stresses and can survive long
   periods on dry surfaces, in water, and in the air.

Post-Test

1. c	6. d	11. d
2. b	7. d	12. a
3. b	8. c	13. b
4. c	9. a	14. b
5. c	10. a	15. a

Marinated mushrooms happened to be one of her husband's specialties. He bought them himself and he himself did all the preparing. Schoenholtz had even got hold of the recipe. It read, "Wash in cold water. Boil in white wine for thirty minutes, and drain. Place in Mason jar, flavor with pepper and cloves, and cover with olive oil. Seal tightly." In other words, nothing that could cause any lurking C. botulinum spores a moment of discomfort. And everything to encourage their growth. But the mushrooms could still have been made perfectly safe. A few minutes of heat before serving would have completely destroyed the toxin. However, that wasn't the old man's way. The jar went straight from the pantry shelf to the table.

Berton Roueche, "Family Reunion," in Eleven Blue Men. New York: Berkeley Publishing, 1953.

CHAPTER OUTLINE

I. Foodborne and Waterborne Bacterial Diseases of Humans

A. Botulism

B. Staphylococcal food poisoning

C. Clostridial food poisoning

D. Typhoid fever

E. Salmonellosis

F. Bacterial dysentery (shigellosis)

G. Asiatic cholera

H. Infantile and traveler's diarrheas

I. Brucellosis

J. Other foodborne and waterborne diseases

OVERVIEW AND OBJECTIVES

Foodborne and waterborne diseases are difficult to control because the organisms that cause them are part of our environment. Often the source of the infection is difficult to identify in epidemic situations. The diseases are sometimes related to particular life styles and their control requires educating people to methods of sanitation and personal hygiene. This may be particularly difficult because it may require changing local and traditional customs.

Several of the diseases discussed in this chapter are well-known, life-threatening diseases, which have plagued humans over the centuries. Botulism is a food-related disease, which is most often associated with preserved (particularly canned) foods. The causative organism produces an exotoxin that is probably the most powerful poison known. Typhoid fever has ravaged humans throughout history. In this disease the victim ingests the bacteria, which ulcerate the linging of the intestine. Asiatic cholera has been known for many years. This disease is characterized by severe dysentery, and 70% of untreated cases are fatal. Bacterial dysentery or Shigellosis is caused by members of the genus Shigella and can be easily transmitted because the infective dose is only a few hundred organisms. Traveler's and infantile diarrheas are caused by Escherichia coli, an organism normally found in the digestive system without causing disease. The disease is caused by strains that have acquired a plasmid which codes for a toxin much like cholera toxin.

Staphylococcal food poisoning has traditionally been known as ptomaine poisoning. This disease is also a result of toxin action, but the symptoms are restricted to the intestine. The disease is seldom fatal. Salmonellosis is caused by several species of the genus Salmonella. It is also a form of food poisoning and is usually allowed to run its course. Clostridial food poisoning is caused by the same bacterium as gas gangrene, which will be discussed in the next chapter. Brucellosis is a disease transmitted by raw milk and infected meat. It has been traditionally called undulant fever because it is associated with fever that is high in the daytime and low in the evening. It is not transmitted from human to human.

After you have read Chapter 18 of your textbook, you should be able to:

1. Define or identify the following terms: botulism, Clostridium botulinum, flaccid paralysis, acetylcholine, fodder disease, limberneck, wound botulism, sudden infant death syndrome (SIDS), staphylococcal food poisoning, ptomaines, Staphylococcus aureus, clostridial food poisoning, Clostridium perfringens, typhoid fever, Salmonella typhi, rose spots, salmonellosis, serotypes, Salmonella species, gastroenteritis, bacterial dysentery (shigellosis), Shigella species, R factors, Asiatic cholera, Vibrio cholerae, biotype, rice-water stools, infantile diarrhea, traveler's diarrhea, Escherichia coli, brucellosis, Brucella abortus, erythritol, undulant fever, Bang's disease, Malta fever, Vibrio parahaemolyticus, Campylobacter jejuni, Bacillus cereus, and Yersinia enterocolitica.

2. List the organisms that cause the diseases discussed and some of their taxonomic characteristics.

3. Group these diseases according to their major symptoms (i. e., diarrheas, food poisonings, etc.)

4. Indicate the major forms of treatment and/or immunization used in fighting these diseases.

5. Identify the diseases in which a toxin is involved and, where possible, indicate the role of the toxin in the disease.

PRE-TEST

1. The only treatment for botulism is:
   a. immunization.
   b. tetracycline.
   c. antitoxin.
   d. chloramphenicol.

2. Staphylococcus aureus is a:
   a. gram(+) rod, which causes staphylococcal food poisoning.
   b. gram(+) coccus, which is often found in the human nose.
   c. gram(-) rod, which causes a form of dysentery.
   d. gram(-) coccus, which is the cause of ptomaine poisoning.

3. A disease that requires only a few hundred organisms as an infective dose can be caused by:
   a. Shigella dysenteriae.
   b. Salmonella enteritidis.
   c. Escherichia coli.
   d. Vibrio parahaemolyticus.

4. Cholera toxin:
   a. inhibits the release of acetylcholine.
   b. stimulates the production of adenyl cyclase.
   c. produces foul-smelling nitrogen compounds called ptomaines.
   d. inhibits protein synthesis.

5. Clostridium perfringens causes both clostridial food poisoning and:
   a. clostridial dysentery.
   b. typhoid fever.
   c. gas gangrene.
   d. Asiatic cholera.

6. Ptomaine poisoning is another name for:
   a. staphylococcal food poisoning.
   b. clostridial food poisoning.
   c. botulism.
   d. brucellosis.

7. A disease caused by an organism found in raw milk is:
   a. brucellosis, which is caused by a bacterium that induces spontaneous abortions in cattle.
   b. brucellosis, which is caused by a sporeforming gram(+) rod.
   c. staphylococcal food poisoning, which is caused by a gram(+) coccus.
   d. staphylococcal food poisoning, which is a disease of the intestine.

8. Malta fever is caused by a:
   a. gram(+) rod, Clostridium perfringens.

b. gram(-) rod, Brucella abortus.
c. gram(+) rod, Brucella abortus.
d. gram(-) rod, Clostridium perfringens.

9. Probably the most potent toxin known is produced by:
   a. Clostridium botulinum.
   b. Clostridium perfringens.
   c. Bacillus cereus.
   d. Brucella abortus.

10. Diarrhea is a symptom of all of the following diseases, except:
    a. infantile diarrhea.
    b. staphylococcal food poisoning.
    c. typhoid fever.
    d. clostridial food poisoning.

11. All of the following are, at least in some cases, caused by Clostridium botulinum, except:
    a. fodder disease.
    b. limberneck.
    c. SIDS.
    d. Bang's disease.

12. Bright red "rose spots" are a symptom is:
    a. botulism.
    b. Asiatic cholera.
    c. typhoid fever.
    d. brucellosis.

13. Salmonellosis is:
    a. caused by hundreds of serotypes of Salmonella.
    b. a form of dysentery almost as severe as cholera.
    c. a form of dysentery caused by members of the genus Shigella.
    d. induced by an infective dose of only a few hundred organisms.

14. An aerobic gram(+) sporeformer that causes food poisoning is:
    a. Clostridium botulinum.
    b. Clostridium perfringens.
    c. Bacillus cereus.
    d. Brucella abortus.

15. One of the most important factors in controlling foodborne and waterborne disease is to:
    a. isolate infected persons because person-to-person infection is so great.
    b. educate people to methods of sanitation and personal hygiene.
    c. control animal pests that may transfer the organisms into the water supply.
    d. inoculate as many people as possible against the diseases in order to control epidemics.

PRACTICE EXERCISES

1. True or False. Decide whether each of the following statements

is true or false; then place a T for true or an F for false on the line provided.

_____ a. In botulism, the bacterium is ingested and produces a toxin in the body, which affects the nervous system.

_____ b. Clostridium perfringens, traditionally an agent for gas gangrene, also causes a form of food poisoning due to a toxin produced by the organism.

_____ c. Rapid thawing and quick cooking of frozen foods are recommended because Staphylococcus aureus is generally resistant to killing by freezing.

_____ d. Gastroenteritis and enteritis are alternative names for shigellosis.

_____ e. The Widal test can use extracts of flagella or cellular antigens to diagnose typhoid fever.

_____ f. Sudden infant death syndrome is sometimes caused by a form of botulism and for this reason honey should not be included in infants' diets.

_____ g. Fodder disease is another name for brucellosis and is so named because it is spread to farmers and their livestock from cattle feed.

_____ h. Foul-smelling nitrogen compounds called ptomaines appear in the intestine of a person suffering from staphylococcal food poisoning.

_____ i. Rose spots are an indication that hemorrhaging is taking place in the skin and are a symptom of salmonellosis.

_____ j. Asiatic cholera has been recognized for centuries in human populations, and the last pandemic is in progress.

2. In a short phrase describe the action of the toxin associated with each of the following diseases.

a. Botulism:

_____

b. Clostridial food poisoning:

_____

c. Shigellosis:

_____

223

d.   Asiatic cholera:

_____

e.   Traveler's diarrhea:

_____

f.   Brucellosis:

_____

3. Matching. Match the bacterial species in the left-hand column
   with the best description of the species in the right-hand column
   by placing the corresponding number on the line provided. Descriptions in the right-hand column may be used more than once or not
   at all. (You may wish to review Table 18.2 before answering this
   exercise.)

_____	a. Clostridium botulinum	1.	Gram(+), aerobic, spore-forming rod
_____	b. Salmonella typhi	2.	Gram(-) curved rod
		3.	Gram(-) rod, which does not produce exotoxins
_____	c. Brucella abortus		
		4.	Gram(+), anaerobic, spore-forming rod
_____	d. Pathogenic Escherichia coli		
		5.	Gram(+) rod, which produces exotoxin but no spores
_____	e. Campylobacter jejuni		
		6.	Gram(-) rod, which produces exotoxin
_____	f. Bacillus cereus		
		7.	Gram(-) coccus, which does not produce exotoxin
_____	g. Clostridium perfringens		
		8.	Gram(+) coccus, which pro-duces exotoxin
_____	h. Salmonella serotypes		
_____	i. Staphylococcus aureus		
_____	j. Vibrio cholerae		

4. Listed below are several treatments and immunizations used for
   various foodborne and waterborne bacterial diseases. Identify one
   disease discussed in this chapter for which each is recommended.
   (You may wish to review Table 18.2 before answering this exercise.)

a. Antitoxin:

_____

b. Rehydration:

_____

c. Ampicillin:

_____

d. Tetracycline:

_____

e. Killed bacteria vaccine:

_____

f. Chloramphenicol:

_____

5. Each of the following phrases is descriptive of a condition associated with one or more airborne or waterborne bacterial diseases.
   Identify each condition by writing its name on the line provided.

   a. The limbs have little tone and become flabby.

   _____

   b. Bright red splotches, which indicate that hemorrhaging is
      taking place in the skin; associated with typhoid fever.

   _____

   c. The result of conversion of intestinal contents to a thin
      material like barley soup, this condition is an important
      signal of Asiatic cholera.

   _____

   d. A fever that is high in the daytime and low in the evening.

   _____

   e. A disease marked by frequent watery stools, often with blood
      and mucus, and characterized by pain and dehydration.

   _____

6. Fill in the blanks. Several foodborne and waterborne diseases are
   among the classical series of bacterial infections that have

ravaged humans for centuries. Antibiotics are of no value in (a)
_____ _____, because the person is (b) _____
_____ rather than infected. Large doses of (c) _____
are administered, and life support systems such as a respirator are
utilized in treatment of the disease. The disease is caused by (d)
_____ _____.

(e) _____ _____ differs from other food
poisoning in that the victim ingests bacteria rather than toxins
and soon becomes infected rather than poisoned. The causative
agent (f) _____ _____, is a gram(-) rod that
is very resistant to (g) _____ extremes.

The most severe form of dysentery is associated with (h) _____
_____ _____. In this disease, caused by (i) _____
_____ _____, the patient experiences vomiting and
violent cramps with unrelenting loss of fluid. The causative
bacterium is a (j) _____ rod, which is gram(-). This
bacterium produces a toxin that stimulates the production of the
enzyme (k) _____ _____. This enzyme increases
the level of (l) _____ _____, which leads to
the abundant secretion of fluid by the intestine.

CONCEPT EXERCISES

1. Typhoid fever can be treated with antibiotics such as chloramphenicol. Patients who recover are usually asymptomatic carriers of
   the organism. Why are antibiotics not effective in clearing the
   patient of the organisms completely?

   _____

   _____

   _____

   _____

   _____

   _____

2. Brucellosis is a disease with both physical and economic consequences to the dairy and meat producer. Explain why this is
   true.

   _____

   _____

   _____

   _____

_____

_____

3. What physiological characteristics of the causative agent of botulism make it particularly suited to produce food poisoning in canned foods?

_____

_____

_____

POST-TEST

1. A fever that often is high in the daytime and low in the evening is associated with brucellosis. This gives the disease its alternative name of:
   a. ptomaine poisoning.
   b. limberneck fever.
   c. undulant fever.
   d. saddleback fever.

2. A gram(-) rod that causes foodborne and waterborne disease in children, which is characterized by sharp, appendicitis-like pain, is:
   a. Bacillus cereus.
   b. Yersinia enterocolitica.
   c. Campylobacter jejuni.
   d. Vibrio parahaemolyticus.

3. In 1979, the CDC recommended that honey be eliminated from the diet of infants because it:
   a. might contain botulism spores, which can germinate in anaerobic pockets in an infant's intestine.
   b. can be aspirated into the respiratory tract and lead to Salmonella infection.
   c. is often the source of staphylococcal food poisoning, which can be fatal in very young children.
   d. often contains the spores of Clostridium perfringens, which can cause both food poisoning and gas gangrene.

4. The chief source of Salmonella typhi is:
   a. fresh water.
   b. food.
   c. human carriers.
   d. animal fomites.

5. Bacterial dysentery is caused by members of the genus:
   a. Shigella.
   b. Salmonella.
   c. Staphylococcus.
   d. Serratia.

227

6. In typhoid fever, the carriers harbor the organism in their:
   a. intestine.
   b. stomach.
   c. pancreas.
   d. gall bladder.

7. _Brucella_ _abortus_ grows actively on the placenta of the pregnant cow because:
   a. its growth is stimulated by the hormones produced during pregnancy.
   b. fetal cows provide a good growth medium for the organism.
   c. the rich blood supply to the placenta provides nutrients.
   d. the placenta of the cow contains the sugar erythritol, which stimulates the growth of the organism.

8. The last pandemic of Asiatic cholera:
   a. was during the reign of Queen Victoria.
   b. killed at least half of the population of Europe.
   c. is going on today.
   d. caused 75,000 deaths in 1878.

9. R factors are:
   a. virulence factors produced by _Vibrio_ _cholerae_.
   b. antibiotics useful in the treatment of botulism.
   c. extra-chromosomal elements that contain drug-resistant genes.
   d. spores produced by _Bacillus_ _cereus_, an organism recently identified as causing food poisoning.

10. Heating of food to _____ degrees Celsius for ten minutes will destroy botulism toxin.
    a. 50
    b. 70
    c. 90
    d. 110

11. Each of the following diseases causes dysentery or diarrhea severe enough to require rehydration therapy, except:
    a. Asiatic cholera.
    b. infantile diarrhea.
    c. salmonellosis.
    d. shigellosis.

12. The most effective therapy in the treatment of botulism is:
    a. chloramphenicol.
    b. killed bacteria vaccines.
    c. antitoxin.
    d. ampicillin.

13. Botulism toxin acts by:
    a. increasing the amount of AMP in the cell.
    b. inhibiting the release of acetylcholine.
    c. inhibiting protein synthesis.
    d. increasing water secretion in the latter part of the small intestine.

14. Vibrio cholerae is best described as a:
    a. gram(-) elongated rod.
    b. gram(-) curved rod.
    c. gram(-) coccus.
    d. gram(+) coccus.

15. The symptoms of typhoid fever include all of the following, except:
    a. intestinal ulcers.
    b. diarrhea.
    c. fever.
    d. skin spots.

ANSWERS TO EXERCISES

Pre-Test

1. c   6. a   11. d

2. b   7. a   12. c

3. a   8. b   13. a

4. b   9. a   14. c

5. c   10. c   15. b

Practice Exercises

1. a. F; b. T; c. T; d. F; e. T; f. T; g. F; h. T;

   i. F; j. T.

2. a. Inhibits release of the neurotransmitter, acetylcholine.

   b. Increases the water secretion in the latter part of the small
   intestine leading to a brief diarrhea.

   c. The nature and mode of action of this toxin is still unknown.

   d. Stimulates the production of the enzyme adenyl cyclase.

   e. Stimulates the production of the enzyme adenyl cyclase.

   f. Symptoms are thought to be caused by endotoxin production.

3. a. 4; b. 3; c. 6; d. 6; e. 3; f. 1; g. 4; h. 3;

   i. 8; j. 2. (All answers to this exercise can be found in

   Table 18.2.)

4. a. botulism and clostridial food poisoning; b. bacterial

   dysentery, Asiatic cholera, infantile diarrhea, and traveler's diarrhea; c. bacterial dysentery; d. bacterial dysentery, Asiatic cholera, and brucellosis; e. typhoid fever and Asiatic cholera; f. typhoid fever. (All answers to this exercises can be found in Table 18.2.)

5. a. flaccid paralysis; b. rose spots; c. rice-water stools; d. undulating fever; e. dysentery.

6. a. botulism therapy; b. intoxicated; c. antitoxin; d. Clostridium botulinum; e. Typhoid fever; f. Salmonella typhi; g. environmental; h. Asiatic cholera; i. Vibrio cholerae; j. curved; k. adenyl cyclase; l. adenosine mono-phosphate.

Concept Exercises

1. The organism has a predilection for the gall bladder, and anti-biotics do not appear to be effective in this organ. Hence, "cured" people retain organisms in the gall bladder. It is often necessary to remove the gall bladder to prevent any further shedding of bacteria through the bile duct.

2. Brucellosis can be acquired by the milk and meat producer from handling infected milk and meat. It is economically important because the organism causes abortions in cows and other animals. This eliminates the infected animal from the breeding herd and costs the farmer money.

3. It is an anaerobic sporeforming organism. Hence, it can survive the heat of the canning process and grow in the anaerobic can producing its toxin.

Post-Test

1. c	6. d	11. c
2. b	7. d	12. c
3. a	8. c	13. b
4. c	9. c	14. b
5. a	10. c	15. b

19 Soilborne and Arthropodborne Bacterial Diseases of Humans

Professor Max Gottlieb was about to assassinate a guinea pig with anthrax germs, and the bacteriology class were [sic] nervous.

They had studied the forms of bacteria, they had handled Petri dishes and platinum loops, they had proudly grown on potato slices the harmless red cultures of Bacillus prodigiosus, and they had come now to pathogenic germs and the inoculation of a living animal with swift disease. These two beadyeyed guinea pigs, chittering in a battery jar, would in two days be stiff and dead.

Sinclair Lewis, Arrowsmith.
New York: Signet Classics, 1961.

CHAPTER OUTLINE

I.   Soilborne and Arthropodborne Diseases of Humans

A.   Anthrax

B.   Tetanus

C.   Gas gangrene

D.   Listeriosis

E.   Leptospirosis

F.   Bubonic plague

G.   Tularemia

H.   Relapsing fever

I.   Bartonellosis

OVERVIEW AND OBJECTIVES

Plague, anthrax, tetanus, and gas gangrene--all of these diseases are well known in the history of mankind, and all are either soilborne or arthropodborne diseases. Several times bubonic plague has reduced the population of the world by half. It is spread by fleas. Anthrax was the disease used by Robert Koch to demonstrate his germ theory of disease. Tetanus is among the most dangerous of human diseases. It is common and is caused by the second most powerful toxin known. Gas gangrene is always prevalent in wars and literally consumes tissue as it progresses. In this chapter we will discuss these and other diseases, which are acquired directly from the soil through cuts, abrasions, deep wounds, or inhalation or are acquired through the bite of an arthropod

231

vector.

Listeriosis has only recently been recognized. It is particularly significant in neonatal situations, where it can cause severe damage to the fetus and newborn child. The disease does not appear to be communicable among humans. Leptospirosis is transmitted from animals to humans through contact with contaminated soil or water. The spiral bacterium that causes the disease initially infects the bloodstream and causes gastric hemorrhages.

Tularemia is a disease native to America. It can be spread by handling contaminated animals, such as rabbits. It may also be transmitted by arthropods that inhabit the fur of these animals. The disease is one of the most difficult bacterial diseases to diagnose. A disease transmitted by lice is called relapsing fever because the disease recurs at regular intervals (often once a week). Bartonellosis is a little-known disease that occurs mainly in the northern regions of South America. It is transmitted by sandflies.

After you have read Chapter 19 of your textbook, you should be able to:

1. Define or identify the following terms: anthrax, epizootic, Bacillus anthracis, woolsorter's disease, Ascoli test, tetanus, Clostridium tetani, tetanospasmin, lockjaw, gas gangrene, Clostridium species, fecithinase, hyperbaric oxygen (HBO), listeriosis, Listeria monocytogenes, listeric meningitis, leptospirosis, Leptospira interrogans, bubonic plague, bipolar staining, Pasteurella pestis, Yersinia pestis, buboes, black death, septicemic plague, pneumonic plague, tularemia, Francisella tularensis, rabbit fever, ulceroglandular, oculoglandular, typhoidal form, pulmonary tularemia, relapsing fever, Borrellia recurrentis, Jarisch-Herxheimer reaction (JHR), bartonellosis, Bartonella bacilliformis, and Carrion's disease.

2. Discuss the historical importance of the diseases described.

3. Identify the causative bacterium of each disease and some of each bacterium's taxonomic characteristics.

4. List the diagnostic tests used to identify the diseases.

5. Describe the treatments and immunizations used to control these diseases.

PRE-TEST

1. An epizootic disease is one that is:
   a. found only in animals.
   b. transferred from animals to humans.
   c. found in epidemic proportions around animals.
   d. transmitted from humans to animals.

2. Woolsorter's disease is another name for:

a. anthrax.
b. plague.
c. tetanus.
d. tularemia.

3. <u>Listeria monocytogenes</u> is <u>best</u> described as a:
   a. gram(+) rod that becomes gram(-) with age.
   b. gram(-) rod.
   c. gram(+) rod that forms long filaments.
   d. gram(+) coccus.

4. Hyperbaric oxygen is a(n):
   a. symptom in which the lungs collect oxygen but cannot expel
      carbon dioxide.
   b. treatment in which oxygen is forced into a wound to make it
      aerobic.
   c. treatment in which oxygen is forced into the lungs.
   d. symptom in which oxygen cannot enter muscle tissue, causing
      muscles to contract.

5. In the typhoidal form of tularemia:
   a. an arthropod contact or a bite produces a skin ulcer.
   b. the cause is the splashing of bacteria--contaminated animal
      fluids into the eye.
   c. there are no skin lesions, but a high fever and severe abdominal
      pains are present.
   d. animal fluids are aerosolized and breathed into the lungs.

6. The Jarisch-Herxheimer reaction is a:
   a. symptom of bubonic plague.
   b. type of endotoxin shock.
   c. laboratory test used to diagnose relapsing fever.
   d. reaction to an exotoxin.

7. A disease caused by a spirochete is:
   a. leptospirosis.
   b. listeriosis.
   c. anthrax.
   d. tularemia.

8. All of the following diseases are caused by sporeforming organisms,
   <u>except</u>:
   a. anthrax.
   b. tetanus.
   c. gas gangrene.
   d. bubonic plague.

9. Antitoxin is an effective treatment for:
   a. tetanus.
   b. gas gangrene.
   c. tularemia.
   d. bubonic plague.

10. Tetanospasmin is:

a. the name given to the symptoms of tetanus.
b. a toxin produced by Clostridium tetani.
c. a drug used to treat tetanus.
d. a mild form of tetanus.

11. Each of the following organisms causes gas gangrene, except:
 a. Clostridium perfringens.
 b. Clostridium septicum.
 c. Clostridium tetani.
 d. Clostridium novyi.

12. A disease that causes vague flu-like symptoms in a pregnant woman, miscarriages, and physical and mental retardation in the child is:
 a. listeriosis.
 b. leptospirosis.
 c. tularemia.
 d. relapsing fever.

13. All of the following virulence factors are produced by Clostridium perfringens, except:
 a. hyaluronidase.
 b. hemolysin.
 c. fecithinase.
 d. tetanospasmin.

14. Tetanus is caused by a:
 a. gram(-) aerobic rod.
 b. gram(-) anaerobic rod.
 c. gram(+) aerobic rod.
 d. gram(+) anaerobic rod.

15. Bartonellosis is a disease:
 a. caused by a gram(+) aerobic rod.
 b. spread by sandflies.
 c. spread by lice.
 d. caused by a gram(-) coccus.

PRACTICE EXERCISES

1. Each of the following diseases is spread by one or more vectors. Write the name of one common vector for each disease on the line provided.

 a. Bubonic plague:

 _____

 b. Relapsing fever:

 _____

 c. Bartonellosis:

 _____

d. Tularemia:

---

2. True or False. Indicate whether each of the following statements is true or false by placing a T for true or an F for false on the line provided.

_____ a. Anthrax spores rapidly germinate on contact with human tissues. The cells are surrounded by a thick capsule that impedes phagocytosis.

_____ b. Bubonic plague is caused by a gram(+) rod that stains heavily at the ends of the cell.

_____ c. Rabbit fever is another name for tularemia because handling or consuming rabbit meat is a vehicle for transmission of the disease.

_____ d. Tularemia is among the easiest of bacterial diseases to recognize.

_____ e. Jarisch-Herxheimer reaction is observed in relapsing fever, syphilis, and trypanosomiasis.

_____ f. Francisella tularensis is very resistant to environmental conditions and may remain active for long periods of time in raw hides or in frozen meat.

_____ g. In pneumonic plague the bacterium does not enter the lung but remains in the blood.

_____ h. Tetanus toxin inhibits the removal of acetylcholine from the nerve synapse.

_____ i. When a person is bitten by a dog, the concern for tetanus is often greater than for rabies.

_____ j. Hemolysin, which induces hemorrhages in the capillaries and leads to general anemia, is not produced by Clostridium novyi.

3. The following characteristics include those that can be used to describe the organisms listed, each of which causes a soilborne or arthropodborne bacterial disease. Choose the appropriate characteristic(s) for each organisms and write the number(s) on the line provided.

1. gram(-)   5. spirochete

2. gram(+)   6. bipolar staining

3. rod   7. sporeforming

4. coccus   8. toxin producing

a. <u>Yersinia pestis</u>: _____

b. <u>Listeria monocytogenes</u>: _____

c. <u>Francisella tularenisis</u>: _____

d. <u>Bacillus anthracis</u>: _____

e. <u>Borrellia recurrentis</u>: _____

f. <u>Bartonella bacilliformis</u>: _____

g. <u>Clostridium tetani</u>: _____

h. <u>Leptospira interrogans</u>: _____

i. <u>Clostridium septicum</u>: _____

4. <u>Matching</u>. Match the disease in the left-hand column with the phrase that <u>best</u> describes it in the right-hand column by placing the appropriate number on the line provided.

_____ a. Anthrax	1.	Transmitted by sandflies
_____ b. Tetanus	2.	Toxins provoking sustained contraction of the muscles
_____ c. Gas gangrene	3.	Causes miscarriage and malformations in fetuses
_____ d. Listeriosis		
_____ e. Leptospirosis	4.	Buboes formed
_____ f. Bubonic plague	5.	Enzymes produced that digest surrounding tissue
_____ g. Tularemia	6.	Disease caused by handling of contaminated rabbits
_____ h. Relapsing fever		
_____ i. Bartonellosis	7.	Symptoms return each week
	8.	An epizootic disease that causes hemorrhaging in the liver and spleen
	9.	A zoonosis caused by a spirochete

5. Each of the following is a short definition of a characteristic or treatment of one or more of the soilborne and arthropodborne diseases described in this chapter. Identify each of these characteristics by writing its name on the line provided.

a. A disease that infects large numbers of animals simultaneously.

b. A treatment that uses the forcing of high-pressure oxygen into a wound to establish an aerobic environment.

_____

c. A toxin that dissolves cell membranes, causing disintegration.

_____

d. A disease that can be transmitted from animals to humans.

_____

e. Swelling of the lymph nodes caused by hemorrhaging.

_____

f. A sudden onset of fever accompanied by pains in the joints, a fit of coughing, temporary delirium, and diarrhea. The fever abates after the victim breaks into a sweat, and sleep usually follows.

_____

6. Each of the following is considered an effective treatment or immunization for one or more diseases discussed in this chapter. Identify one disease for which each of the following is used. (You may wish to review Tables 19.1 and 19.2 before answering this exercise.)

a. Penicillin:

_____

b. Toxoid:

_____

c. Tretracycline:

_____

d. Killed bacteria vaccine:

_____

e. Antitoxin:

_____

f.   Streptomycin:

_____

CONCEPT EXERCISES

1. For several diseases discussed in this chapter (including relapsing
   fever) chemotherapy, while successful, may lead to additional
   complications. Why?

   _____

   _____

   _____

2. An epidemiologist is faced with finding the source of 20 cases of
   anthrax contracted by middle-class homemakers in a Chicago suburb.
   What are some of the questions he might ask of the affected individuals?

   _____

   _____

   _____

   _____

   _____

   _____

3. Tularemia has been misdiagnosed as several other diseases. When
   it was first identified, McCoy and Chapin were studying a "plague-
   like" disease of squirrels in Tulare County, California. The disease has also been thought to be typhoid fever at times. Explain
   how these mistakes could be made by discussing the symptoms of the
   various forms of the disease.

   _____

   _____

   _____

POST-TEST

1. Lockjaw is an alternative name for a disease caused by:
   a. Clostridium tetani.
   b. Clostridium perfringens.
   c. Clostridium septicum.
   d. Clostridium novyi.

2. A disease spread by fleas and ticks and which causes skin ulcers is:
   a. relapsing fever.
   b. bubonic plague.
   c. bartonellosis.
   d. tularemia.

3. Penicillin is a recommended treatment for each of the following diseases, except:
   a. anthrax.
   b. listeriosis.
   c. tetanus.
   d. gas gangrene.

4. Characteristic signs of relapsing fever include:
   a. skin ulcers.
   b. recurring fever and jaundice.
   c. intermittent fever without jaundice.
   d. buboes.

5. The "second most powerful toxin known to science" is produced by:
   a. Clostridium botulinum.
   b. Clostridium perfringens.
   c. Salmonella typhi.
   d. Clostridium tetani.

6. A disease caused by a small gram(+) rod and results in headaches, stiff neck, delirium, and coma is:
   a. tetanus.
   b. listeriosis.
   c. leptospirosis.
   d. anthrax.

7. One of the distinctive characteristics of Yersinia pestis is:
   a. production of polar spores.
   b. acid-fast staining.
   c. bipolar staining.
   d. spirochete cell type.

8. A form of tularemia in which there are no skin lesions, but that produces a high fever and severe abdominal pains as the bacteria invade the visceral organs, is called:
   a. ulceroglandular.
   b. oculoglandular.
   c. pulmonary.
   d. typhoidal.

9. One communicable disease discussed in this chapter is:
   a. bubonic plague.
   b. tularemia.
   c. tetanus.
   d. gas gangrene.

10. Antitoxin is recommended in the treatment of:

a. anthrax.
b. gas gangrene.
(c) tetanus.
d. bubonic plague.

11. Fleas and/or ticks are involved in the transmission of all of the following diseases, except:
   a. bubonic plague.
   b. tularemia.
   c. relapsing fever.
   (d) bartonellosis.

12. The Ascoli test:
   (a) is a precipitation test useful in the detection of anthrax spores.
   b. identifies gas gangrene by cytological analysis of affected tissue.
   c. is a serological test for tetanus toxins.
   d. can be used to distinguish bubonic plague and tularemia.

13. The isolation of Listeria monocytogenes is:
   a. easily accomplished on blood-agar plates.
   (b) hampered by the fact that it grows poorly in the laboratory environment.
   c. only possible under anaerobic conditions.
   d. difficult because human amnionic fluids must be added to the culture medium.

14. Pneumonic plague is a(n):
   a. less virulent disease than bubonic plague.
   (b) infection of the lung by Yersinia pestis similar to anthrax.
   c. disease actually caused by Francisella tularensis.
   d. condition resulting from the swelling of the lymph nodes.

15. A disease often caused when the victim comes into contact with soil or water contaminated with the urine or tissues of an infected animal is:
   (a) leptospirosis.
   b. listeriosis.
   c. bubonic plague.
   d. bartonellosis.

ANSWERS TO EXERCISES

Pre-Test

1. c	6. b	11. c
2. a	7. a	12. a
3. c	8. d	13. d
4. b	9. a	14. d
5. c	10. b	15. b

Practice Exercises

1. a. rats and fleas; b. fleas, ticks, and other arthropods;
   c. ticks and lice; d. sandflies. (All answers to this exercise
   can be found in Table 19.2.)

2. a. T; b. F; c. T; d. F; e. T; f. T; g. F; h. T;
   i. T; j. F.

3. a. 1, 3, 6; b. 2, 3; c. 1, 3, 6; d. 2, 3, 7; e. 5;
   f. 1, 3; g. 2, 3, 7; h. 5; i. 2, 3, 7. (All answers to this
   exercise can be found in Table 19.1 and 19.2.)

4. a. 8; b. 2; c. 5; d. 3; e. 9; f. 4; g. 6; h. 7;
   i. 1.

5. a. epizootic; b. hyperbaric oxygen; c. fecithinase;
   d. zoonosis; e. buboes; f. Jarisch-Herxheimer reaction.

6. a. anthrax, tetanus, gas gangrene, and leptospirosis;
   b. tetanus; c. listeriosis, bubonic plague, tularemia, relapsing fever, and bartonellosis; d. bubonic plague;
   e. tetanus; f. tularemia. (All answers to this exercise can be
   found in Tables 19.1 and 19.2.)

Concept Exercises

1. As the bacteria disintegrate in the bloodstream, they release endotoxins that complicate the infection. This can lead to several
   different conditions. In cases of relapsing fever, the Jarisch-
   Herxheimer reaction may be induced.

2. Anthrax can be acquired in a number of ways. These include coming
   in contact with contaminated animals or animal products, consumption of contaminated meat, and contact with airborne spores.
   Questions to determine whether such contact could have been common to the 20 women should be asked, such as:

   a. Is your home near a farm with cows?

   b. Do you use real wool yarn in knitting?

   c. Where have you purchased meat recently?

241

3. The skin ulcers caused by the disease resemble buboes caused by bubonic plague. One form of the disease, typhoidal form, has symptoms resembling typhoid fever, including high fever and abdominal pains.

Post-Test

1. a	6. b	11. d
2. d	7. c	12. a
3. b	8. d	13. b
4. b	9. a	14. b
5. d	10. c	15. a

After this, the vengeance on the whole camp! or, rather, the
Neapolitan bone-ache, for that, methinks, is the curse depending on
those that war for a placket.

>William Shakespeare, Troilus and Cressida,
>Act II, scene III.

CHAPTER OUTLINE

I. Contact and Endogenous Bacterial Diseases of Humans

   A. Gonorrhea

   B. Syphilis

   C. Chancroid (soft chancre)

   D. Granuloma inguinale

   E. Ureaplasma urethritis

   F. Leprosy (Hansen's disease)

   G. Yaws

   H. Rat bite fever

   I. Actinomycosis

   J. Nocardiosis

   K. Trench mouth (ANUG)

   L. Toxic shock syndrome (TSS)

   M. Urinary tract infections

   N. Burn infections

   O. Bacteroides infection

OVERVIEW AND OBJECTIVES

Venereal diseases are among the most common groups of infectious diseases known. In 1979, gonorrhea was the most frequently reported disease to CDC and syphilis was third on the CDC list. These diseases
have been known throughout recorded history, and references to them
appear in literature from the Old Testament onward. The quote above

from Shakespeare's play Troilus and Cressida is a good example. It also points out some of the thoughts and prejudices of his day concerning venereal disease. First, it was associated with one's enemies in any war. Hence, the English called it the "French disease" and here, the "Neapolitan bone-ache." "Bone-ache" was a well-recognized symptom of severe syphilis. It was also recognized that the disease was transmitted sexually. The "placket" (a slit or opening) is a metaphoric allusion to Helen of Troy, the cause of the war with which the play deals. In this chapter, we will examine several of the more common venereal diseases and other diseases that are contracted through contact with an infected person. We will also explore several diseases caused by endogenous species of bacteria (i.e., bacteria that are normally found in or on the body).

Among the most common bacterial venereal diseases are gonorrhea and syphilis. Both can be severe if untreated. It is no wonder that, historically, people have considered them the curse of God for an intemperate sex life. Gonorrhea can lead to sterility and blindness. It is particularly dangerous to the newborn. Syphilis often is fatal and congenital syphilis is a cause of many stillbirths. It is believed that five of the six children of Katherine of Aragon and Henry VIII of England were born dead or died shortly after birth because of his syphilis. The one child who survived, Mary I (Bloody Mary), also showed many signs of congenitally acquired syphilis. Other sexually transmitted bacterial diseases include chancroid and granuloma inguinale.

Leprosy is a contact-acquired disease, which has been a scourge throughout history. The Bible refers to its victims as unclean and banishes them from human society. The disease has a long incubation period (3 to 6 years) and is caused by an acid-fast organism that still has not been grown in pure culture. Yaws is another disease transmitted by contact. It is related to syphilis and is also caused by a spirochete. Two unrelated organisms can cause a disease acquired through contact with contaminated animals. This disease is known as rat bite fever.

Endogenous diseases of humans include actinomycosis, nocardiosis, trench mouth, toxic shock syndrome, urinary tract infections, burn infections, and bacteroides infections. The organisms that cause these diseases are normally found on the skin or in the gastrointestinal tract of humans. Under certain circumstances, where the individual is otherwise cjmpromised, these organisms may cause disease.

After you have read Chapter 20 of your textbook, you should be able to:

1. Define or identify the following terms: gonorrhea, Neisseria gonorrhoeae, gonococcus, Neisseria meningitidis, keratitis, penicillinase, penicillinase-producing Neisseria gonorrhoeae (PPNG), spectinomycin, gonococcal ophthalmia, Chlamydia trachomatis, non-gonococcal urethritis (NGU), syphilis, Treponema pallidum, primary syphilis, chancre, secondary syphilis, tertiary syphilis, gummas, chancroid (soft chancre), Haemophilis ducreyi, granuloma inguinale, Calymmatobacterium granulomatis, Donovan bodies, Leprosy (Hansen's

disease), <u>Mycobacterium leprae</u>, lepromatous leprosy, lepromas,
tuberculoid leprosy, Mitsuda reaction, yaws, hejel, pinta,
<u>Treponema pertenue</u>, mother yew, frambesia, rat bite fever,
<u>Streptobacillus moniliformis</u>, Haverhill fever, <u>Spirillum minor</u>,
sodoku, actinomycosis, <u>Actinomyces israelii</u>, cervicofacial actinomycosis, lumpy jaw, sinus, sulfur granules, nocardiosis, <u>Nocardia</u>
<u>asteroides</u>, Madura foot, trench mouth, acute necrotizing ulcerative
gingivitis (ANUG), <u>Leptotrichia buccalis</u>, <u>Treponema vincentii</u>,
Vincent's agina, fursiform, fursospirochetal disease, <u>Eikenella</u>,
toxic shock syndrome (TSS), <u>Staphylococcus aureus</u>, urinary tract
infections, <u>Escherichia coli</u>, <u>Pseudomonas aeruginosa</u>, burn infections, bacteroides infection, and <u>Bacteroides fragilis</u>.

2. List the causative organisms of each of the diseases described.
   Include some relevant taxonomical characteristics.

3. Describe the treatments for the various diseases discussed.

4. Describe the mode of transmission of each contact bacterial disease discussed.

5. Explain the importance of the appearance of PPNG.

6. Explain how an otherwise nonpathogenic endogenous organism can
   cause an infection in particular circumstances.

PRE-TEST

1. Each of the following diseases is caused by a spirochete, <u>except</u>:
   a. trench mouth.
   b. yaws.
   c. gonorrhea.
   d. syphilis.

2. Primary syphilis is:
   a. characterized by the chancre.
   b. associated with gummas.
   c. characterized by flat, wartlike lesions over the entire body.
   d. lethal in one fourth to one half of its victims.

3. Jarisch-Herxheimer reaction is associated with:
   a. gonorrhea.
   b. syphilis.
   c. chancroid.
   d. granuloma inguinale.

4. <u>Haemophilis ducreyi</u> is the causative organism of:
   a. gonorrhea.
   b. syphilis.
   c. chancroid.
   d. granuloma inguinale.

5. The Mitsuda reaction is a test used to identify early cases of:
   a. yaws.

245

    b. syphilis.
    c. leprosy.
    d. rat bite fever.

6. Actinomycosis can be diagnosed because its causative organism,
   Actinomyces israelii:
    a. is acid-fast.
    b. is a fungus.
    c. produces sulfur granules.
    d. moves by an external axial filament characteristic of spiro-
        chetes.

7. All of the following organisms are endogenous species that can
   produce urinary tract infections, except:
    a. Escherichia coli.
    b. Treponema pallidum.
    c. Klebsiella pneumoniae.
    d. Pseudomonas aeruginosa.

8. Pseudomonas aeruginosa is a(n):
    a. endogenous organism that causes burn infections.
    b. sexually transmitted organism.
    c. gram(+) rod.
    d. organism that does not exhibit resistance to antibiotics.

9. Staphylococcus aureus is associated with:
    a. urinary tract infections.
    b. burn infections.
    c. venereal disease.
    d. toxic shock syndrome.

10. One of the difficulties in controlling gonorrhea is the fact that:
    a. the male is asymptomatic.
    b. the causative organism is resistant to many antibiotics
    c. 50% of female infections may be asymptomatic.
    d. penicillin is not effective against the organism because all
        strains produce penicillinase.

11. Gummas are:
    a. the circular, purplish ulcers associated with primary syphilis.
    b. lesions, which destroy the elastic tissue and weaken major
        blood vessels.
    c. the "great pox."
    d. associated with the endogenous disease called lumpy jaw.

12. An endogenous disease resembling tuberculosis or pneumonia is:
    a. yaws.
    b. actinomycosis.
    c. bacteroides infection.
    d. nocardiosis.

13. Haverhill fever is:
    a. caused by a streptobacillus and is another name for a rat
        bite fever.

b. an alternative name for urinary tract infections caused by a number of endogenous organisms, including <u>Escherichia coli</u>.
c. caused by a spirochete normally found on the skin.
d. a gram(-) anaerobic rod that produces pseudohyphae.

14. <u>Mycobacterium leprae</u> is best described as a:
    a. gram(-) rod.
    b. spirillum.
    c. acid-fast rod.
    d. spirochete.

15. An organism characterized by a sweet odor and a fluorescent glow is:
    a. <u>Escherichia coli</u>.
    b. <u>Actinomyces israelii</u>.
    c. <u>Serratia marcescens</u>.
    d. <u>Pseudomonas aeruginosa</u>.

PRACTICE EXERCISES

1. <u>True or False</u>. Indicate whether each of the following statements is true or false by placing a T for true or an F for false on the line provided.

_____ a. The disease caused by <u>Neisseria gonorrhoeae</u> is a sexually transmitted disease in which more than 50% of the infected males are asymptomatic.

_____ b. JHR is a hypersensitive reaction caused by release of antigens by disrupted spirochetes associated with relapsing fever and syphilis.

_____ c. Tertiary syphilis is due more to an allergic reaction than to an infectious disease.

_____ d. Yaws is caused by an organism resembling the syphilis agent, and some consider the disease to be nonvenereal syphilis.

_____ e. <u>Treponema pertenue</u>, the causative agent of the sexually transmitted disease syphilis, is a spirochete.

_____ f. Koch's postulates have never been fulfilled for leprosy because the causative agent has not yet been grown in pure culture.

_____ g. Bejel and pinta diseases are closely related to leprosy.

_____ h. A major cause of urinary tract infections is <u>Escherichia coli</u>, an organism normally found in the intestine.

_____ i. Trench mouth is caused by two organisms that exist in a synergistic relationship.

_____ j. The term Madura foot is often used to indicate a complicated
       infection of the foot with <u>Actinomyces</u> <u>israelii</u>.

2. <u>Matching</u>. Match the bacterial species in the left-hand column
   with an appropriate description of the species from the list in
   the right-hand column by placing the corresponding number on the
   line provided. Descriptions in the right-hand column may be used
   <u>more</u> <u>than</u> <u>once</u> or <u>not</u> <u>at</u> <u>all</u>. (You may wish to review Tables 20.1
   and 20.2 before answering this exercise.)

   _____ a. Escherichia coli   1. Gram(+) anaerobic rod

   _____ b. Neisseria   2. Spirochete
             gonorrhoeae
                                       3. Gram(-) rod
   _____ c. Treponema
             pallidum   4. Spirillum

   _____ d. Spirillum minor   5. Gram(-) streptobacillus

   _____ e. Mycobacterium   6. Acid-fast rod
             leprae
                                       7. Gram(+) staphylococcus

                                       8. Gram(+) aerobic rod

                                       9. Gram(+) diplococcus

                                      10. Gram(-) diplococcus

3. Identify a disease discussed in this chapter for which each of
   the following antibiotics and drugs is considered an effective
   treatment. (You may wish to review Tables 20.1 and 20.2 before
   answering this exercise.)

   a. Penicillin:

   _____

   b. Aminoglycosides:

   _____

   c. Spectinomycin:

   _____

   d. Gentian violet:

   _____

   e. Tetracycline:

   _____

f. Sulfonamides:

_____

g. Dapsone:

_____

h. Rifampin:

_____

4. Each of the following statements is descriptive of a disease, or one of its symptoms, discussed in this chapter. Identify the disease or symptom described by writing its name on the line provided.

a. In the cervicofacial type of this disease, the organism enters the gum tissues and forms a firm, red swelling that becomes lumpy and as hard as wood.

_____

b. This disease, contracted from the bite of an infected animal, is not communicable among humans and only develops following about 10% of the bites from infected animals.

c. This disease results from a synergistic relationship between Treponema vincentii and Leptotrichia buccalis.

_____

d. This disease is caused by an organism that may be a natural inhabitant of the vagina and is associated with the use of tampons.

_____

e. Caused by a major inhabitant of the intestine, this disease occurs when the organism enters the bloodstream, causing blood clots that clog the vessels.

_____

f. An infection of the eye associated with the gonococcus.

_____

g. A circular, purplish ulcer with a raised margin, which forms the site of entry of Treponema pallidum.

_____

h. A condition associated with the engulfing of bacteria by phagocytes, especially monocytes.

_____

i. A red, raised lesion at a wound or abrasion where Treponema pertenue has entered the body.

_____

j. An infection of the superficial nerves with Mycobacterium leprae, which deprives the muscles of nerve stimulation and leads to their atrophy.

_____

5. Fill in the blanks. Many tests are used to diagnose syphilis. In one test, the serum from a patient is combined with spirochetes obtained from an infected rabbit's (a) _____. If syphilis (b) _____ are present in the patient's serum, they will attach to the spirochetes and immobilize them. This test is called the (c) _____ _____ _____ _____, or (d) ____, test. A second test mixes patient test serum with fluorescent-tagged (e) _____ _____ _____ and live spirochetes. This test is called the (f) _____ _____ _____, or (g) _____, test. The (h) _____ and (i) _____ _____ _____ _____ tests are screening procedures for syphilis. In still another test, disrupted syphilis organisms are absorbed into the surface of sheep red blood cells, and the patient's serum is added. If syphilis (j) _____ are present, they will induce agglutination of the red blood cells. This test is called the (k) _____ _____ _____, or (1) ____, test. These tests and others are largely responsible for the early diagnosis and treatment of syphilis. This has contributed to a decline in the incidence of the disease in modern times.

6. Each of the following organisms is considered an endogenous form. Identify (1) the normal site and (2) the abnormal (or disease) site of colonization for each.

   a. Leptotrichia buccalis:

      1. _____

      2. _____

   b. Escherichia coli:

      1. _____

      2. ____ _ _____

c. Bacteroides fragilis:

    1. _____

    2. _____

d. Treponema vincentii

    1. _____

    2. _____

e. Staphylococcus aureus:

    1. _____

    2. _____

CONCEPT EXERCISES

1. The "sexual revolution" of the 1970s saw the increase of many
venereal diseases, especially gonorrhea. The threat of these diseases did not seem to inhibit the participants in this revolution.
Yet a 1982 issue of Time magazine suggested that the sexual revolution may come to an end because of another venereal disease--
venereal herpes. What characteristics does this disease have that
makes it more threatening than gonorrhea or syphilis? (A review
of Chapter 9 may be helpful in answering this question.)

_____

_____

_____

_____

_____

_____

2. What disease caused by Chlamydia trachomatis has been such a problem to public health officials? Why?

_____

_____

_____

_____

_____

_____

3. When the penicillinase-producing strains of <u>Neisseria gonorrhoeae</u> were first introduced into the United States from Southeast Asia, it was feared that within a matter of months or a few years all isolated strains of the gonococcus would be penicillin resistant. Public health officials quickly began to find alternative treatments for gonorrhea. Yet in 1982, penicillin is still an effective treatment in a majority of cases of gonorrhea and the frequency of PPNG strains is still relatively low.

    a. Why were the public health officials so concerned that all <u>Neisseria gonorrhoeae</u> strains would soon be penicillin resistant?

_____

_____

_____

_____

_____

_____

    b. What characteristics of a plasmid-associated drug resistance could be responsible for the fact that the officials' fears have not realized to the extent they predicted?

_____

_____

_____

_____

_____

    c. In many developing countries, antibiotics are available without a prescription or even a physician's recommendation. Do you think that this practice may have helped to create the problem of drug resistance in the first place? How?

_____

_____

_____

_____

1. Chlamydia trachomatis causes:
   a. gonorrhea.
   b. syphilis.
   c. nonspirochetal syphilis.
   d. nongonococcal urethritis.

2. Yaws is sometimes known as frambesia because:
   a. it was first reported in the provence of Frambesia in France.
   b. of the raspberry-like appearance that can be produced by the bursting of the mother yaw.
   c. it may deform the leg bones.
   d. of the permanent scars it produces.

3. Hansen's disease has an incubation period of 3 to 6:
   a. days.
   b. weeks.
   c. months.
   d. years.

4. A draining abscess associated with actinomycosis is referred to as a(n):
   a. sinus.
   b. sodoku.
   c. thorac.
   d. madura.

5. Acute necrotizing ulcerative gingivitis is another name for:
   a. syphilis.
   b. toxic shock syndrome.
   c. trench mouth.
   d. yaws.

6. Pseudomonas aeruginosa is a severe problem in burn infections. This is due in part to the fact that:
   a. the organism is normally associated with flammable materials such as wood.
   b. this bacterium has developed resistance to many antibiotics.
   c. P. aeruginosa is anaerobic.
   d. the organism is normally found on the skin and in the intestinal tract of almost all people.

7. The gram(-) bacillus Eikenella may be involved in:
   a. venereal disease.
   b. urinary tract infections.
   c. toxic shock syndrome.
   d. ANUG.

8. The causative organism of actinomycosis is a:

a. gram(+) anaerobic rod.
b. gram(+) aerobic rod.
c. gram(-) anaerobic rod.
d. fungus.

9. Organisms in the genus <u>Treponema</u> are involved in all of the following diseases, <u>except</u>:
   a. yaws.
   b. leprosy.
   c. syphilis.
   d. ANUG.

10. An antibiotic recommended as an effective treatment for PPNG is:
    a. streptomycin.
    b. sulfonamide.
    c. spectinomycin.
    d. penicillin.

11. Gummas appear to be an allergic reaction associated with _____ _____ syphilis.
    a. primary
    b. secondary
    c. tertiary
    d. thoracic

12. Madura foot is a form of:
    a. nocardiosis.
    b. actinomycosis.
    c. leprosy.
    d. bacteroides infection.

13. A gram(-) anaerobic rod is responsible for:
    a. actinomycosis.
    b. bacteroides infection.
    c. toxic shock syndrome.
    d. gonorrhea.

14. This disease begins with a red, pimplelike papule on the external genital organs. It can be distinguished from syphilis because substantial swelling of the inguinal lymph nodes in the groin area occurs. This disease is:
    a. chancroid.
    b. granuloma inguinale.
    c. gonorrhea.
    d. nongonococcal urethritis.

15. Tumorlike growths on the skin and along the respiratory tract are characteristic of:
    a. tuberculoid leprosy.
    b. thoracic actinomycosis.
    c. lepromatous leprosy.
    d. abdominal actinomycosis.

ANSWERS TO EXERCISES

1. c	6. c.	11. b
2. a	7. b	12. d
3. b	8. a	13. a
4. c	9. d	14. c
5. c	10. c	15. d

Practice Exercises

1. a. F; b. T; c. T; d. T; e. F; f. T; g. F; h. T;
   i. T; j. F.

2. a. 3; b. 10; c. 2; d. 4; e. 6. (All answers to this
   exercise can be found in Tables 20.1 and 20.2.)

3. a. gonorrhea, syphilis, yaws, rat bite fever, actinomycosis, and
   nocardiosis; b. urinary tract infections and burn infections;
   c. gonorrhea; d. trench mouth; e. gonorrhea, granuloma inguinale, rat bite fever, and bacteroides infections; f. chancroid;
   g. leprosy; h. leprosy. (All answers to this exercise can be
   found in Tables 20.1 and 20.2.)

4. a. actinomycosis; b. rat bite fever; c. trench mouth;
   d. toxic shock syndrome; e. bacteroides infection; f. keratitis;
   g. chancre; h. Donovan bodies; i. mother yaw; j. tuberculoid
   leprosy.

5. a. testicle; b. antibodies; c. Treponema pallidum immobili-
   zation; d. TPI; e. antiglobulin antibodies; f. fluorescent
   treponemal antibody absorption; g. FTA-ABS; h. VDRL;
   i. rapid plasma reagin; j. antibodies; k. Treponema pallidum
   hemagglutination; 1. TPHA.

6. a. 1. mouth, 2. gums, pharynx; b. 1. intestine, 2. uri-

255

nary tract; c. 1. intestine, 2. blood; d. 1. mouth, 2. gums, pharynx; e. 1. vagina or skin, 2. blood.

Concept Exercises

1. Venereal herpes is a viral infection that cannot be treated with antibiotics. In addition, the virus has long periods of dormancy in which it is not susceptible to the body's immune system. These characteristics make the disease essentially incurable at present. (See Chapter 9.)

2. Chlamydia trachomatis is a penicillin-resistant organism that causes nongonococcal urethritis. This disease is very similar to gonorrhea. With the appearance of penicillin-resistant forms of Neisseria gonorrhoeae, it has been very difficult to distinguish between the two diseases.

3. a. The treatment of the disease with penicillin (the traditional antibiotic) forms a strong selective pressure for the penicillin-resistant strains, as only they can survive. Hence, public health officials assumed that these forms would soon predominate.

   b. The presence of a plasmid in most organisms reduces their growth rate so that they will grow somewhat more slowly. This may have allowed the penicillin-sensitive forms to predominate in untreated cases of the disease. Since less than half of the causes of gonorrhea are reported and treated, this may have acted to counteract the selective pressure for the penicillinase-producing strains in the treated cases. This is probably not the whole story, however.

   c. It has been suggested that penicillin and other antibiotics are used in Southeast Asia much as we use aspirin. This indiscriminate use of penicillin for everything from headaches to viral infections has led to a constant selective pressure for antibiotic-resistant forms of many organisms, including Neisseria gonorrhoeae.

Post-Test

1. d	6. b	11. c
2. b	7. d	12. a
3. d	8. a	13. b
4. a	9. b	14. a
5. c	10. c	15. c

21 Physical Methods for Controlling Microorganisms

Early in the history of bacteriology the problem of the death of bacteria by heating was studied. The bacteriologist, who usually must begin his work with sterilized materials, generally finds heat the most convenient sterilizing agency for his purposes. For successful sterilization the most heat resistant types must be destroyed, namely, bacterial endospores.

> C. Lamanna and M. F. Mallette, Basic Bacteriology: Its Biological and Chemical Background, 3rd. ed. Baltimore: Williams and Wilkins, 1965.

CHAPTER OUTLINE

I. Physical Control with Heat

    A. Direct flame

    B. Hot-air oven

    C. Boiling water

    D. Autoclave

    E. Fractional sterilization

    F. Pasteurization

    G. Hot oil

II. Physical Control by Other Methods

    A. Filtration

    B. Ultraviolet light

    C. Other radiations

    D. Ultrasonic vibrations

    E. Preservation methods

OVERVIEW AND OBJECTIVES

Control of microbial growth is necessary for good health. In addition, the study of microbiology would be impossible without the ability to limit bacterial growth in a medium to those organisms under study. In this chapter, we will discuss physical methods for controlling microbial growth; in the following two chapters, we will discuss chemical

methods for control of growth and the chemotherapeutic use of antibiotics to control growth in disease.

As the quote above points out, the most commonly used physical
method to sterilize material is heat. The form of heat sterilization
chosen is dependent both on the substance to be sterilized and on the
types of organisms to be removed. These methods depend on the ability
of high temperatures to cause biochemical changes in the organic molecules necessary for life of the cell. These methods range from pasteurization, which kills thermal-resistant vegetative cells but does not
destroy endospores, to autoclaving, which will destroy heat-resistant
bacterial spores.

Other physical methods for the control of microbial growth are also
used. Filtration removes bacteria (and, in some cases, viruses) by
restricting their passage through a membrane or other physical barrier.
Ultraviolet light, X rays, gamma rays, microwaves and ultrasonic vibrations are also able to destroy living microorganisms by causing
chemical changes in nucleic acids and/or proteins. Food can be preserved by several methods, including drying, salting, and freezing.
These methods are often not bacteriocidal but simply bacteriostatic.

After you have read Chapter 21 of your textbook, you should be able
to:

1. Define or identify the following terms: thermal death time,
   thermal death point, sterilization, direct flame method, incineration, hot-air oven, boiling water, autoclave, sterilizing chamber,
   steam jacket, prevacuum autoclaves, fractional sterilization,
   tyndallization, intermittent sterilization, Arnold sterilizer,
   pasteurization, holding method, Mycobacterium tuberculosis,
   Coxiella burnetti, flash pasteurization method, ultrapasteurization method, hot oil, filtration, filtrate, Seitz filter, diatomaceous earth, diatoms, membrane filter, ultraviolet light,
   X rays, gamma rays, ionizing radiations, microwaves, ultrasonic
   vibrations, cold boiling, cavitation, cavitron, drying, osmotic
   pressure, osmosis, low temperatures, and bacteriostatic.

2. Distinguish among the various methods of sterilization by heat.

3. List the materials for which each method of sterilization is best
   suited.

4. Distinguish between thermal death time and thermal death point.

5. Distinguish between sterilization and bacteriostasis.

6. Explain the physical basis for sterilization by each of the agents
   discussed.

PRE-TEST

1. The most rapid sterilization method is:
   a. autoclaving.
   b. boiling water.

c. ultraviolet light.
d. incineration.

2. You have done an experiment and discovered that at 160°C it takes
   25 min to kill a certain bacterium. In this experiment, you have
   determined the:
   a. thermal death time.
   b. thermal death point.
   c. both thermal death time and thermal death point.
   d. neither thermal death time nor thermal death point.

3. Ultraviolet light kills by:
   a. coagulating proteins.
   b. forming covalent links between adjacent thymine molecules in
       DNA.
   c. denaturing proteins.
   d. forming peroxides that can denature DNA and RNA.

4. Cold boiling is produced by:
   a. ultraviolet light.
   b. microwaves.
   c. ultrasonic vibration.
   d. ionizing radiations.

5. A method of sterilization that also allows quantitation of the
   microorganisms which were in the solution before sterilization is:
   a. autoclaving.
   b. ultraviolet light.
   c. filtration through a Berkefeld filter.
   d. filtration through a membrane filter.

6. The temperature required to kill bacterial spores in two hours by
   the dry heat method is:
   a. 100°C.
   b. 140°C.
   c. 160°C.
   d. 220°C.

7. An object that can be sterilized by the direct flame method is a:
   a. disposable hospital gown.
   b. solution of amino acids to be added to a growth medium.
   c. wooden hospital bed.
   d. fruit to be used in canning.

8. A rare beef roast is an example of:
   a. the use of the incineration method of sterilization.
   b. a bacteriostatic method of food preservation.
   c. the inefficiency of heat transfer by dry air.
   d. a proper method of preparation of food that has been preserved
       by freezing.

9. A method for the "sterilization" of milk that allows it to retain
   its palatability is:
   a. ultraviolet light.

    b.   tyndallization.
    c.   pasteurization.
    d.   autoclaving.

10. Hot oil is sometimes used to sterilize:
    a.   culture medium.
    b.   wooden objects.
    c.   metal dental instruments.
    d.   cloth objects.

11. A Seitz filter is composed of:
    a.   asbestos.
    b.   diatomaceous earth.
    c.   cellulose acetate.
    d.   polycarbonate.

12. A method of sterilization called cavitation utilizes _____
    _____ as the physical agent.
    a. heat.
    b.   ultraviolet light.
    c.   microwaves.
    d.   ultrasonic vibrations.

13. Low temperature is:
    a.   bacteriocidal.
    b.   a good method of sterilization.
    c.   bacteriostatic.
    d.   as effective as high temperature in coagulating proteins.

14. A method of preserving food that depends upon osmosis is:
    a.   treating the food with high concentrations of sugar.
    b.   freezing the food at low temperature in a "frost-free" freezer.
    c.   drying the foods in the sun.
    d.   treating the food with ultrasonic waves.

15. In an autoclave under 15 lb/in^2 steam pressure, the approximate
    temperature will be _____. (You may wish to review
    Figure 21.5 before answering this exercise.)
    a.   115.5°C.
    b.   121.5°C.
    c.   126.5°C.
    d.   134.5°C.

PRACTICE EXERCISES

1. List the conditions necessary to kill bacterial spores by each of
   the following methods.

    a.   Direct flame:

      _____

    b.   Hot oil:

      _____

c. Pressurized steam:

_____

d. Filtration:

_____

e. Fractional sterilization:

_____

f. Hot air:

_____

g. Boiling water:

_____

2. Consider the following graph, which describes thermal death of a test bacterium.

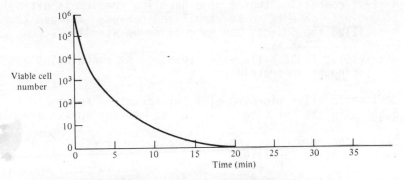

a. What is the thermal death time of the test organism under these conditions?

_____

b. If you wanted to shorten the thermal death time, what could you do?

_____

c. If you lowered the temperature by 10°C, what would you expect to happen to the thermal death time?

_____

d. If the method were autoclaving, what would you expect to happen to the thermal death time if you increased the steam pressure by 5 lb/in² ?

3. List four important considerations in determining the time and temperature for microbial destruction with heat.

   a. _____

   b. _____

   c. _____

   d. _____

4. True or False. Determine whether each of the following statements is true or false; then place a T for true or an F for false on the line provided.

___ a. Bacterial spores may require two hours for destruction by boiling water.

___ b. The thermal death point is the time at which an organism dies at a given temperature.

___ c. A strip containing spores of a Bacillus species is often included with objects to be sterilized because if these spores are killed the objects can be considered sterile.

___ d. Ultraviolet light kills microorganisms by coagulating and denaturing their proteins.

___ e. Cavitation kills microorganisms by formation and implosion of bubbles in the solution in which the microorganisms are placed.

___ f. Drying can be used to preserve meat because water is a necessary requisite for life.

___ g. Pasteurization is effective in killing all microorganisms in milk.

___ h. The Berkefeld filter utilizes glass, porcelain, or asbestos to trap microorganisms.

___ i. X rays and gamma rays are ionizing radiations. The ions produced cause the formation of unusual molecules that may change the structure or chemistry of microorganisms.

___ j. The most effective wavelength of ultraviolet light for killing bacteria is 265 nm.

5. Matching. Match the physical method of controlling microorganisms in the left-hand column with the statement in the right-hand column that is most closely related to it.

   _____ a. Autoclave   1. Cavitation

_____ b. Ultraviolet light

_____ c. Ultrasonic
          vibrations

_____ d. Hot oil

_____ e. Pasteurization

_____ f. Dry heat

_____ g. Boiling water

_____ h. Direct flame

_____ i. Tyndallization

_____ j. Filtration

2. Traps organisms in pores of
    asbestos

3. Heat under steam pressure

4. Thymine dimers formed

5. Kills by coagulating proteins

6. Is not assumed to achieve
    sterility

7. Fractional sterilization

8. Requires rinsing after
    sterilization

9. Disposable items only

10. Does not transfer heat well

6. Give an example of materials sterilized by each of the following
   methods. (You may wish to review Table 21.2 before answering this
   exercise.)

   a. Direct flame:

   _____

   b. Filtration:

   _____

   c. Ultraviolet light:

   _____

   d. Fractional sterilization:

   _____

   e. Pressurized steam:

   _____

   f. Hot air:

   _____

   g. Pasteurization:

   _____

h. Ultrasonic vibrations:

_____

i. Boiling water:

_____

j. Hot oil:

_____

CONCEPT EXERCISES

1. New mothers are often told, "Boil your baby's bottle for 10-15
   minutes before using it in order to sterilize it." Explain why
   this statement is not really true.

   _____

   _____

   _____

2. Explain the relationship between "thermal death point" and "thermal
   death time."

   _____

   _____

   _____

   _____

   _____

   _____

3. a. Why is it important to cook frozen meat and other frozen foods
       as soon as possible after they are thawed?

       _____

       _____

       _____

   b. Would it be better to thaw meat in a microwave oven or on the
       kitchen counter? Explain.

       _____

       _____

264

c. Would it be better to thaw meat in the refrigerator or on the kitchen counter? Explain.

_____

_____

_____

POST-TEST

1. The development of which of the following methods of sterilization made possible the canning of "real draft beer"?
   a. pasteurization
   b. membrane filtration
   c. autoclaving
   d. ultraviolet light sterilization

2. Fractional sterilization utilizes treatment with free-flowing steam for 30 minutes on three consecutive days. This repeated treatment is required to:
   a. keep the proteins in the solution from denaturing.
   b. kill bacterial spores that germinate between treatments.
   c. allow enough growth of vegetative cells to cloud the solution is contaminated.
   d. keep fungi from sporulating in the solution.

3. Hot-air ovens require a temperature of 160°C for two hours to sterilize pipettes because:
   a. any moisture on the pipettes must be evaporated.
   b. pipettes must be put into metal cans for sterilization.
   c. the small openings in pipettes allow the collection of bacteria in very large numbers.
   d. dry heat does not penetrate materials well.

4. In an autoclave set at 15 lb/in^2, the recommended time to sterilize empty glassware is:
   a. 15 min.
   b. 30 min.
   c. 1 hr.
   d. 2 hr.

5. An effective way to sterilize large surfaces, such as a counter, on which bacterial media are to be prepared would be:
   a. autoclaving.
   b. hot air.
   c. ultraviolet light.
   d. ultrasonic vibration.

6. An Arnold sterilizer is used for:
   a. pasteurization.
   b. filtration.

265

c. fractional sterilization.
   d. hot oil sterilization.

7. Radiations with wavelengths between 400 nm and 800 nm are considered:
   a. X rays.
   b. visible light.
   c. ultraviolet light.
   d. gamma rays.

8. Filters prepared from diatomaceous earth are especially advantageous
   because:
   a. the inorganic fibers are very closely spaced.
   b. microorganisms trapped on the filter can be grown and
      quantitated.
   c. the organic molecules of the filter attract the organic comp-
      onents of the microorganisms.
   d. viruses can also be trapped by these filters.

9. A method used to collect microorganisms for electronmicroscopy is
   by:
   a. filtering them in Berkefeld filters.
   b. passing them through a Seitz filter.
   c. utilizing membrane filters to trap the organisms.
   d. drying them in solutions of various concentrations of salt.

10. Cavitrons are used:
   a. by dentists to clean teeth.
   b. to sterilize dental instruments.
   c. to incinerate disposable items.
   d. to produce small holes (cavities) in the bacterial cell wall.

11. The conditions necessary to kill Mycobacterium tuberculosis by
   pasteurization are:
   a. 30 min at 62.9°C.
   b. 2 hr at 160°C.
   c. 2 hr at 100°C.
   d. 30 min at 100°C.

12. A method that kills Coxiella burnetti in three seconds at 82°C is
   called:
   a. standard pasteurization.
   b. autoclaving.
   c. flash pasteurization.
   d. ultrapasteurization.

13. Of the following, the most efficient method for sterilization of a
   bacteriological transfer loop is:
   a. dry heat.
   b. hot oil.
   c. autoclaving.
   d. incineration.

14. Sterilization is the removal of all:

a. pathogenic bacteria.
b. life forms.
c. bacterial growth.
d. vegetative bacteria.

15. Peroxides and other toxic chemicals are often produced when an organic solution is exposed to:
a. ultraviolet light.
b. X rays.
c. microwaves.
d. ultrasonic vibrations.

ANSWERS TO EXERCISES

Pre-Test

1. d   6. c   11. a
2. a   7. a   12. d
3. b   8. c   13. c
4. c   9. c   14. a
5. d   10. c   15. b

Practice Exercises

1. a. extreme heat; b. 160°C, 1 hr.; c. 121°C, 15 min., 15 lb/in^2 steam; d. entrapment in pores; e. 100°C, 30 min./day, 3 days; f. 160°C, 2 hr.; g. 100°C, 2 hr. (All answers to this exercise can be found in Table 21.2.)

2. a. 20 min.; b. Raise the temperature; c. It would increase in lenght; d. It would shorten in length.

3. a. The type of organism to be killed; b. The type of material to be treated; c. The presence of organic matter; d. The acidic or basic nature of the material.

4. a. T; b. F; c. T; d. F; f. T; g. F; h. F; i. T; j. T.

5. a. 3; b. 4; c. 1; d. 8; e. 6; f. 10; g. 5; h. 9; i. 7; j. 2.

6. a.   laboratory instruments;   b.   fluids;   c.   surfaces and   air;
   d.   chemicals destroyed by other methods;   e.   instruments, surgical
   materials, bacteriological media, solutions;   f.   glassware, pow-
   ders, oily substances;   g.   dairy products, beer;   h.   fluids;
   i.   a wide variety of objects;   j.   instruments.   (All answers to
   this exercise can be found in Table 21.2.)

Concept Exercises

1. Sterilization is the elimination of all life forms; the definition
   cannot be qualified.   Boiling for 15 minutes is not sufficient to
   kill bacterial spores and therefore the bottles are not sterile.

2. Thermal death point is the temperature necessary to kill an organism
   in a given time; thermal death time is the time necessary to kill
   an organism at a given temperature.   These two measurements show
   an inverse relationship; i.e., as one becomes larger (longer), the
   other becomes smaller (shorter).

3. a.   Freezing is only bacteriostatic.   The organisms are not killed
      but only inhibited from growth.   As the food warms, the
      bacteria are again able to grow and contaminate the food.

   b.   It would be better to thaw the food in the microwave oven.
      First, the time required is shorter.   Second, microwaves are
      effective bacteriocidal agents.

   c.   It would be better to thaw the food in the refrigerator because
      at the temperature (approximately 7°C) of the refrigerator
      the growth rate of the bacteria will still be slower than at
      room temperature (approximately 21°C).

Post-Test

1. b	6. c	11. a
2. b	7. c	12. d
3. d	8. c	13. d
4. a	9. c	14. b
5. c	10. a	15. b

22 Chemical Methods for Controlling Microorganisms

<u>Only those substances can be anchored at any particular part of
the organism which fit into the molecule of the recipient combination
as a piece of mosaic fits into a certain pattern.</u>

Paul Ehrlich. Quoted in K. V. Thimann, <u>The Life
of Bacteria</u>, 2nd ed. New York: Macmillan, 1963.

CHAPTER OUTLINE

  I. General Principles

      A. Origins of disinfection practices

      B. Terminology of disinfection

      C. Selection of antiseptics and disinfectants

 II. Important Chemical Agents

      A. Halogens

      B. Phenol and phenol derivatives

      C. Heavy metals

      D. Alcohol

      E. Alkylating agents

      F. Hydrogen peroxide

      G. Soaps and detergents

      H. Dyes

      I. Acids

OVERVIEW AND OBJECTIVES

As the quotation above points out, chemicals that are effective in
controlling bacterial growth are those which are able to interfere with
the reactions and structures necessary for life. In this chapter, we
discuss chemicals that are available for the inhibition of bacterial
growth on surfaces of both inanimate objects (<u>disinfectants</u>) and humans
(<u>antiseptics</u>). In the next chapter, we will investigate antimicrobial
agents that can be used to inhibit growth of pathogenic organisms
within the host organism.

Several terms are used to describe disinfectants and antiseptics.

Bactericidal agents kill bacterial organisms, whereas bacteriostatic agents only inhibit the growth of organisms. Disinfectants can be used to achieve different levels of decontamination. The term degerm means to remove organisms from a surface; "to sterilize" means to remove all living organisms; and "to sanitize" simply means to reduce the microbial population to a "safe level." Many disinfectants and antiseptics are able to sanitize a surface but few, if any, are able to sterilize materials. Several important criteria should be considered in selecting a disinfectant. These criteria, which are discussed in the chapter, include standards of effectiveness, safety, and economy.

Chemical disinfectants usually inhibit growth by altering proteins or nucleic acids, or by changing the permeability of the cell wall and membrane. Halogens are compounds that contain chlorine or iodine. They appear to inhibit the cell by inactivating enzymes important to cellular metabolism. Phenol and its derivatives act on bacteria by coagulating their proteins. Proteins are also inactivated by heavy metals such as mercury, copper, and silver. These tend to form bridges between protein molecules. Alcohol not only inactivates protein by denaturing it but also dissolves lipids, leading to disintegration of the cell membrane.

Both protein and nucleic acid structures are altered by alkylating agents. Formaldehyde, the traditional component of embalming fluid, is one of the alkylating agents commonly used as a disinfectant. Restructuring of protein molecules by hydroxyl ions is now thought to be the mechanism of disinfection by hydrogen peroxide. This compound is often used to rinse wounds, scrapes, and abrasions. Soaps and detergents are wetting agents, which reduce surface tension. They may interact with phosphate groups in the cell membrane leading to leakage of important metabolic compounds from the cytoplasm. Dyes interact with macromolecules and many are specific for nucleic acids. When bound, these compounds inhibit DNA and RNA synthesis. Acids are also useful as disinfectants because they lower the pH to levels where many metabolic enzymes are inactivated. They are also used in conjunction with other disinfectants because they enhance the effectiveness of many of the other disinfecting compounds.

After you have read Chapter 22 of your textbook, you should be able to:

1. Define or identify the following terms: disinfectant, antiseptic, bactericidal, bacteriostatic, sepsis, septicemia, antiseptic, aseptic, sanitize, degerm, phenol coefficient (PC), halogen, hypochlorites, chloramines, tincture of iodine, iodophors, phenol, cresol, bisphenol, orthophenylphenol, hexachlorophene, hexylresorcinol, heavy metal, mercury, copper, silver, alcohol, ethyl alcohol, isopropyl alcohol, alkylating agents, formaldehyde, paraformaldehyde, formalin, ethylene oxide, beta-propiolactone, glutaraldehyde, hydrogen peroxide, soap, detergent, wetting agent, anionic, cationic, quaternary ammonium compounds (quats), triphenylmethane dyes, acridine dyes, benzoic acid, salicylic acid, undecylenic acid, lactic acid, acetic acid, and propionic acid.

2. Distinguish between a disinfectant and an antiseptic. Discuss the differences in the criteria for selection of these two types of chemicals.

3. Distinguish between bactericidal and bacteriostatic agents. Give some examples of each.

4. Indicate how each of the chemical methods for control of microorganisms discussed works.

5. Explain the meaning of the phenol coefficient and how it is used in the evaluation of various antimicrobial agents.

PRE-TEST

1. A compound containing which of the following elements would be classified as a halogen?
   a. Cl
   b. Hg
   c. Ag
   d. Cu

2. The most common (and most effective) concentration of ethyl alcohol used for disinfection is:
   a. 30%.
   b. 50%.
   c. 70%.
   d. 100%.

3. Alkylating agents act by:
   a. producing hydroxyl ions.
   b. forming bridges between proteins and nucleic acids.
   c. "wetting" the membrane so that compounds leak from the cellular cytoplasm.
   d. coagulating proteins.

4. A disinfectant that combines directly with DNA and halts RNA synthesis is:
   a. an acridine dye.
   b. soap.
   c. hydrogen peroxide.
   d. silver.

5. An agent that temporarily prevents multiplication of a microorganism without necessarily killing it is called a:
   a. bactericidal agent.
   b. sanitizing agent.
   c. sterilizing agent.
   d. bacteriostatic agent.

6. A disinfectant with a PC of 100 is:
   a. 100 times more effective than phenol as a disinfectant.
   b. 100 times less effective than phenol as a disinfectant.
   c. 100 times more corrosive than phenol.
   d. 100 times less corrosive than phenol.

271

7. Iodine acts by:
   a. releasing atomic oxygen that may combine with cytoplasmic proteins.
   b. coagulating proteins.
   c. releasing hydroxyl ions that cause restructuring of proteins.
   d. combining with tyrosine in proteins.

8. A criterion that is <u>more</u> important in the selection of an antiseptic than in the selection of a disinfectant is its:
   a. ability to kill microorganisms.
   b. toxicity to animals and humans.
   c. shelf life.
   d. corrosiveness to instruments.

9. Silver in the form of a 1% solution of silver nitrate is used in the prevention of:
   a. neonatal infections of <u>Neisseria</u> <u>gonorrhoeae</u>.
   b. <u>Bacillus</u> infections.
   c. <u>Candida</u> infections.
   d. infections of the mouth, such as trench mouth.

10. Synthetic chemicals developed for their ability to be strong wetting agents and surface tension reducers are:
    a. soaps.
    b. dyes.
    c. alkylating agents.
    d. detergents.

11. Quats are:
    a. acridine dyes, which combine directly with DNA and halt RNA synthesis.
    b. cationic detergents, which act as wetting agents.
    c. anionic detergents, which act on the cell wall.
    d. alkylating agents, which cause "cold burns" on contact with the skin.

12. A disinfectant that appears to act by releasing water, which in turn yields hydroyl ions that cause restructuring of proteins molecules, is:
    a. an alkylation agent.
    b. an alcohol.
    c. hydrogen peroxide.
    d. phenol.

13. A sanitizing agent:
    a. sterilizes a solution.
    b. removes organisms from a surface.
    c. reduces the microbial population to a safe level.
    d. frees a solution from microbial contamination.

14. All of the following disinfectants contain mercury, <u>except</u>:
    a. mercurochrome.
    b. merthiolate.
    c. hexylresorcinol.
    d. metaphen.

15. Glutaraldehyde is a(n):
    a. heavy-metal-containing antiseptic.
    b. alkylating agent.
    c. phenol derivative.
    d. iodophor.

PRACTICE EXERCISES

1. Different disinfectants and antiseptics have different antimicrobial spectra. For each of the compounds listed below, identify it
   as a

   1. fungicidal agent   3. sporicidal agent

   2. viricidal agent   4. bactericidal agent

   by placing the corresponding number(s) on the line provided. (You
   may wish to review Table 22.4 before answering this exercise.)

   __4__ a. Acridine dyes

   _1,2,3,4_ b. Glutaraldehyde

   _1,2,4_ c. Alcohol

   __4__ d. Hydrogenperoxide

   __4__ e. Silver

   __4__ f. Ethylene oxide

   _1,2,3,4_ g. Copper

   _1,4_ h. Phenols

   _1,2,4_ i. Iodine

   _1,2,4_ j. Chlorine

2. For each of the antiseptics and disinfectants listed below, describe briefly the mechanism of microbial inactivation.

   a. Phenol:

   _____

   _____

   b. Iodine:

   _____

   _____

273

c. Acridine dyes:

_____

_____

d. Heavy metals:

_____

_____

e. Alcohol:

_____

_____

f. Chlorine:

_____

_____

g. Alkylating agents:

_____

_____

h. Soap:

_____

_____

3. In laboratory test using Staphylococcus aureus, a 1:10,000 dilution of phenol killed the organisms after 10 minutes but not after
   5 minutes. Several other disinfectants were also tested. They
   are listed below with the dilution that killed the S. aureus in the
   5-10-minute time period. Give the phenol coefficient of each disinfectant.

   a. Disinfectant M: 1:1000 dilution killed. _____

   b. Disinfectant A: 1:100,000 dilution killed. _____

   c. Disinfectant Z: 1:50,000 dilution killed. _____

   d. Disinfectant Y: 1:7500 dilution killed. _____

4. True or False. Indicate whether each of the statements below is
   true or false by placing a T for true or an F for false on the
   line provided.

_F_ a. All disinfectants have the same PC for Staphylococcus aureus and Salmonella typhi.

_T_ b. Iodine reacts with tyrosine to halogenate this amino acid. This is believed to change the structure of the protein containing the tyrosine.

_T_ c. Hexylresorcinol is a phenol derivative used in mouthwase and topical antiseptics.

_F_ d. Brain damage has been traced to copper exposure.

_T_ e. Seventy-percent solutions of ethyl alcohol are more effective than 100% solutions because the water contained in the 70% solution prevents rapid evaporation and helps penetration into the tissues.

_T_ f. Hydrogen peroxide is effective against anaerobic microorganisms because they may be inhibited by the oxygen released by the chemical's breakdown.

_F_ g. Heavy metals are very reactive with nucleic acids and are thought to bind DNA to RNA in a covalent bridge.

_T_ h. One agent that is effective against Pseudomonas infections of burns is silver nitrate.

_F_ i. Beta-propiolactone is always used in preference to ethylene oxide because it is less explosive and just as effective in penetrating materials.

_T_ j. Acids are effective because they lower pH. In general, they enhance the effects of other disinfectants and can be used to help solubilize other disinfectants.

5. Because of their individual characteristics, different disinfectants and antiseptics have different uses. For each of the chemicals listed, give at least one important application.

    a. Chlorine:

    _____

    b. Acids:

    _____

    c. Alcohol:

    _____

    d. Phenols:

    _____

275

e. Silver:

_____ _____

f. Ethylene oxide:

_____

g. Mercury:

_____ ___ _____

h. Acridine dyes:

_____

i. Iodine:

_____

j. Formaldehyde:

_____ __ _____

6. Matching. Match each term in the left-hand column with its best
    description or definition in the right-hand column by placing the
    corresponding number on the line provided. Each entry in the
    right-hand column can be used only once.

_4_	a. Disinfectant	1.	Free from contamination
_12_	b. Viricidal agent	2.	Free from all life
_6_	c. PC	3.	Temporarily prevents multi-plication of bacteria
_8_	d. Iodophor		
_1_	e. Aseptic	4.	Removes pathogens from table tops
_7_	f. Degerm	5.	Kills microorganisms
_10_	g. Sanitize	6.	Standard of effectiveness
_2_	h. Sterilize	7.	Removes organisms from a surface
_9_	i. Sepsis		
_5_	j. Bactericidal	8.	Mixture of a halogen and a detergent
_3_	k. Bacteriostatic	9.	Contaminated with micro-organisms
_11_	l. Iodine	10.	Reduces contamination to a safe level

11. Halogenates tyrosine

12. Kills viruses

CONCEPT EXERCISES

1. Alkylating agents and acridine dyes are effective disinfectants. In addition, these agents are powerful mutagenic compounds. Explain the chemical characteristics of these compounds that account for both of these observations.

_____

_____

_____

_____

_____

_____

2. As pointed out by Paul Ehrlich, inhibition of bacterial growth by chemical and physical agents must fit into the general scheme of the processes of bacterial growth. What are some of the general processes of the cell that are good candidates for chemical inhibition?

_____

_____

_____

_____

_____

_____

_____

_____

3. a. In choosing an antiseptic for sanitizing a burn from infection with Pseudomonas aeruginosa, what criteria would you consider to be most important?

_____

_____

_____

_____

_____

_____

   b.   In choosing a disinfectant for sanitizing a hospital room from contamination with <u>Pseudomonas aeruginosa</u>, what criteria would you consider to be most important?

_____

_____

_____

_____

_____

_____

POST-TEST

1. Aseptic is a term meaning:
   a. free from contaminating microorganisms.
   b. free from all living organisms.
   c. a safe level of microbial contamination.
   d. contaminated with microorganisms.

2. A group of disinfectants formed by replacing the hydrogen atom of an amino group on a carrier molecule with chlorine is called:
   a. hypochlorites.
   b. iodophors.
   c. chloramines.
   d. tincture of chlorine.

3. A compound effective in killing bacteria in 10, but not 5 minutes in a 1:500,000 dilution is compared to phenol. In this test a 1:10,000 dilution of phenol can kill the bacteria in 10, but not 5 minutes. The PC of the compound being tested is:
   a. 50.
   b. 5.
   c. 0.2.
   d. 0.02.

4. Compounds that interact with nucleic acids include all of the following, <u>except</u>:
   a. formaldehyde.
   b. ethylene oxide.
   c. acriflavine.
   d. hexachlorophene.

5. A physician wants to remove any bacterial endospores that may be contaminating her surgical instruments. She would choose which of the following compounds as the disinfectant:
   a. silver nitrate.
   b. cresol.
   c. glutaraldehyde.
   d. cationic detergents.

6. Ethylene oxide might be preferred to autoclaving in the sterilization of:
   a. surgical instruments.
   b. water for use in making sterile solutions.
   c. plastic petri dishes.
   d. salt solutions for the preparation of culture medium.

7. Acids are useful as bactericidal and fungicidal agents in food preservation because they:
   a. are used in such low concentrations that they do not change the taste of the food.
   b. lower the pH of the food, causing a bacteriostatic effect.
   c. decompose the materials the microorganism could use for energy to a form that is not metabolizable.
   d. coagulate the microorganisms' proteins, leading to a bactericidal condition.

8. A compound that can effectively kill bacteria, fungi, and other forms of microorganisms is referred to as:
   a. bactericidal.
   b. fungiostatic.
   c. germiostatic.
   d. germicidal.

9. Washing with soap and water before eating is best classified as:
   a. antiseptic.
   b. sanitization.
   c. degerming.
   d. sterilization.

10. All of the following are drawbacks to the use of the phenol coefficient, except:
    a. It is done in the laboratory.
    b. There is no consideration of tissue toxicity.
    c. It does not consider the types of organisms to be killed.
    d. The effective dilution of the disinfectant is not considered.

11. Iodophors are:
    a. halogenated derivatives of compounds containing amino groups.
    b. solutions of ethyl alcohol containing low concentrations of iodine and sodium iodide.
    c. used in very dilute solutions for the disinfection of swimming pools.
    d. complexes of iodine and detergents that release iodine over long periods of time.

12. Hexachlorophene is no longer used in toothpaste and soaps because it:
    a. was found that soaps inactivated it.
    b. is neurotoxic in newborn rats and monkeys.
    c. was associated with brain damage in Japan, where it contaminated fish.
    d. has a very short effective half-life on the skin.

13. Copper is particularly active against:
    a. gram(+) bacteria.
    b. chlorophyll-containing organisms.
    c. gram(-) bacteria.
    d. anaerobic organisms.

14. Anionic detergents are limited in their usefulness because they:
    a. are only effective against gram(-) organisms.
    b. are not sporicidal.
    c. have a positive charge, which repels negatively charged bacteria.
    d. are hydrophobic and therefore are not easily absorbed through the bacterial cell membrane.

15. Perhaps the best antiseptic to remove anaerobic microorganisms from a wound would be:
    a. alcohol.
    b. hydrogen peroxide.
    c. merthiolate.
    d. mercurochrome.

ANSWERS TO EXERCISES

Pre-Test

1. a   6. a   11. b

2. c   7. d   12. c

3. b   8. b   13. c

4. a   9. a   14. c

5. d   10. d   15. b

Practice Exercises

1. a. 4; b. 1, 2, 3, 4; c. 1, 2, 4; d. 4; e. 4; f. 1, 2,
   3, 4; g. 1; h. 1, 4; i. 1, 2, 4; j. 1, 2, 4. (All answers
   to this exercise can be found in Table 22.4.)

2. a. Phenol acts by coagulating protein; b. Iodine acts by halogenating tyrosine and altering protein structure; c. Acridine

dyes act by combining directly with DNA and they halt RNA synthesis; d. Heavy metals are very reactive with proteins, particularly the sulfhydryl groups, and are thought to bind two protein molecules, forming a bridge between them; e. Alcohol acts by denaturing proteins and dissolving lipids; f. Chlorine is thought to act by releasing atomic oxygen that combines with and inactivates important cytoplasmic proteins; g. Alkylating agents react with amino and hydroxyl groups in nucleic acids and proteins, and with carboxyl and sulfhydryl groups in proteins. In so doing, they change the structure and chemistry of the nucleic acid or protein; i. Soaps act as wetting agents and may act by altering the cell membrane allowing leakage of cytoplasmic components.

3. a. 0.1; b. 10; c. 5; d. 0.75.

4. a. F; b. T; c. T; d. F; e. T; f. T; g. F; h. T; i. F; j. T.

5. a. water treatment, skin antisepsis, equipment spraying, food processing, and toilet facilities.

b. skin infections and food preservatives.

c. instrument disinfectant and skin antiseptic.

d. general preservatives and skin antisepsis with soap.

e. skin antiseptic and eyes of newborns.

f. sterilization of plastics, instruments, equipment, and heat-sensitive objects.

g. skin antiseptics and disinfectants.

h. skin infections.

i. skin antisepsis, equipment spraying, food processing, and preparation.

j. embalming, vaccine production, and gaseous sterilization.

(All answers to this exercise can be found in Table 22.4.)

6. a. 4; b. 12; c. 6; d. 8; e. 1; f. 7; g. 10;
   h. 2; i. 9; j. 5; k. 3; l. 11.

Concept Exercises

1. Both types of compounds interact with DNA to change its structure.
   This can lead either to killing of the organism (bactericidal effect) or to mutation through introduction of mistakes in DNA replication by DNA polymerase (mutagenic effect).

2. Several different features of general microbial physiology and
   cytology can be identified, four of which are:

   1. Interference with the energy supply of the cell.

   2. Reduction of the supply of material, especially of the most
       critical materials (such as vitamins) needed in small amounts
       and not replaceable.

   3. Interference with the synthetic process itself, especially
       with its most vulnerable participants, the nucleic acids.

   4. Damage to the cell wall or membrane, so that both cell enlarge-
       ment and the mechanism for taking up solutes are impaired.

   The general processes of the cell are acted upon by both chemical
   and physical inhibitors of microbial growth, including the antibiotics discussed in the next chapter.

3. a. Many criteria are important in selection of an antiseptic.
       Since it is to be used on a living organism, the toxicity to
       animals and humans is among the most important. Other general
       considerations include its effectiveness, shelf life, and cost.
       Also to be considered are the time required for its antimicro-
       bial action and its ability to penetrate well.

   b. Many of the same criteria considered in part (a) are still
       important. However, since this disinfectant is to be used on
       lifeless objects, its corrosive properties are probably more
       important than its toxicity to animals and humans. This is
       particularly true if sufficient time is allowed for inacti-
       vation of the disinfectant's toxic properties before the ob-
       ject comes in contact with animals or humans.

Post-Test

1. a   2. c   3. a   4. d   5. c   6. c   7. b   8. d   9. c   10. d

11. d   12. b   13. b   14. c   15. b

23 Chemotherapeutic Agents and Antibodies

The major source of antibiotics is the venerable family of parasitic and saprophytic plants known as fungi. Its members include smuts, rusts, molds, yeasts, mildews and mushrooms. Nearly all fungi evolve bactericidal material of one sort or another, but that exuded by the various molds appears to lend itself most efficiently to therapeutic use. The curative properties of fungi have been sensed, at least dimly, for centuries. They are conspicuous in the folk pharmacopoeias of practically all races.

> Berton Roueché, "Something Extraordinary," in *Eleven Blue Men*. New York: Berkley Publishing, 1953.

CHAPTER OUTLINE

OVERVIEW AND OBJECTIVES

Until the 1940s, medicine was primarily a diagnostic science. When antibiotics were discovered and came into wide use, physicians suddenly were able to cure disease, and medicine was revolutionized. In this chapter we will discuss the various chemotherapeutic agents and antibiotics. Chemotherapeutic agents (often called chemotherapeutic drugs) are synthetic chemicals that inhibit bacterial growth and are often bactericida. Antibiotics are also chemicals having these characteristics but are produced by organisms as wastes or byproducts of metabolism. Many are produced by fungi and moldlike bacteria (the actinomycetes). These compounds are useful because they are toxic to the infectious microorganism, while having little or no toxic effect on the host eukaryotic organism.

The most important group of chemotherapeutic agents are the sulfonamides. The first of these agents, identified as bactericidal by Domagk in the 1930s, was sulfanilamide. It acts as a competitive inhibitor of folic-acid metabolism. Since higher eukaryotes such as humans do not make their own folic acid, but must have it supplied, the sulfonamides have little effect on the host. Other chemotherapeutic agents in this group inhibit other reactions important to bacterial metabolism.

Several families of antibiotics are in use today. They also inhibit important reactions necessary for the growth of bacteria. The penicillins inhibit the synthesis of the peptidoglycan in actively growing bacteria, causing the cell to swell and burst. Because of the importance of the peptidoglycan in the gram(+) cell wall, the penicillins are most effective against gram(+) infections. The cephalosporins also inhibit cell-wall biosynthesis and are most effective against gram(+) organisms. The aminoglycosides including streptomycin inhibit protein synthesis. They are most effective in treating gram(-) infections. Chloramphenicol is another antibiotic that inhibits protein synthesis. It is effective against gram(+) and gram(-) bacteria, as well as several rickettsiae and fungi. Because of the great variety of microorganisms inhibited, it is referred to as a broad-spectrum antibiotic. The tetracyclines also are a group of broad-spectrum antibiotics that inhibit protein synthesis. Other antibiotics inhibit cell-wall synthesis (vancomycin, bacitracin, polymyxin, nystatin, and amphotericin B), protein synthesis (erythromycin and spectinomycin), and nucleic-acid synthesis (rifampin and griseofulvin). Several of these antibiotics are used primarily for the treatment of fungal infections.

When an organism is isolated from a patient, it is necessary to determine the range of antibiotics to which the organism is sensitive. Several tests can be used to determine the antibiotic sensitivity spectrum of the organism. These include the tube dilution method and the agar diffusion method. The Kirby-Bauer test is a tube dilution method that has been standardized for influencing factors and is regulated by standards established by the federal Food and Drug Administration.

After you have read Chapter 23 of your textbook, you should be able to:

1. Define or identify the following terms: Salvarsan, sulfanilamide, sulfonamide, competitive inhibition, folic acid, para-amino-benzoic acid (PABA), metabolite, sulfamethoxazole, trimethoprim, sulfacetamide, sulfabenzamide, sulfathiazole, sulfisoxazole, isonicotinic acid hydrazide (INH), isoniazid, nalidixic acid, nitrofurantoin, metronidazole, chloroquine, primaquine, dapsone, penicillin, antibiotic, beta lactam, penicillinase, ampicillin, methicillin, nafcillin, cephalosporin, streptomycin, gentamicin, neomycin, kanamycin, amikacin, R factors, chloramphenicol, broad-spectrum antibiotic, aplastic anemia, gray syndrome, tetracycline, nystatin, erythromycin, vancomycin, rifampin, clindamycin, lincomycin, pseudomembranous colitis, bacitracin, polymyxin, spectinomycin, nystatin, candicidin, griseofulvin, amphotericin B, minimum inhibitory concentration (MIC), Kirby-Bauer test, and zone of inhibition.

2. Explain the difference between a chemotherapeutic agent and an antibiotic.

3. Identify the metabolic function inhibited by each of the antibiotic and chemotherapeutic agents described.

4. Indicate the group(s) of organisms against which each of the antiniotics and chemotherapeutic agents are most effective.

5. Describe the various antibiotic sensitivity tests and indicate the various factors that must be considered when comparing and standardizing MICs.

PRE-TEST

1. A zone of inhibition is:
   a. obtained through a tube dilution antibiotic sensitivity test.
   b. indicates the areas of the body protected by an antibiotic.
   c. indicative of sensitivity of an organism to the test antibiotic.
   d. the area surrounding a fungus in which a bacterium cannot grow.

2. An antifungal antibiotic that degrades the cell membrane of fungal cells is:
   a. nystatin.
   b. griseofulvin.
   c. penicillin.
   d. amphotericin B.

3. An antibiotic that is the product of sporeforming bacterium is:
   a. penicillin.
   b. tetracyclin.
   c. polymyxin.
   d. griseofulvin.

4. Penicillin:
   a. has an amino-containing carbohydrate as its basic structural unit.
   b. is a component of the red dye prontosil.

c. contains a beta lactam nucleus.
d. is most effective against gram(-) bacteria.

5. Ampicillin is preferable to penicillin because it:
   a. stimulates fewer allergic reactions.
   b. is absorbed more easily from the intestine when taken orally.
   c. is more active against gram(+) bacteria.
   d. cannot be detoxified by penicillinase.

6. Cephalosporins act by:
   a. inhibiting protein synthesis.
   b. interfering with cell-wall biosynthesis.
   c. competitively inhibiting folic-acid biosynthesis.
   d. inhibiting RNA synthesis.

7. A physician has determined that he must prescribe chloramphenicol to treat an infection. He should:
   a. check for an allergic reaction.
   b. test for hearing defects induced.
   c. place the patient in the hospital and check for development of aplastic anemia.
   d. be aware of the possibility of eye damage.

8. Tetracycline antibiotics interfere with:
   a. protein synthesis.
   b. RNA synthesis.
   c. cell-wall biosynthesis.
   d. DNA replication.

9. Penicillin is most effective against:
   a. log phase gram(-) bacteria.
   b. stationary phase gram(-) bacteria.
   c. log phase gram(+) bacteria.
   d. stationary phase gram(+) bacteria.

10. Carbenicillin is best classified as a:
    a. synthetic chemotherapeutic agent.
    b. natural antibiotic.
    c. natural fungicide.
    d. semisynthetic antibiotic.

11. A physician wants to treat a fungal infection of the skin. An antibiotic she might prescribe is:
    a. penicillin.
    b. streptomycin.
    c. amphotericin B.
    d. chloramphenicol.

12. Tetracycline is the drug of choice in treating:
    a. gram(+) bacterial infections.
    b. fungal infections.
    c. gram(-) infections.
    d. rickettsial infections.

13. Gray syndrome is a serious condition of newborn children and is
associated with the use of:
    a.   tetracycline.
    b.   chloramphenicol.
    c.   cephalosporin.
    d.   oxacillin.

14. The MIC is the:
    a.   minimum concentration of an antibiotic that will inhibit the
        growth of a microorganism.
    b.   minimum concentration of an antibiotic that will kill a micro-
        organism.
    c.   maximum concentration of an antibiotic that can be absorbed in-
        to the bloodstream without damage.
    d.   mean diameter of the zone of inhibition in a Kirby-Bauer test.

15. Sulfanilamide inhibits:
    a.   cell-wall biosynthesis.
    b.   folic-acid metabolism.
    c.   protein synthesis.
    d.   cell-wall permeability.

PRACTICE EXERCISES

1. Several families of antibiotics are discussed in this chapter.
They are distinguished by their basic chemical structures, among
other criteria. Identify each of the following as a (1) penicillin,
(2) tetracyclin, (3) amino glycoside, or (4) chloramphenicol by
placing the appropriate number on the line provided.

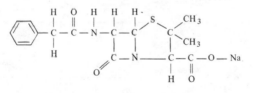

a. ——

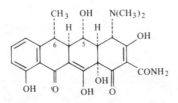

b. ——

287

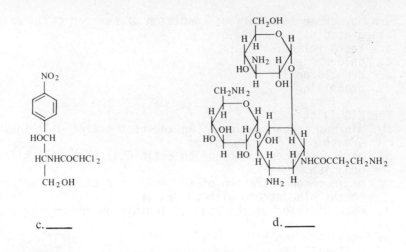

c.____   d.____

2. For each of the following antibiotics, indicate which metabolic
   function it inhibits.

   a. Penicillin:

   _____

   b. Sulfanilamide:

   _____

   c. Chloramphenicol:

   _____

   d. Cephalosporin:

   _____

   e. Isoniazid:

   _____

   f. Streptomycin:

   _____

   g. Rifampin:

   _____

h. Erythromycin:

_____

i. Polymyxin:

_____

j. Griseofulvin:

_____

3. You want to determine the MIC of nalidixic acid for a strain of
   Pseudomonas aeruginosa isolated from the lungs of a child with
   cystic fibrosis. You make the following dilution series of the
   drug in Mueller-Hinton medium and inoculate each tube with 0.1 ml
   of a suspension of the P. aeruginosa strain you are testing. Tube
   1 contained nalidixic acid in a concentration of 1000 u mg of
   nalidixic acid/ml of Mueller-Hinton medium.

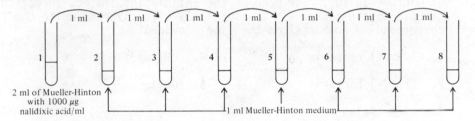

After incubation for 17hr at 37°C, you detect growth in tubes 5-8
but no growth in tubes 1-4. What is the MIC of nalidixic acid for
this strain of P. aeruginosa?

_____

4. True or False. Decide whether each of the following statements is
   true or false; then place a T for true or an F for false on the
   line provided.

___F___ a. Penicillin is more effective against gram(-) organisms than
           against gram(+) organisms because of the composition of their
           cell walls.

___T___ b. Lysozyme is a nonspecific enzyme effective in killing gram(+)
           bacteria.

___T___ c. Sulfanilamide was first discovered to be inhibitory to gram(+)
           bacteria because it is a component of the red dye prontosil.

___T___ d. The first chemotherapeutic agent, Salvarsan, was discovered
           by Paul Ehrlich in 1910. It was very effective against
           Treponema pallidum.

___F___ e. Sulfanilamide is a noncompetitive inhibitor of an enzyme in-
           volved in folic-acid synthesis.

_F_ f. Neomycin is easily absorbed when taken orally and therefore
         it is not useful in control of infections of the intestine.

_T_ g. Chloramphenicol was the first broad-spectrum antibiotic to be
         discovered. It is so named because it inhibits a wide variety
         of gram(+) and gram(-) bacteria as well as rickettsiae and
         fungi.

_F_ h. Streptomycin inhibits cell-wall biosynthesis in gram(-) bacteria.

_T_ i. One important drawback to the use of penicillin is the fact
         that it causes severe anaphylactic reactions in persons allergic
         to it.

_F_ j. Penicillinase is an enzyme that detoxifies penicillin by
         cleaving the amino group containing the carbohydrate nucleus
         of the molecule.

5. Different antibiotics are most effective against different groups
    of microorganisms. For each of the antibiotics listed, select the
    group(s) against which it is especially effective and write the
    corresponding number(s) on the line provided.

    1. Gram(+) bacteria   4. chlamydiae

    2. Gram(-) bacteria   5. fungi

    3. rickettsiae

    a. Rifampin: _____

    b. Aminoglycosides: _____

    c. Tetracycline: _____

    d. Cephalosporin: _____

    e. Penicillin: _____

    f. Streptomycin: _____

    g. Amphotericin: _____

    h. Chloramphenicol: _____

    i. Polymyxin: _____

    j. Nystatin: _____

CONCEPT EXERCISES

1. Not surprisingly, there are many fewer antibiotics effective
    against fungi than against bacteria. Many potentially useful
    fungicidal agents have severe side effects, which limit their use.

What characteristic(s) of the fungal cell would you identify to explain these observations?

_____

_____

_____

_____

_____

_____

2. Genes leading to resistance to drugs can be either chromosomal or plasmid in origin. Two major catagories of mechanisms for resistance are encoded by these genes. One category leads to alterations in the target site for the antibiotic so that the antibiotic no longer has an inhibitory effect on the cellular process involved. An example of this is the modification of a ribosomal protein so that streptomycin no longer binds to the ribosome and inhibits protein synthesis. The other category of mechanisms detoxifies the antibiotic by changing the chemical structure of the antibiotic itself. An example of this type is the inactivation of penicillin by penicillinase.

a. Would you expect streptomycin resistance of the type described above to most likely be of chromosomal or plasmid origin? Why?

_____

_____

_____

b. Would you expect penicillin resistance of the type described above to most likely be of chromosomal or plasmid origin? Why?

_____

_____

_____

_____

_____

3. Explain the mechanism of <u>competitive inhibition</u> of an enzyme by a

molecule such as sulfanilamide.

_____

_____

_____

_____

_____

_____

_____

_____

POST-TEST

1. Chloroquine is effective against:
   a. syphilis.
   b. malaria.
   c. tuberculosis.
   d. fungal infection.

2. The beta lactam nucleus is the basic structure of the:
   a. penicillins.
   b. tetracyclines.
   c. chloramphenicols.
   d. aminoglycosides.

3. Cephalosporins must be injected because:
   a. they are broken down by stomic acid.
   b. oral intake may cause damage to the mucous membranes.
   c. they cannot be absorbed from the gastrointestinal tract.
   d. effective half-life is very short.

4. R factors are:
   a. extrachromosomal genes coding for drug resistance.
   b. found only in gram(+) bacteria.
   c. compounds found in fungi and the actinomycetes that protect
       them from the antibiotics they produce.
   d. elements that must be standardized in the Kirby-Bauer test for
       antibiotic resistance.

5. All of the following are elements that must be standardized to a
   constant value before two MICs can be compared, except:
   a. temperature of incubation.
   b. inoculum size.
   c. incubation time.
   d. concentration of drug.

292

6. Lincomycin and Clindamycin are alternative antibiotics for use
   with infections that prove to be resistant to:
   a. streptomycin.
   b. erythromycin.
   c. penicillin.
   d. tetracycline.

7. An antibiotic effective against anaerobic bacterial infections
   such as those caused by <u>Clostridium</u>, <u>Bacteroides</u>, and <u>Actinomyces</u>
   is:
   a. clindamycin.
   b. bacitracin.
   c. polymyxin.
   d. spectinomycin.

8. A drug that has been used effectively for the treatment of cases
   of gonorrhea caused by PPNG is:
   a. clindamycin.
   b. bacitracin.
   c. polymyxin.
   d. spectinomycin.

9. The antibiotic shown

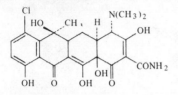

   should be classified as a(n):
   a. penicillin.
   b. tetracycline.
   c. chloramphenicol.
   d. aminoglycoside.

10. Chloramphenicol:
    a. inhibits RNA synthesis.
    b. cannot be absorbed from the intestine.
    c. can cause aplastic anemia and gray syndrome.
    d. is effective only against gram(-) infections.

11. All of the following are true statements about nystatin, <u>except</u>:
    a. It changes the permeability of the fungal-cell membrane.
    b. It is a product of <u>Streptomyces</u>.
    c. It cannot be used internally.
    d. It is sold as ointment, cream, and in suppository form.

12. The MIC of an antibiotic can be determined from the:
    a. Kirby-Bauer test.
    b. zone of inhibition.
    c. tube dilution method.
    d. agar diffusion method.

13. Erythromycin inhibits:
    a. protein synthesis.
    b. RNA synthesis.
    c. DNA replication.
    d. cell-wall biosynthesis.

14. Because of its mode of action, penicillin cannot inhibit members
    of the genus:
    a. Bacillus.
    b. Clostridium.
    c. Escherichia.
    d. Mycoplasma.

15. Trimethoprim inhibits:
    a. protein synthesis by binding to the ribosome.
    b. folic-acid biosynthesis by acting as a analog of PABA.
    c. the enzyme that converts folic acid to folinic acid.
    d. the cross-linking of the peptidoglycan layer of the gram(-)
        bacterial cell wall.

ANSWERS TO EXERCISES

Pre-Test

1. c	6. b	11. c
2. d	7. c	12. d
3. c	8. a	13. b
4. c	9. c	14. a
5. b	10. d	15. b

Practice Exercises

1. a. 1 (Figure 23.5); b. 4 (Figure 23.10); c. 2 (Figure 23.14);

   d. 3 (Figure 23.9).

2. a. cell-wall biosynthesis; b. folic-acid metabolism;

   c. protein synthesis; d. cell-wall synthesis; e. niacin and/or

   vitamin-B metabolism; f. protein synthesis; g. RNA synthesis;

   h. protein synthesis; i. cell-membrane function; j. nucleic-

   acid synthesis. (All answers to this exercise can be found in

   Table 23.3).

3. 125 u mg/ml.

4. a. F; b. T; c. T; d. T; e. F; f. F; g. T; h. F;

   i. T; j. F.

5. a. 2 (Table 23.3); b. 2 (Table 23.3); c. 2, 3, 4 (Table 23.3);

   d. 1 (Table 23.3); e. 1 (Table 23.3); f. 2 (Table 23.3);

   g. 5 (Table 23.3); h. 1, 2, 3, 5; i. 2 (Table 23.3);

   j. 5 (Table 23.3).

Concept Exercises

1. Fungi are eukaryotic organisms. In addition, they do not have the unique cell wall of bacteria, which contains the peptidoglycan. Because of their greater similarity in biochemistry and cytology to their eukaryotic host (e.g., humans), it is more difficult to find drugs that will inhibit the fungal cell without having a similar effect on the host organism.

2. a. Because the organelle being modified (i.e., the ribosome) is a constituent of all cells, it is most likely that the genetic modifications is chromosomal in origin.

   b. Since the modification is a new function of the cell (an enzyme capable of cleaving the beta-lactam ring), it is most likely that the drug resistance is of plasmid origin. If it were of chromosomal origin we would expect all cells to have it because mutation of the chromosome usually leads to loss of function, not to the acquisition of a new enzymatic activity.

3. Competitive inhibition of an enzyme by an antibiotic takes place when the structure of the antibiotic is close enough to the natural substrate of the enzyme that it can successfully compete with the natural substrate for the active site of the enzyme. When the inhibition is competitive, both compounds (both the substrate and the inhibitor) can bind to the active site in the presence of the other, and whichever compound is in greater excess will be bound most often to the enzyme.

Post-Test

1. b
2. a
3. c
4. a
5. d

6. c
7. a
8. d
9. b
10. c

11. c
12. c
13. a
14. d
15. c

The technique of making sauerkraut has hardly changed since it was recorded by the ancient Romans, who seem to have acquired it from the Orient. It consists of adding salt to shredded cabbage and then allowing the cabbage to ferment. The method was forgotten by Europeans until the conquering Tatar hordes, bringing it from China, reintroduced it to Austria in the 13th Century. The Austrians gave sauerkraut its name (literally, "sour plant") and passed it along to their neighbors, among whom none welcomed it more warmly than the Germans.

Nika Standen Huzelton, The Cooking of Germany.
New York: Time-Life Books, 1969.

CHAPTER OUTLINE

I. Food Spoilage

A. The conditions of spoilage

B. The chemisty of spoilage

C. Meats and fish

D. Poultry and eggs

E. Breads and bakery products

F. Spoilage of other foods

II. Food Preservation

A. Heat

B. Low temperature

C. Drying

D. Osmotic pressure

E. Chemical preservatives

F. Radiation

G. Foodborne disease

III. The Positive Role of Microorganisms in Foods

OVERVIEW AND OBJECTIVES

Microbiology and public health are closely related. Many of the considerations of the public health official involve microorganisms. Bacteria and other microbes have both positive and negative roles in food and dairy processing, in the sanitation of water and sewage, and in many other industries (including the textile and paper industries). These roles will be discussed in the remaining chapters of your textbook. In addition, a short discussion of multicellular parasites is included.

This chapter discusses the diseases and uses of microorganisms in the food industry: the process of food spoilage, methods of preserving foods from spoilage, and the role of microbes in the production of several fermented foods.

The food industry is vitally concerned with microorganisms. Contamination of foods by bacteria and fungi can have devastating economic consequences to the food processor. The dawn of modern microbiology began with Louis Pasteur's investigation of the diseases of wine. On the other hand, many processed foods (including wine) depend on bacterial fermentation for their production. Among these foods are pickles, sauerkraut, and olives, as well as the livestock food product, silage.

When humans developed a social structure that allowed collection of more food than could be eaten at one time, the process of spoilage had to be confronted. As the quote from Louis Pasteur that opens Chapter 5 points out, this is a natural process which is necessary to return the elements trapped in dead biological tissue to the environment for recycling in the development of new biological tissue. This process is initiated by microorganisms. Many of the conditions associated with spoilage are not necessarily harmful but reduce the palatability of food. The introduction of spices into the diet was mainly a tool for masking these effects of spoilage. The undesirable changes associated with spoilage are caused by the degradation of protein, carbohydrates, and fats. Food can be divided into three categories according to their susceptibility to spoilage: highly perishable, semiperishable, and nonperishable.

Food preservation depends on retarding the rate of growth of microorganisms in food products. Many of the methods for controlling bacterial growth discussed in Chapters 21 and 22 are used by the food industry and the homemaker for this purpose. Heat kills microorganisms that are contaminating the food. Low temperatures do not eliminate viable organisms from food but retard their metabolism and, hence, spoilage. Drying has been used by humans since before recorded history and depends on the elimination of water from food. Water is necessary for life and, without it, bacterial growth is eliminated or, at least, greatly reduced. Osmotic pressure can be increased by the addition of high concentrations of salt or sugar. This form of preservation has also been used by humans throughout history. (Bees also use this method to preserve honey.) Modern methods of preservation include the addition of chemical preservatives to processed food and radiation, which kills bacteria on the surface of food. One very important goal of food preservation and sanitation is the elimination of pathogenic organisms. Many diseases can be transmitted by food, as discussed in Chapter 18.

After you have read Chapter 24 of your textbook, you should be able to:

1. Define or identify the following terms: spoilage, highly perishable, semiperishable, nonperishable, tryptophan, indole, skatole, <u>Serratia marcescens</u>, <u>Lactobacillus</u>, <u>Leuconostoc</u>, <u>Streptococcus</u>, <u>Salmonella</u>, <u>Proteus</u>, black rot, red rot, <u>Pseudomonas</u>, green rot, <u>Bacillus</u>, ropy, <u>Aspergillus</u> <u>flavus</u>, aflatoxin, <u>Claviceps purpurae</u>, ergot disease, canning, blanching, flipper, springer, soft swell, hard swell, flat sour, thermoduric, thermophilic, spray dryer, heated drum, belt heater, lyophilization, osmotic pressure, osmosis, sorbic acid, benzoic acid, propionic acid, smoking, sulfur dioxide, ethylene oxide, ultraviolet light, gamma rays, microwaves, sauerkraut, pickles, and silage.

2. Discuss the chemistry of spoilage, including the compounds broken down, the degradation products, and the effects of this process on food.

3. List the methods used for preservation of food and explain their effects on the growth of microorganisms.

4. Describe the uses of microorganisms in the production of processed foods.

5. Identify some of the genera of bacteria and fungi associated with various forms of food spoilage.

PRE-TEST

1. <u>Serratia marcescens</u> is associated with:
   a. black rot of eggs.
   b. ropy spoilage of bread.
   c. contamination of bread with "blood."
   d. ergot disease.

2. Lyophilization is a process in which:
   a. materials are first frozen and then dryed under vacuum.
   b. sugar is added to foods to preserve them.
   c. bacteria are killed by heating materials to high temperatures.
   d. low temperatures are used to kill bacteria by forming ice crystals within the cytoplasm.

3. Perhaps the <u>best</u> way to thaw frozen meat is to:
   a. place it on the kitchen counter.
   b. thaw it in a microwave oven on defrost cycle.
   c. place it in the refrigerator, where it will thaw in an environment that reduces bacterial growth.
   d. submerge it in hot water where it will thaw quickly.

4. The formation of slime on the outer casings of frankfurters may be

due to:
a. Streptococcus.
b. Pseudomonas.
c. Bacillus.
d. Proteus.

5. Contamination of eggs by Serratia marcescens leads to a condition called:
a. black rot.
b. green rot.
c. ropy rot.
d. red rot.

6. Blanching:
a. is a form of freezer burn.
b. destroys many enzymes in food and prevents further cellular metabolism.
c. is the loss of color in foods due to the growth of contaminating bacteria.
d. kills bacteria by subjecting them to high heat.

7. An organism that can survive and grow at refrigerator temperatures is termed:
a. thermoduric.
b. thermophilic.
c. thermotropic.
d. psychrotropic.

8. Foods that spoil at an intermediate rate are termed:
a. highly perishable.
b. semiperishable.
c. perishable.
d. nonperishable.

9. Gas is caused in sealed cans from the:
a. decomposition of protein to amino acids.
b. metabolism of carbohydrates.
c. breakdown of fats to fatty acids.
d. production of indole and skatole from trypthophan.

10. Most foods fall in a pH range of:
a. 1-3.
b. 5-7.
c. 7-10.
d. 10-14.

11. Ropy is a condition:
a. associated with the growth of Bacillus in bread.
b. caused by the contamination of eggs with Pseudomonas.
c. that develops when meat is kept too long in the refrigerator.
d. brought about by the growth of Aspergillus flavus in grains.

12. LSD is derived from:
a. aflatoxin.

b. the toxin produced by <u>Bacillus</u>.
c. enterotoxin.
d. the toxin produced by <u>Claviceps purpurae</u>.

13. The flat, sour taste sometimes associated with canned foods is caused by:
a. gas production by microorganisms.
b. acid production by microorganisms.
c. the degradation of fats to fatty acids.
d. the production of indol from tryptophan.

14. Large ice crystals, which can tear and shred microorganisms and may kill them, are formed most often at:
a. 32°C.
b. 5°C.
c. -5°C.
d. -60°C.

15. A method useful for the preservation, transport, and storage of microorganisms is:
a. heat drying.
b. freezing at -5°C.
c. lyophilization.
d. chemical preservation in sorbic acid.

PRACTICE EXERCISES

1. <u>Matching</u>. Many food products are produced by microorganisms. Identify the organism in the right-hand column that is used in the production of each of the food products in the left-hand column by placing the appropriate number on the line provided. Entries in the right-hand column may be used <u>more than once</u> or <u>not at all</u>.

_____ a. Soy sauce	1. Lactic and acetic acid bacteria
_____ b. Sourdough bread	2. Yeasts
_____ c. Sauerkraut	3. Lactic acid bacteria with yeast
_____ d. Fermented olives	
_____ e. Alcoholic beverages	4. <u>Aspergilluys flavus</u>
_____ f. Ginger bread	5. Anaerobic bacteria
_____ g. Vanilla	6. <u>Aspergillus oryzae</u>
_____ h. Sausage	7. <u>Serratia marcescens</u>
_____ i. Vinegar	8. Propionic acid bacteria
_____ j. Pickles	

2. Indicate the degredation products of each of the following components of food and the effects of these products on the taste, smell,
   and/or appearance of the food.

   a. Cysteine:

   _____

   _____

   b. Carbohydrates:

   _____

   _____

   c. Tryptophan:

   _____

   _____

   d. Fats:

   _____

   _____

3. Identify one organism that commonly causes each of the following
   conditions, which are associated with the spoilage of food.

   a. Red rot of eggs:

   _____

   b. The greening of the surface of meat:

   _____

   c. Slime formation on the outer casings of frankfurters and
      bologna:

   _____

   d. Ropy bread:

   _____

   e. Green rot of eggs:

   _____

   f. Contamination of grains with aflatoxin:

   _____

g. Black rot of eggs:

_____

h. Ergot disease:

_____

i. Salmonellosis associated with poultry and egg products:

_____

j. Historical incidents of bread contaminated with blood:

_____

4. Describe in one or two sentences how each of the following methods
of food preservation is used to inhibit bacterial growth in a
food product.

a. Drying:

_____

_____

_____

b. Osmotic pressure:

_____

_____

_____

c. Smoking:

_____

_____

_____

d. Ultraviolet light:

_____

_____

_____

e. Belt heater:

_____

_____

_____

f. Canning:

_____

_____

_____

g. Freezing at -5°C:

_____

_____

_____

h. Sorbic acid:

_____

_____

_____

i. Microwaves:

_____

_____

_____

j. Addition of high concentrations of sugar:

_____

_____

_____

5. <u>True or False</u>. Indicate whether each of the following statements
   is true or false by placing a T for true or an F for false on the
   line provided.

____ a. Microwaves work primarily by energizing water molecules, and
        the heat of friction results in quick cooking.

_____ b. Silage is a fermented product of grass, corn, leaves, stems, grain stalks, and other materials, which is both nutritious to animals and inexpensive for the farmer.

_____ c. Pickles are produced by yeast fermentation.

_____ d. Hard swell is a condition of canned foods caused by the production of acid by bacteria.

_____ e. Blanching is a process in which food to be canned is subjected to steam heat for 3-5 minutes. It destroys many enzymes in the food product and prevents further cellular metabolism.

_____ f. pH is not an important factor in the spoilage of food because bacteria can grow at all pHs.

_____ g. The chemical composition of food may be a determining factor in the type of microorganisms responsible for its spoilage.

_____ h. The sour taste associated with the spoilage of many foods results from the decomposition of protein to amino acids.

_____ i. Chocolate toppings and sweet icings on bakery goods do not require refrigeration because neither bacteria nor fungi can grow in the high-sugar environment.

_____ j. Ergot disease is associated with the contamination of grains by _Claviceps purpurae_. This mold produces a toxin from which LSD is derived.

CONCEPT EXERCISES

1. Food becomes contaminated in many different ways. As a public health official, what aspects of a food-packing plant would you particularly investigate in determining whether measures were being taken to minimize microbial contamination?

_____

_____

_____

2. Many bacteriology and cell-biology laboratories store bacterial
   and eukaryotic cell lines in ultralcold freezers. Why don't the
   scientists use the freezer compartments contained in the refriger-
   ators that are also found in every laboratory for the storage of
   their important strains and cell lines?

_____

_____

_____

_____

_____

_____

_____

_____

3. You are in the research and development department of a company
   that makes salad dressings. You are asked to select a preservative
   for bottled Russian dressing. What criteria would be helpful to
   your selection of an appropriate preservative?

_____

_____

_____

_____

_____

_____

_____

_____

POST-TEST

1. A good method for the decontamination of the surface of a steak during the aging process would be:
   a. drying.
   b. microwave.
   c. ultraviolet light.
   d. salting.

2. All of the following organisms are involved in the fermentation of silage, except:
   a. anaerobic organisms such as Lactobacillus.
   b. naturally occurring yeasts.
   c. aerobic organisms such as Bacillus.
   d. coliform bacteria from the soil.

3. Ethylene oxide is used in the decontamination of all of the following, except:
   a. petri dishes.
   b. nuts.
   c. spices.
   d. meats.

4. Alcohol is introduced into foods during the spoilage process by:
   a. acid-producing bacteria decomposing carbohydrates.
   b. the decomposition of fats.
   c. yeasts, which decompose carbohydrates to ethanol.
   d. proteiolytic bacteria decomposing cysteine.

5. The natural resistance of egg white to spoilage is in part due to the presence of:
   a. lysozyme.
   b. hydrogen sulfide.
   c. sulfur dioxide.
   d. propionic acid.

6. A food intoxication caused by bacteria is:
   a. typhoid fever.
   b. botulism.
   c. salmonellosis.
   d. shigellosis.

7. A combination of lactic acid bacteria and yeast are responsible for the production of:
   a. ginger beer.
   b. sauerkraut.
   c. red wine.
   d. vanilla.

8. Which of the following forms of meat is likely to be the least perishable?
   a. Hamburger
   b. Spiced sausage
   c. T-bone steak
   d. Frankfurters

9. Several pathogenic organisms are associated with foods. These include typhoid bacilli, cholera vibrios, amoebic cysts, and hepatitis viruses. All of these causative agents of disease may accumulate in:
    a. dairy products.
    b. shell fish, such as clams.
    c. eggs.
    d. beef.

10. Listed below are several diseases of eggs and their causative agents. Identify which disease is <u>not</u> caused by the organism indicated.
    a. Black rot--<u>Proteus</u>
    b. Green rot--<u>Pseudomonas</u>
    c. Red rot--<u>Bacillus</u>
    d. Salmonellosis--<u>Salmonella</u>

11. A condition caused by the contamination of grains, which may produce convulsions and hallucinations, is:
    a. aflatoxin poisoning.
    b. ergot disease.
    c. salmonellosis.
    d. amoebiasis.

12. A process that both dries food and deposits chemical preservatives in it is:
    ·a. lyophilization.
    b. spray drying.
    c. smoking.
    d. osmosis.

13. A common food that is not palatable until it is fermented is:
    a. the olive.
    b. the pickle.
    c. sauerkraut.
    d. soy sauce.

14. Sulfur dioxide is often used to perserve:
    a. fresh meats.
    b. breads.
    c. dairy products.
    d. dried fruits.

15. Macaroni, flour, dried beans, and cereals are considered to be:
    a. highly perishable foods.
    b. nonperishable foods.
    c. semiperishable foods.
    d. perishable foods.

ANSWERS TO EXERCISES

Pre-Test

1. c   6. b   11. a

307

2. a	7. d	12. d
3. b	8. b	13. b
4. a	9. b	14. c
5. d	10. b	15. c

Practice Exercises

1. a. 6; b. 3; c. 1; d. 1; e. 2; f. 3; g. i; h. i;

   i. 1; j. 1. (All answers to this exercise can be found in

   Table 24.4.)

2. a. hydrogen sulfide, which imparts a rotten-egg smell to food.

   b. yeast will produce ethanol, which gives juices an alcoholic taste; other microorganisms may produce acid, giving food a sour taste and producing gas in canned foods.

   c. indole and skatole, which give food a fecal odor.

   d. fatty acids, which give foods a rancid odor.

3. a. Serratia marcescens; b. Lactobacillus and Leuconostoc;

   c. Lactobacillus, Leuconostoc, and Streptococcus; d. Bacillus

   and other capsule-producing bacteria; e. Pseudomonas;

   f. Aspergillus flavus; g. Proteus; h. Claviceps purpurae;

   i. Salmonella; j. Serratia marcescens.

4. a. Drying preserves food by the elimination of water, which is necessary for life processes.

   b. Osmotic pressure preserves food by withdrawing water from both the microorganisms and the food product.

   c. Smoking preserves food by both drying it and by adding chemical preservatives to the food.

   d. Ultraviolet light will decontaminate the surface of food such as meat during the aging process. It inactivates nucleic acids and proteins found in bacteria.

   e. The belt heater preserves food by drying.

   f. Canning preserves food by subjecting it to high heat under pressure. It is simlar to autoclaving.

g. Freezing at -5°C preserves food by reducing the metabolism of microorganisms. The ice crystals formed may also disrupt the bacterial cell and kill it.

h. Sorbic acid is a chemical preservative that is thought to act by interfering with the uptake of certain essential organic substances by the microbial cell.

i. Microwaves act to energize water molecules. The heat of friction produced may be capable of killing microorganisms in food.

j. The addition of high concentrations of sugar to food inhibits microbial growth by increasing the osmotic pressure causing water to be lost from both the bacteria and the food product.

5. a. T; b. T; c. F; d. F. e. T; f. F; g. T; h. F;

   i. F; j. T.

Concept Exercises

1. Several areas should be investigated. the air filtering system of the plant should be inspected to determine whether it is increasing the contamination of airborne organisms. If the plant is a meat-packing plant, the handling of meat products should be monitored to be sure that contamination with intestinal flora is kept to a minimum. When plants packaging fruits and vegetables are inspected, methods for the removal of soil from the fresh produce should be considered to determine whether they are adequate to minimize soilborne contamination. In plants handling shellfish, methods should be used to remove possibly contaminated water from the organisms, perhaps by allowing them to live in clear water for a period of time before final packing. And, in all types of plant, general cleanliness is necessary to ensure that contamination from insects and rodents is reduced as much as possible.

2. Scientists want to preserve the viability of their stock cultures. The large ice crystals that form at the -5° to -20°C temperatures of the refrigerator freezer can cause tearing and shredding of the bacterial or mammalian cells, which can cause their death. The -60° to -80°C ultracold freezer produces smaller ice crystals that cause less harm to the cells. To reduce the size of the ice crystals, most investigators quick-freeze their stock cultures, using liquid nitrogen, when storing them.

3. In selecting a chemical preservative for the salad dressing, you should consider several factors. Not only must the agent be inhibitory to microorganisms, but it must also be broken down and eliminated by the body without side effects. In addition, it should be economical, extend the shelf life of the product, not reduce the quality of the product, not retard the activity of digestive enzymes, and be distributed uniformly in the product.

309

Also, the preservative in the food should be easily detectable by chemical analysis to allow for quality-control testing.

Post-Test

1. c	6. b	11. b
2. c	7. a	12. c
3. d	8. c	13. a
4. c	9. b	14. d
5. a	10. c	15. b

NO ARTIFICIAL ANYTHING -- A cultured lowfat milk product made from
cultured pasteurized Grade A milk and nonfat milk solids. -- REAL
CHERRIES, WATCH FOR PITS.

Dannon Lowfat Cherry Yogurt Label.

CHAPTER OUTLINE

   I. The Composition of Milk

  II. Milk Spoilage

      A. Milkborne disease

      B. Pasteurization

 III. Laboratory Microbiology of Dairy Products

      A. The phosphatase test

      B. Standard plate count

      C. The reduction test

      D. The breed counting procedure

      E. The antibiotic detection test

  IV. The Positive Role of Microorganisms in Milk

      A. Cheese

OVERVIEW AND OBJECTIVES

Milk and dairy products have long been part of the human diet. Today
they make up about 20 percent of our diet, and through the use of
microbial fermentation, we have developed a large variety of different
foods derived from milk. In this chapter, the spoilage of milk and its
preservation is explored. We will also look at the methods of testing
milk for contaminating bacteria and antibiotics. Last, we will explore
some of the important bacterially derived dairy products.

    Milk is a complete food. It contains protein, carbohydrate, and
fat, as well as several vitamins. These characteristics make it just
as good a food for microorganisms as it is for mammals. Many microorganisms are active in the spoilage of milk and growth of these
organisms leads to various types of spoilage. In addition, milk can
harbor several types of pathogenic organisms. To prevent the trans-

mission of these diseases by dairy products, milk is pasteurized to eliminate pathogenic organisms. This process is effective and does not significantly change the palatability of the milk. Several different methods of pasteurization are currently in use.

Several laboratory tests are used to assess the degree of microbial contamination in milk. The phosphatase test relies on the fact that the enzyme phosphatase is inactivated at the temperature used in the pasteurization process to kill microorganisms. The enzyme is normally found in milk and its activity is easily assayed. If the milk has been properly pasteurized, no phosphates activity will be found in the milk sample. The standard plate count uses a standard dilution of a milk sample followed by plating of the dilution on culture media that detect (1) the total viable cells/ml and (2) the number of coliform bacteria/ml. This second count is important because it is a measure of possible fecal contamination. The reduction test is rapid and determines the number of bacteria in the milk sample by measuring the length of time required to change the color of a dye added to the sample. The Breed counting procedure is a direct microscopic count of the organisms in the milk sample. It has the disadvantages of not being able to distinguish between living and dead organisms, and between coliform and noncoliform bacteria. If the cows that produce the milk are being treated with antibiotics, the antibiotics can pass into the milk and may cause allergic reactions in persons who drink it. For this reason an antibiotic detection test is run on milk samples. This test detects antibiotics in the milk samples by their ability to inhibit the growth of test microorganisms.

Many dairy products are produced by inoculating milk with specific bacterial and fungal strains and allowing them to grow. Some of the most common are yogurt, cultured buttermilk, acidophilus milk, kefir, kumiss, and cheese.

After you have read Chapter 25 of your textbook, you should be able to:

1. Define or identify the following terms: casein, lactalbumin, lactose, sweet curding, stormy fermentation, lipase, colostrum, aflatoxins, pasteurization, holding method (LTLT), flash method (HTST), ultrapasteurization, thermoduric, thermophilic, phosphatase test, standard plate count (SPC), reduction test, reductase, Breed counting procedure, antibiotic detection test, Bacillus subtilis, cultured buttermilk, starter, yogurt, acidophilus milk, Lactobacillus acidophilus, sweet acidophilus milk, kefir, kumiss, rennin, and Propionibacterium.

2. List the various types of milk spoilage and the types of organisms that produce them.

3. Distinguish among the various methods of pasteurization.

4. Outline the methods used to test the quality of milk and define the standards milk must meet to be given a "Grade A" rating.

5. Identify some of the dairy products produced by microbial fermentation and list some of the organisms that carry out fermentation.

PRE-TEST

1. The protein that gives milk its white color is:
   a. lactalbumin.
   b. lactose.
   c. casein.
   d. bovine serum albumin.

2. A method of sanitizing milk in which the milk is heated to 82°C for 3 seconds is called:
   a. pasteurization.
   b. the holding method.
   c. ultrapasteurization.
   d. the flash method.

3. Pasteurization is virtually useless against:
   a. viruses.
   b. thermophilic bacteria.
   c. psycrophilic bacteria.
   d. fungi.

4. A method used to determine the effectiveness of pasteurization by testing for the inactivation of an enzyme is the:
   a. phosphatase test.
   b. standard plate count.
   c. reduction test.
   d. Breed counting procedure.

5. The time required for a milk sample to change the color of added resazurin is the basis for the:
   a. phasphatase test.
   b. standard plate count.
   c. reduction test.
   d. Breed counting procedure.

6. Violet-red bile agar is a selective medium for the detection of:
   a. Lactobacillus.
   b. Clostridium.
   c. coliform bacteria.
   d. anaerobic bacteria.

7. If a microscopic field is 0.01 mm^2, and 0.01 ml of milk is counted in a Breed counting procedure, the microscope factor is:
   a. 500,000.
   b. 10,000.
   c. 1,000,000.
   d. 250,000.

8. Lactobacillus bulgaricus and Streptococcus thermophilus are important starter organisms for the production of:

313

a.   cultured buttermilk.
b.   yogurt.
c.   acidophilus milk.
d.   blue cheese.

9. In the antibiotic detection test, penicillin is identified by:
    a.   using Escherichia coli, a penicillin-sensitive gram(-) organism,
         as the test bacterium.
    b.   dropping a milk sample onto a plate inoculated with a penicil-
         lin-resistant organism.
    c.   treating the milk sample with penicillinase and then testing
         for inhibition of bacterial growth.
    d.   heating the milk and then testing for growth inhibition.

10. Lactobacillus acidophilus:
    a.   establishes itself in the human intestine and promotes good
         health by assisting the digestion process.
    b.   causes ropiness of milk.
    c.   is an important pathogen, which is transmitted in unpasteurized
         milk.
    d.   can never be present in Grade A milk in concentrations higher
         than 10/ml.

11. The major carbohydrate in milk is:
    a.   glucose.
    b.   galactose.
    c.   lactalbumin.
    d.   lactose.

12. The souring of milk can be caused by:
    a.   Streptococcus sp.
    b.   Serratia marcescens.
    c.   Alcaligenes sp.
    d.   Bacillus sp.

13. Coliform bacteria causes:
    a.   sweet curdling of milk.
    b.   lipid digestion in milk.
    c.   gas production in milk.
    d.   gray rot of milk.

14. The bacterial limit for prepasteurized Grade A milk is:
    a.   20,000/ml.
    b.   200/ml.
    c.   200,000/ml.
    d.   2000/ml.

15. The clear liquid remaining after casein has separated when milk
    spoils is called:
    a.   curd.
    b.   lactalbumin.
    c.   whey.
    d.   butterfat.

PRACTICE EXERCISES

1. Each of the following organisms causes one or more different types of milk spoilage. Identify one type that each microorganism causes. (You may wish to review Table 25.2 before answering this exercise.)

   a. <u>Clostridium</u> sp.:

   _____

   b. <u>Penicillium</u> sp.:

   _____

   c. <u>Lactobacillus</u> sp.:

   _____

   d. <u>Enterobacter</u> sp.:

   _____

   e. <u>Bacillus</u> sp.:

   _____

   f. <u>Alcaligenes</u> sp.:

   _____

   g. <u>Micrococcus</u> sp.:

   _____

   h. Coliform bacteria:

   _____

   i. <u>Proteus</u> sp.:

   _____

   j. <u>Serratia marcescens</u>:

   _____

2. a. You are carrying out a Breed counting procedure. After counting a 0.1 ml milk sample in a compound microscope with a field area of 0.02 mm^2, you determine that the average field contains 14 bacterial cells. What is the cell count/ml of milk? _____

   b. What is the microscope factor? _____

315

3. a. In a standard plate count, you detect 37 colonies on the
      1:1000 dilution plate and 320 on the 1:1000 dilution plate
      when the sample was plated on plate count agar. The colony
      count of violet-purple colonies was 4 on the 1:1000 dilution
      and 31 on the 1:100 dilution when violet-red bile agar was
      used. What is the total number of bacteria/ml of milk?

      _____

   b. What was the coliform count in this milk sample? _____
      ___

   c. Would this sample of milk be graded as Grade A? _____

   d. A second sample of milk was plated on tryptone, glucose, yeast
      extract agar. The plate counts were 26 on the 1:1000 dilution
      and 198 on the 1:100 dilution. What is the viable cell count/
      ml of this milk sample? _____

4. True or False. Determine whether each of the following statements
   is true or false; then place a T for true or an F for false on the
   line provided.

____ a. The Breed counting method is useful because it can separate
        live bacteria from dead ones.

____ b. Viruses go undetected in the standard plate count method of
        determining the quality of milk.

____ c. Lactobacillus acidophilus produces a product called acidophilus
        milk. It is considered healthful because the bacterium estab-
        lishes itself in the human intestine and promotes the digestion
        process by keeping mold in check.

____ d. Lactalbumin is not considered a whey protein because it is
        found in the milk curd after casein separates when milk spoils.

____ e. Organisms that cause milk to sour are members of the genera
        Lactobacillus and Streptococcus.

____ f. Phosphatase is an enzyme normally found in milk and has a heat
        tolerance similar to that of Coxiella burnetii and Mycobacterium
        bovis.

____ g. Organisms that can grow at 60°C but not at 70°C are termed
        thermophilic.

____ h. The blue veins found in Roquefort, blue, and Gorganzola cheeses
        are actually the harmless mold Penicillium, which grows during
        the ripening process and gives the cheeses their unique tastes.

____ i. Rennin is added to cheese to retard bacterial growth during
        the curing process.

____ j. In the HTST method of pasteurization, the milk is heated to

69.5°C for 30 minutes.

5. Each of the following sentences and phrases describes or defines a term associated with dairy microbiology. Identify the term by writing it on the line provided.

a. A process by which the bacterial count of milk is reduced by heating the milk to 71.6°C for a period of 15-17 seconds.

_____

b. The protein that gives milk its white color. It makes up 2.5% of the substance of milk.

_____

c. A process where milk turns gray in color and develops a foul smell.

_____

d. A disease that causes abortions in pregnant cows.

_____

e. A protein found normally in milk, which has a heat tolerance similar to Mycobacterium bovis.

_____

f. An enzyme that uses the electrons liberated by the bacterial fermentation of lactose to cause a change in the color of methylene blue.

_____

g. A test used to detect the presence of penicillin in milk.

_____

h. A fermented product of milk produced by Streptococcus lactis, streptococcus cremoris, and Leuconostoc citrovorum growing in the milk.

_____

i. An organism used to detect antibiotics in milk.

_____

j. A condition of milk caused by the gram(-) rods Alcaligenes, Klebsiella, or Enterobacter, in which a gummy material accumulates in the milk.

_____

317

1. In testing the quality of milk, particular care is taken to culture milk samples on violet-red bile agar. What types of organisms
   does this selective medium detect? Explain why neutral red and
   bile are added to the agar.

   _____

   _____

   _____

   _____

   _____

   _____

   _____

   _____

2. A bacteriologist prepares the following dilution series of a
   sample of culture medium in which he has grown an organism.

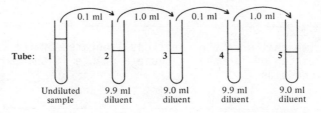

   He plates 0.1 ml of each dilution onto a petri plate. After incubation, he records the following results:

Plate Number	Tube Sampled	Number of colonies on plate
1	Tube 1:	Confluent growth
2	Tube 2:	Confluent growth
3	Tube 3:	Confluent growth
4	Tube 4:	276 colonies
5	Tube 5:	21 colonies

   a. What is the total dilution of the sample in each tube?

   _____

b. What is the total dilution of the sample represented on each plate?

_____

_____

c. What is the number of bacteria/ml of the original culture?

_____

_____

d. Which dilution did you use to calculate the answer in part (c)? Why?

_____

_____

3. Table 25.3 lists the microbiological standard for milk and milk products in the state of New York. Explain why each is important in ensuring the quality and palatability of milk.

_____

_____

_____

_____

_____

_____

_____

_____

POST-TEST

1. Gray rot of milk is caused by:
   a. Pseudomonas sp.
   b. Clostridium sp.
   c. Achromobacter sp.
   d. Serratia marcescens.

2. A mixture of lipids removed in the production of skim milk is:
   a. casein.
   b. curd.
   c. whey.
   d. butterfat.

3. Lactobacillus or Streptococcus:
   a. can sour milk with the production of a curd.
   b. produce curd in milk without the production of acid.
   c. curdle milk with the production of gas.
   d. deposit gummy materials in milk, leading to a condition refer-
      red to as ropiness.

4. An influenza-like disorder transmitted in raw milk is caused by:
   a. Mycobacterium bovis.
   b. Brucella abortus.
   c. Coxiella burnetii.
   d. Aspergillus flavus.

5. The HTST method of pasteurization heats milk to:
   a. 62.9°C for 30 min.
   b. 82°C for 3 sec.
   c. 82°C for 3 min.
   d. 71.6°C for 15-17 sec.

6. Reductase is:
   a. a protein that makes up 0.1% of milk solids.
   b. inactivated by the same temperature as Mycobacterium bovis.
   c. capable of using electrons to cause a color change in the dye
      resazurin.
   d. used in selective media to identify coliforms in milk.

7. In the standard plate count method, plates used to determine the
   bacterial count of milk should have _____ colonies.
   a. 10-100
   b. 20-200
   c. 30-300
   d. 40-400

8. Newman-Lampert stain is used in the:
   a. phosphatase test.
   b. Breed counting procedure.
   c. standard plate count method.
   d. reduction test.

9. The characteristic holes of Swiss cheese are produced by:
   a. oxygen produced by Lactobacillus.
   b. carbon dioxide produced by Propionibacterium.

c. hydrogen produced by <u>Streptococcus</u>.

d. the growth of <u>Penicillum</u> during the ripening process.

10. The standard plate count can detect <u>only</u> which of the following groups of organisms?
   a. anaerobic bacteria
   b. viruses
   c. aerobic bacteria
   d. yeasts

11. Grade A pasteurized milk may have no more than:
   a. 10,000 total bacteria and 10 coliforms/ml of milk.
   b. 20,000 total bacteria and 1 coliform/ml of milk.
   c. 10,000 total bacteria and 1 coliform/ml of milk.
   d. 20,000 total bacteria and 10 coliforms/ml of milk.

12. <u>Escherichia coli</u> causes a kind of spoilage of milk with the following distinctive characteristic(s):
   a. stringy or slimy milk.
   b. gray coloration and foul smell.
   c. curd formation with explosion of the curds.
   d. sour taste and curd formation.

13. Red rot of milk is caused by:
   a. <u>Clostridium</u> sp.
   b. <u>Serratia marcescens</u>.
   c. <u>Bacillus</u> sp.
   d. <u>Geotrichum</u> sp.

14. Lactose is:
   a. a monosaccharide found only in milk.
   b. one of the whey proteins.
   c. a disaccharide that can be digested by only a relatively few bacteria.
   d. a component of the butterfat removed in the skimming process.

15. The most heat-resistant contaminate of milk, which is eliminated by pasteurization, is:
   a. <u>Mycobacterium</u> <u>bovis</u>.
   b. <u>Bacillus</u> <u>sterothermophilus</u>.
   c. <u>Lactobacillus</u> <u>casei</u>.
   d. <u>Coxiella</u> <u>burnetii</u>.

ANSWERS TO EXERCISES

Pre-Test

1. c	6. c	11. d
2. c	7. c	12. a
3. b	8. b	13. c
4. a	9. c	14. a

5. c   10. a   15. c

Practice Exercises

1. a. gas production, gray rot; b. dairy mold; c. souring;

   d. ropiness, gas production; e. sweet curdling; f. ropiness;

   g. sweet curdling; h. gas production i. sweet curdling;

   j. red rot. (All answers to this exercise can be found in Table

   25.2.)

2. a. 7×10; b. 5×10^5.

3. a. 37,000/ml; b. 3100/ml; c. No (Both the total cell count

   and the coliform cell counts are much too high.); d. 19,800/ml

   (This number should probably be rounded off to 20,000/ml.)

4. a. F; b. T; c. T; d. F; e. T; f. T; g. F; h. T;

   i. F; j. F.

5. a. flash method; b. casein; c. gray rot (Table 25.2);

   d. brucellosis; e. phosphatase; f. reductase;

   g. antiobiotic detection test; h. cultured buttermilk;

   i. Bacillus subtilis; j. ropiness.

Concept Exercises

1. Violet-red bile agar is a selective medium for the detection of
   coliform bacteria such as Escherichia coli and Salmonella sp. It
   is important to detect these organisms because their presence
   suggests fecal contamination of the milk. The bile salts are
   added because they retard the growth of most bacteria but do not
   effect the growth of coliforms. Neutral red is added because it
   is taken up by coliforms giving a violet-purple color to their
   colonies. In addition, a thin layer of agar is poured over the
   plate before it is incubated to produce a semianaerobic environment, which also favors the growth of coliforms.

2. a. Tube 1 is the undiluted culture to be tested, Tube 2 is a
       $1:10^2$ dilution, Tube 3 is a $1:10^3$ dilution, Tube 4 is a
       $1:10^5$ dilution, and Tube 5 is a $1:10^6$ dilution.

   b. Each plate is essentially a 1:10 dilution of the corresponding
       tube. Therefore the total dilutions represented by each plate
       are: Plate 1, 1:10; Plate 2, $1:10^3$; Plate 3, $1:10^4$; and Plate

322

4, $1:10^6$; and Plate 5, $1:10^7$.

c. 2.76×10^8 cells/ml (or, rounded off, 2.8×10^8 cells/ml).

d. Plate 4 should be used. Plates 1-3 contain too many bacteria to allow counting of individual colonies. Plate 5 has too few colonies to be statistically significant.

3. Temperature should be kept low to retard bacterial growth. The number of bacteria should be low to reduce spoilage and the chance of pathogenic contamination. Coliform count is particularly important here because it is an indication of fecal contamination. If fecal contamination has occurred, the probability of Salmonella contamination is greatly increased. Contamination with inhibitory substances must be avoided because antibiotics may cause allergic reactions and disinfectants may be toxic. Phosphatase levels in pasteurized milk should be low to ensure the effectiveness of the pasteurization process in removing such pathogenic contaminants as Coxiella burnetii.

Post-Test

1. b	6. c	11. d
2. d	7. c	12. c
3. a	8. b	13. b
4. c	9. b	14. c
5. d	10. c	15. d

All the nitrogen in the world found in different nitrogenous compounds has its origin in the atmosphere, and . . . by far the greater part of it has been formed through the activity of micro-organisms.

> A. I. Virtanen (1947), quoted in K. V. Thimann, The Life of Bacteria, 2nd ed. New York: Macmillan, 1963.

CHAPTER OUTLINE

I.   Various Water Environments

   A.   Types of water

   B.   An unpolluted water environment

   C.   A polluted water environment

   D.   A marine environment

   E.   Types of water pollution

   F.   Diseases transmitted by water

II. Treatment of Water and Sewage

   A.   Water purification

   B.   Sewage treatment

III. Laboratory Microbiology of Water

   A.   Bacteriological analysis of water

IV. The Positive Role of Microorganisms in Water and Soil

   A.   The carbon cycle

   B.   The sulfur cycle

   C.   The nitrogen cycle

OVERVIEW AND OBJECTIVES

Water is the most abundant molecule on earth, and it is probably the most important compound to biological life. The amount of potable water is limited. Much of the water on earth is not available to living organisms because it is saltwater. In addition, much of the

water that is fresh has become polluted. We can purify contaminated
water, but we are learning that we must also protect available water
by not contaminating it in the first place. In this chapter, we will
examine the various types of polluted and unpolluted water environments, and the types of microscopic and macroscopic life forms each can
sustain. We will look at the methods for treating polluted and contaminated water to make it potable, and at the laboratory tests commonly used to test the purity of water. Our final consideration will
be of the essential role that water and soil microorganisms play in the
cycling of the essential elements into and out of the biological and
nonbiological worlds.

Three major types of water environments are discussed. The unpolluted freshwater environment has low concentrations of organic materials.
These bodies of water do not support large quantities of microbial
life, most of which are soil organisms that have been introduced
through runoff. Many autotrophic bacteria are found in these environments. Polluted water environments are high in organic materials.
They often contain much higher bacterial counts, and many heterotrophic forms are found. If fecal contamination is present, large
numbers of coliform bacteria may be present. The marine (saltwater)
environment is a third type, which supports an entirely different
group of microorganisms. These organisms are halophilic, which means
that they are able to grow in water containing high salt concentrations.
Most are also psychrophilic.

Pollutants of water can be divided into three groups: (1) physical
pollutants, which include particulate matter and make the water cloudy;
(2) Chemical pollutants, which include laundry detergents, acids, and
radioactive wastes from domestic and industrial sources; and (3)
Biological pollutants, which include organisms that utilize oxygen
and may turnstagnant water into an anaerobic environment. The amount
of biological pollution in a body of water can be estimated by
determining the biochemical oxygen demand (BOD) of a water sample.

Biologically contaminated water may be a source of disease because
it harbors the causative bacterial, viral, and protozoan organisms.
Because of possible contamination with these pathogenic organisms,
the purity of water must be ensured through water treatment and testing.
Drinking water is purified before distribution to the public, and
sewage is removed from water before it is released to rejoin the
natural water table. Several methods are used to assess the bacterial
content of water. Membrane filter techniques and standard plate count
techniques are used to estimate the number of bacteria in water
samples. The most probable number (MPN) method is also used. This
method is a fairly quick way to estimate the number of coliforms,
which are often present in low numbers. The presence of these
organisms indicate fecal contamination.

Bacteria are essential in the cycling of important elements (including carbon, sulfur, and nitrogen) through the biological world.
They are the initial organisms in the decomposition of dead tissues
and the release of these elements into the environment so that they
become available for the production of new living biological tissue.

In addition, they are essential in the primary processing of sulfur
and nitrogen into forms that can be used by higher organisms to produce new biological material. Photosynthetic microorganisms also contribute significantly to the total fixation of carbon into carbohydrate.

After you have read Chapter 26 of your textbook, you should be
able to:

1. Define or identify the following terms: groundwater, surface
   water, contaminated, polluted, potability, actinomycetes, autotrophic, heterotrophic, coliform bacteria, halophilic, psychrophilic, barophilic, oceanic zone, littoral zone, benthic zone,
   abyssal zone, physical pollution, eutrophication, chemical pollution, biological pollution, biochemical oxygen demand (BOD),
   sedimentation, flocs, flocculation, filtration, slow sand filter,
   schmutzdecke, rapid sand filter, chlorine, privy, cesspool, septic
   tank, oxidation lagoons, primary treatment, secondary treatment,
   sludge tanks, tertiary treatment, membrane filter technique,
   standard plate count technique (SPC), most probable number (MPN),
   carbon cycle, sulfur cycle, nitrogen cycle, Nitrosomonas,
   Nitrobacter, Rhizobium, and legumes.

2. Describe the various water environments and the types of organisms
   each will support.

3. Characterize the various types of water pollution and the consequences to the water environment of each.

4. Outline the methods of water purification and sewage treatment.

5. Describe the major methods for testing the biological purity of
   water.

6. Outline the carbon, sulfur, and nitrogen cycles. Include the
   genera of bacteria that are important in each and, where appropriate, the reactions they carry out in the cycle.

PRE-TEST

1. In one method for estimating the biological purity of water,
   samples of water are taken, dilutions are made, and these dilutions
   are plated on agar medium and incubated. This method is called
   the:
   a. membrane filter technique.
   b. most probable number.
   c. standard plate count technique.
   d. secondary treatment technique.

2. Escherichia coli is most probably found in a:
   a. nonpolluted water environment.
   b. polluted water environment.
   c. marine water environment.
   d. benthic water environment.

3. Eutrophication is a term used to describe:
   a. the chemical pollution of a freshwater environment.
   b. a condition caused by the upsetting of the ecological balance through pollution.
   c. the abyssal zone of a marine environment.
   d. a condition associated with the overgrowth of dinoflagellates, commonly known as the "red tide."

4. All of the following viral diseases are commonly transmitted by polluted water, except:
   a. type A hepatitis.
   b. Coxsackie viruses.
   c. type A herpes virus.
   d. ECHO viruses.

5. Which of the following sequences is used in the purification of water?
   a. Sedimentation ⟶ chlorination ⟶ filtration.
   b. Flocculation ⟶ filtration ⟶ chlorination.
   c. Sedimentation ⟶ flocculation ⟶ chlorination.
   d. Chlorination ⟶ flocculation ⟶ filtration.

6. In the treatment of sewage, sludge tanks:
   a. take advantage of anaerobic bacteria to digest sedimented material.
   b. use aerobic bacteria to digest sewage.
   c. encourage the growth of yeast to oxidize the liquid phase of sewage.
   d. collect sedimented material that cannot be digested by micro-organisms.

7. Desulfovibrio species (a-c) convert or (d) fix:
   a. sulfide to sulfate.
   b. nitrate to nitrite.
   c. sulfur to hydrogen sulfide.
   d. nitrogen as ammonia.

8. Legumes develop symbiotic relationships with nitrogen-fixing bacteria belonging to the genus:
   a. Nitrosomonas.
   b. Nitrobacter.
   c. Rhizobium.
   d. Azotobacter.

9. All of the following genera of bacteria are capable of releasing sulfur from hydrogen sulfide, except:
   a. Thiobacillus.
   b. Beggiatoa.
   c. Desulfovibrio.
   d. Thiothrix.

10. Water found in lakes, streams, and shallow wells is called:
   a. groundwater.
   b. benthic water.

c.   unpolluted water.
d.   surface water.

11. The BOD of a water sample is a measure of the:
    a.   chemical pollution of a water environment.
    b.   oxygen requirement by the metabolism of organisms in the water
         environment.
    c.   amount of particulate matter dissolved in a water environment.
    d.   biological oxidation of detergent pollution in a water environ-
         ment.

12. Microorganisms found on the ocean floor are said to be found in
    the _____ zone.
    a.   oceanic
    b.   benthic
    c.   abyssal
    d.   barophilic

13. In an MPN test the following results are obtained. Two lactose
    broth tubes containing 10 ml of the water sample and one tube con-
    taining 1 ml of the sample were found to be producing gas. These
    results tell you that the number of coliform organisms is most
    probably (see Table 26.2):
    a.   7.6.
    b.   7.
    c.   5.
    d.   unknown.

14. Barophilic organisms:
    a.   are salt-loving.
    b.   grow best at low temperatures.
    c.   are pressure-loving.
    d.   found on the ocean floor.

15. A free-living bacterium capable of fixing nitrogen is:
    a.   Rhizobium.
    b.   Spirillum.
    c.   Thiobacillus.
    d.   Beggiatoa.

1. Below is a pictorial representation of the nitrogen cycle. Identify the group of organisms that carries out each of the indicated steps by writing its name or description in the space provided. Be as specific as you can.

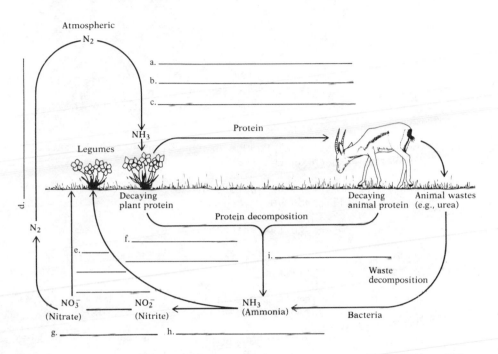

2. The following results are obtained in an MPN test of a water sample. Using Table 26.2, determine the number of coliform organisms in the sample.

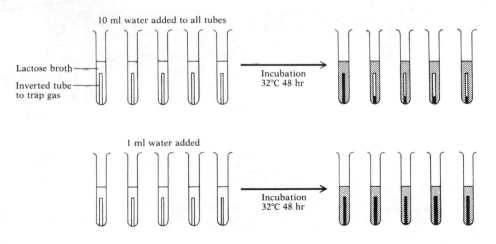

0.1 ml water added

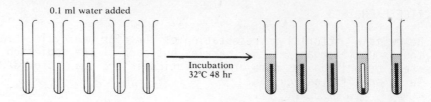

Incubation
32°C 48 hr

3. True or False. Identify each of the following statements as true
or false by placing a T for true or an F for false on the line
provided.

____ a. Non-coliform bacteria produce green colonies with a metallic
fluorescent sheen on EMB agar.

____ b. Fecal coliforms ferment lactose at 44.5°C, whereas nonfecal
coliforms fail to do so.

____ c. Potability refers to the drinkability of water.

____ d. Actinomycetes are typically found in unpolluted water environments.

____ e. Acids are a problem in the pollution of water because bacteria
may convert sulfur or sulfates in water to sulfuric acid.

____ f. The red tide is caused when halophilic bacteria grow to high
numbers in the oceanic zone.

____ g. Heterotrophic bacteria are often found in unpolluted water
environments.

____ h. Flocculation is a process whereby flocs are added to water to
help in the sedimentation of bulky objects.

____ i. A schmutzdecke is a layer of microorganisms that act as an
additional filter in a slow sand filter.

____ j. Thiobacillus is among the genera of bacteria that are able to
convert sulfur to hydrogen sulfide.

4. Each of the following is a description of results that may be
obtained in one of the laboratory tests of the microbiological
purity of water. In a short statement explain what conclusions
can be drawn from each set of data.

a. A number of lactose broth tubes showed gas production when
inoculated with a water sample and incubated at 37°C. When a

330

number of similar tubes were inoculated with a sample of the
same water and incubated at 44.5°C, none showed gas production.

_____   _____

_____

_____

b. One-tenth milliliter of water is spread on an eosin methylene
blue agar plate and incubated. Twenty-two green colonies with
a fluorescent sheen and 87 pink and white colonies without
sheen grow up.

_____

_____

_____

c. One hundred milliliters of water are filtered onto a membrane
filter. The filter pad is transferred to a plate containing
nutrient agar and incubated. Thirty-eight colonies grow up.

_____   ___ _____

_____   ___ _____

_____   _____   _____

d. A dilution series of a water sample is prepared. Each tube is
a 1:10 dilution of the previous tube. The first tube contains
the undiluted water sample. One-tenth milliliter of each tube
is plated onto a nutrient agar plate and incubated. After incubation the plate containing the 0.1 ml sample of the fourth
tube shows 49 colonies.

_____   _____

_____   ___ _____

_____

5. Identify each of the following organisms as typical to

1. unpolluted water environments,

2. polluted water environments, or

3. marine environments,

by placing the appropriate number(s) on the line provided.

a. Actinomycetes: _____

b. Escherichia coli: _____

c. Clostridium spores: _____

d. Clostridium species vegetative cells: _____

e. Halophilic organisms: _____

f. Desulfovibrio: _____

g. Blue-green algae: _____

h. Diatoms: _____

i. Cellulose digesters: _____

j. Autotrophic bacteria: _____

k. Heterotrophic bacteria: _____

l. Enteric viruses: _____

6. Each of the following groups of bacteria is involved in one or more of the carbon, sulfur, and nitrogen cycles. Write the reaction(s) that each carries out in these cycles.

a. Desulfovibrio:

_____

b. Microorganisms that are the primary decayers of animal and plant material:

_____

c. Rhizobium:

_____

d. Thiobacillus:

_____

e. Nitrosomonas:

_____

f. Nitrobacter:

_____

CONCEPT EXERCISES

1. Refer to the quotation of Louis Pasteur that introduced Chapter 5.

In light of the information contained in this chapter of your textbook, explain Pasteur's statement.

_____

_____

_____

_____

_____

_____

2. There have been many reports in the news media recently of improper
   dumping of toxic chemical wastes. Why is such dumping a potential
   health hazard?

   _____

   _____

   _____

3. Escherichia coli is a common inhabitant of the human digestive
   tract. Under normal conditions it does not cause disease, yet the
   majority of laboratory microbiology tests are designed to identify
   E. coli in water. Why?

   _____

   _____

   _____

   _____

   _____

POST-TEST

1. Ten milliliters of a water sample are filtered through a membrane
   filter. After incubation of the filter pad on EMB agar, 32 green
   colonies with a fluorescent metallic sheen develop. The concentration of coliform bacteria in the original water sample was:
   a. 32 bacteria/ml.
   b. 3.2 bacteria/ml.
   c. 320 bacteria/ml.
   d. undetermined, because coliforms will not grow on EMB.

2. A water sample is mixed with a sample of water having a known
   amount of dissolved oxygen. This mixture is placed in a bottle,

stoppered, and incubated at 20°C for five days. This test will measure the water's:
a. BOD.
b. SPC.
c. MPN.
d. EMB.

3. All of the following genera of bacteria carry out the reaction

$$H_2S \longrightarrow SO_4^=,$$

except:
a. Thiobacillus.
b. Beggiatoa.
c. Thiothrix.
d. Desulfovibrio.

4. Legumes are:
a. bacteria capable of carrying out the reaction

$$N_2 \longrightarrow NH_3.$$
b. plants that bear their seeds in pods.
c. plants which have a symbiotic relationship with bacteria that carry out the reaction

$$SO_4^= \longrightarrow H_2S.$$
d. bacteria that decompose carbohydrate with the release of CO_2.

5. The primary treatment of sewage in mechanized sewage treatment facilities is designed to:
a. sediment bacteria and debris.
b. anaerobically ferment sludge.
c. aerobically digest the liquid phase of sewage.
d. separate the digested sludge from water, wich may be treated further.

6. Besides testing water for coliforms such as Escherichia coli, modern laboratories also directly test water for:
a. fecal streptococci.
b. hepatitis virus.
c. Yersinia species.
d. Salmonella species.

7. The most abundant element or molecule in the earth's atmosphere is:
a. CO_2.
b. O_2.
c. N_2.
d. S_2.

8. Sulfur is derived from decaying material through the digestion of:
a. carbohydrates.

b. nucleic acids.
c. proteins.
d. cellulose.

9. A common form of bacteria found in unpolluted water environments
   is _____ bacteria.
   a. halophilic
   b. autotrophic
   c. barophilic
   d. heterotrophic

10. Cellulomonas is:
    a. an actinomycete often found in unpolluted water environments.
    b. usually found only in polluted waters, where it feeds on the
       high concentrations of organic material.
    c. is a halophilic, psychrophilic, and barophilic organism often
       found in the benthic zone.
    d. found in unpolluted water environments, where it digests cel-
       lulose contained in plant cell walls.

11. Potability is used to describe:
    a. the level of pollution in a water sample.
    b. contaminated water that is not polluted.
    c. the drinkability of water.
    d. the BOD of a water sample.

12. Nitrosomonas carries out which one of the following reactions?

    a. $NO_2^- \longrightarrow NO_3^-$.

    b. $NO_3^- \longrightarrow N_2$.

    c. $N_2 \longrightarrow NH_3$.

    d. $NH_3 \longrightarrow NO_2^-$.

13. All of the following release CO_2 into the atmosphere, except:
    a. combustion of coal.
    b. respiration in the ocean.
    c. respiration of land plants.
    d. photosynthesis of land plants.

14. Blood of the horseshoe crab is used in a sensitive assay for:
    a. exotoxin and therefore gram(+) bacteria.
    b. endotoxin and therefore gram(-) bacteria.
    c. endotoxin and therefore gram(+) bacteria.
    d. exotoxin and therefore gram(-) bacteria.

15. Laundry detergents are important chemical pollutants because they:
    a. cloud water, reducing light penetration and photosynthesis.
    b. reduce the surface tension of water and inhibit the growth of
       microorganisms at the surface.
    c. add large amounts of phosphates and nitrates to water, which
       can lead to overgrowth of green algae.

d.   increase the pH of water, leading to increased bacterial growth.

ANSWERS TO EXERCISES

Pre-Test

1. c	6. a	11. b
2. b	7. c	12. b
3. b	8. c	13. a
4. c	9. c	14. c
5. b	10. d	15. b

Practice Exercises

1. a.   nitrogen fixing bacteria; b. yeasts; c. blue-green bacteria;

   d.   various microorganisms; e. nitrate utilization by plants;

   f.   ammonia utilization by plants; g. Nitrobacter species;

   h.   Nitrosomonas species; i. bacteria. (All answers to this

   exercise can be found in Figure 26.22.)

2. 20 (Table 26.2).

3. a.   F; b. T; c. T; d. T; e. T; f. F; g. F; h. T;

   i. T; j. F.

4. a.   The water sample contains bacteria capable of fermenting lactose with the production of gas, but none of these are fecal coliforms.

   b.   The water sample contains a concentration of 220 Escherichia
   coli/ml and 870 non-E. coli bacteria/ml. The total number of
   bacteria in a milliliter of the water is 1090.

   c.   The 38 colonies represent the number of bacteria in 100 ml
   of the original water sample. Therefore the concentration of
   bacteria in one milliliter of that water sample is 0.32.

   d.   The sample of the fourth tube has a total dilution factor of
   1:10,000 (1:1000 in the dilution tube and an additional 1:10 dilution from plating only 0.1 ml). Therefore the number of bacteria
   in 1 ml of the original water sample is 4.9×10^5.

5. a.   1; b. 2; c. 1; d. 2; e. 3; f. 2; g. 2; h. 3;

   i. 1; j. 1; k. 2; 1. 2. (All answers to this exercise can be found in Table 26.1.)

6. a. $SO_4^= \longrightarrow H_2S$.

   b. Organic sulfur in amino acids $\longrightarrow SO_4^=$, Organic carbon CO_2, and Organic nitrogen $\longrightarrow NH_3$.

   c. $N_2 \longrightarrow NH_3$.

   d. $H_2S \longrightarrow S_2$ and $S_2 \longrightarrow SO_4^=$.

   e. $NH_3 \longrightarrow NO_2^-$.

   f. $NO_2^- \longrightarrow NO_3^-$.

Concept Exercises

1. Bacteria play key roles in the carbon, nitrogen, and sulfur cycles; if bacteria were eliminated from the environment, the biologically available forms of these compounds would soon be tied up in dead biological material. None would be available to create new living material, and life would cease to exist.

2. These materials can seep into groundwater and from there, either directly or by way of surface water, into the drinking water supply of both nearby and more distant communities.

3. Escherichia coli is an excellent detector of fecal contamination because of its ecological nitch in the digestive tract of most mammals. If E. coli is found, it can be assumed that the water may be contaminated with several pathogenic forms (such as the agents of typhoid fever, cholera, and bacterial dysentery) that are found in feces and are more difficult to detect because of their lower concentrations in contaminated water.

Post-Test

1. b	6. a	11. c
2. a	7. c	12. d
3. d	8. c	13. d
4. b	9. b	14. b
5. a	10. d	15. c

So far as the helminths in general and those of man in particular are concerned, I believe that Egypt is one of the most suitable countries for their development and study. . . . The tapeworm is so common that the Abyssinian considers it abnormal when no tapeworm segments pass from him. . . . The frequency of the tapeworm in Abyssinia is ascribed to the ingestion of raw meat; people who refrain therefrom--Schimper, our compatriot, for instance--supposedly have been spared. Is it possible that the tapeworm embryos choose animal tissue as a vehicle while the round worms are ingested chiefly through plant food? Insofar as I remember, in Europe, the Ascaris lumbricoides and pin worms are attributed to spoiled flour and bread; here in Egypt the population consumes many vegetables (especially raw leaves and roots) and is plagued in particular by round worms.

> Theodore Bilharz in a letter to C. T. von Siebold, 1 May, 1851. From B. H. Kean, K. E. Mott, and A. J. Russell (eds.), Tropical Medicine and Parasitology, Ithaca, N.Y.: Cornell University Press, 1978.

CHAPTER OUTLINE

I. General Principles

II. Roundworms

    A. Pinworm disease

    B. Whipworm disease

    C. Roundworm disease

    D. Trichinosis

    E. Hookworm disease

    F. Filariasis

    G. Eyeworm disease

III. Flatworms

    A. Beef and pork tapeworm disease

    B. Dwarf tapeworm disease

    C. Dog tapeworm disease

    D. Fish tapeworm disease

E.   Intestinal fluke disease

F.   Liver fluke disease

G.   Chinese liver fluke disease

H.   Blood fluke disease

OVERVIEW AND OBJECTIVES

Parasitology is the study of disease caused by protozoa and multicellular parasites. We discussed the protozoa in Chapter 12, and in this
chapter we will discuss the multicellular parasites, collectively known
as roundworms and flatworms. Although these organisms are classified
in two phyla of the animal kingdom, the Nemathelminthes and the
Platyhelminthes, respectively, we will discuss them because they cause
infectious disease.

The roundworms, or nematodes, are ubiquitous in nature in great
numbers, as the above quote points out. They cause a number of diseases
of humans who are often the definitive host for these animals. The
definitive host is the organism in which the adult form is found. Many
of these animals also have intermediate hosts, in which the immature
forms develop. The intermediate hosts are often other mammals but are
sometimes insects or other forms of life.

Often the symptoms associated with parasitic disease are general
in nature and the specific diseases are often difficult to diagnose.
Pinworm disease is found worldwide and is the most widespread parasitic
disease of humans. The parasite lives in the small intestine and
causes anal itching and diarrhea. Roundworm disease is the second
most prevalent parasitic disease, after pinworm disease, in the United
States. It is caused by the largest of the intestinal nematodes
Ascaris lumbricoides. The use of human feces for fertilizer in many
parts of the world increases the spread of this disease through the
ingestion of contaminated vegetables. One of the most dangerous of
the roundworm diseases is trichinosis, caused by the nematode Trichinella spiralis. This disease is acquired by eating undercooked pork,
as the pig is the other host for the organism. The adult animal lives
in the gastrointestinal tract and causes diarrhea and other symptoms.
Larvae may migrate into the muscles where cysts may form. This can
interfere with breathing, and eye movement, and cause pain. Other
roundworm diseases of humans include whipworm disease, hookworm disease, filariasis, and eyeworm disease.

The parasitic flatworms include the tapeworms and the flukes. The
adult flatworm consists of a scolex, or head, a neck, and a series of
segments called proglottids. The worms are hermaphroditic, with sex
organs of both sexes present in the same worm. Some species of tapeworms may reach lengths of up to 25 feet in the intestine. They may
cause obstruction of the gastrointestinal tract, but they usually
cause few symptoms and may remain with the host for many years. The
beef and pork tapeworms are among the most common. They are acquired
by eating poorly cooked meat of infected animals. Another tapeworm,

the _dwarf_ tapeworm, is the most common cestode in humans and is prevalent in the United States. It is only 25 mm in length. Other tapeworms discussed are the _dog tapeworm_, which may infect humans who come
in contact with infected dogs, and the _fish tapeworm_, which is acquired
from eating raw or poorly cooked fish.

The _flukes_ are the second group of cestodes that commonly cause
human disease. Severe damage to the liver can be caused by _liver fluke_
disease. This fluke is commonly found in sheep and cattle and has a
particular species of freshwater snail as the intermediate host. It
is acquired by eating contaminated vegetation, such as watercress.
Schistosomiasis (also called _blood fluke_ disease and _bilharzia_) is
caused by at least three species of flukes. This disease is common in
the United States. The intermediate host is again the snail and the
parasite can be acquired by swimming in contaminated water. Other important diseases caused by flukes are _intestinal fluke_ disease and
Chinese liver fluke disease.

After you have read Chapter 27 of your textbook, you should be
able to:

1. Define or identify the following terms: _Nemathelminthes_, _Platy-
   helminthes_, helminth, definitive host, pinworm disease, _Enterobius
   vermicularis_, whipworm disease, _Trichuris trichiura_, roundworm
   disease, _Ascaris lumbricoides_, night soil, trichinosis, _Trichinella
   spiralis_, cyst, hookworm disease, _Ancylostoma duodenale_, _Necator
   americanus_, rhabditiform larvae, filariform larvae, filariasis,
   Wuchereria bancrofti, elephantiasis, microfilariae, eyeworm disease,
   Loa loa, hermaphroditic, cestode, tapeworm, scolex, proglottid,
   gravid proglottid, trematodes, flukes, miracidium, metacercaria,
   cercaria, _Taenia saginata_, _Taenia solium_, _Hymenolepsis nana_,
   Echinococcus granulosus, hydatid cyst, _Diphyllobothrium latum_,
   copepod, _Fasciolepsis buski_, _Fasciola hepatica_, _Clonorchis sinensis_,
   Schistosoma mansoni, _Schistosoma japonicum_, _Schistosomahaematobium_
   schistosomiasis, and bilharzia.

2. Describe the general taxonomic features of the _Nemathelminthes_ and
   the _Platyhelminthes_.

3. Identify the various roundworms that cause the diseases of humans
   discussed, the disease each causes, and their alternative hosts
   (where appropriate).

4. Identify the various cestodes and trematodes that cause the diseases of humans discussed, the disease each causes, and the
   alternative host(s) of each.

PRE-TEST

1. The trematodes are commonly called:
   a. tapeworms.
   b. roundworms.
   c. pinworms.
   d. flukes.

2. The gravid proglottids are the:
   a. head sections of a tapeworm.
   b. middle segments of a tapeworm.
   c. the distal segments of a tapeworm containing fertilized eggs.
   d. the proximal segments of a tapeworm, which are the newest segments.

3. The most common roundworm disease in the United States is:
   a. pinworm disease.
   b. roundworm disease.
   c. trichinosis.
   d. whipworm disease.

4. Hardened shells that form around the larvae of many roundworms and flatworms are called:
   a. copepods.
   b. scolexes.
   c. proglottids.
   d. cysts.

5. Ascaris lumbricoides is:
   a. the largest intestinal nematode and the cause of roundworm disease.
   b. found in the southern United States and causes pinworm disease.
   c. found in pork and causes trichinosis.
   d. a nematode with an anterior end resembling a buggy whip and causes whipworm disease.

6. Animals that are termed hermaphroditic:
   a. have alternating male and female generations.
   b. are female when young and become male as they age.
   c. have both male and female sex organs.
   d. reproduce by asexual mechanisms.

7. Taenia solium is the _____ tapeworm.
   a. beef
   b. dog
   c. fish
   d. pork

8. Blood fluke disease is caused by _____ species.
   a. Fasciola
   b. Tasciolopsis
   c. Schistosoma
   d. Clonorchis

9. The snail is an alternative host for the organisms that cause all of the following diseases, except _____ disease.
   a. blood fluke
   b. intestinal fluke
   c. fish tapeworm
   d. liver fluke

10. A disease acquired by eating undercooked pork is:

341

a.   trichinosis.
b.   pinworm disease.
c.   Chinese liver fluke disease.
d.   filariasis.

11. Elephantiasis is:
a.   caused by <u>Ancylostoma</u> <u>duodenale</u>.
b.   a condition where the legs and scrotum become swollen and
     distorted with lymph fluid.
c.   associated with liver fluke disease.
d.   a symptom of diseases acquired from eating beef and pork.

12. The roundworms are classified in the phylum:
a.   <u>Nemathelminthes</u>.
b.   <u>Platyhelminthes</u>.
c.   <u>Trichinella</u>.
d.   <u>Clonorchis</u> <u>sinensis</u>.

13. Copepods are an alternative host for the:
a.   dog tapeworm.
b.   eyeworm.
c.   fish tapeworm.
d.   Chinese liver fluke.

14. Eyeworm disease is caused by:
a.   <u>Trichinella</u> <u>spiralis</u>.
b.   <u>Clonorchis</u> <u>sinensis</u>.
c.   <u>Loa</u> <u>loa</u>.
d.   <u>Ancylostroma</u> <u>duodenale</u>.

15. Microfilariae are:
a.   eel-like embryos of some roundworms.
b.   rod-shaped larvae of roundworms.
c.   rod-shaped larvae of flatworms.
d.   the neck segments of tapeworms.

PRACTICE EXERCISES

1. <u>True or False</u>. Decide whether each of the following statements
   is true or false; then place a T for true or an F for false on the
   line provided.

_____ a. Trematodes are a group of flatworms usually referred to as
          tapeworms.

_____ b. A tapeworm that reaches only 25 mm in length is <u>Hymenolepsis</u>
          <u>nana</u>.

_____ c. <u>Clonorchis</u> <u>sinensis</u>, the Chinese liver fluke, can be transmit-
          ted to humans who eat raw or poorly cooked freshwater fish.

_____ d. Bilharzia is another name for liver fluke disease.

_____ e. A definitive host of a parasite is the one in which the adult,

342

sexually mature form resides.

_____ f. Parasitology is the study of all organisms that cause infectious disease.

_____ g. Rhabditiform larvae are a hairlike or threadlike form of the hookworm.

_____ h. The metacercaria is an encysted form of flukes, which is released from snails and finds its way to the human host.

_____ i. Loa loa is a nematode that can be seen in the cornea of the eye of an infected person.

_____ j. The beef tapeworm may reach 25 feet in length.

2. Animals often act as intermediate hosts for roundworms and flatworms. Identify at least one animal host for the organisms that cause each of the following diseases.

a. Beef tapeworm disease:

_____

b. Chinese liver fluke disease:

_____

c. Filariasis:

_____

d. Pork tapeworm disease:

_____

e. Trichinosis:

_____

f. Hookworm disease:

_____

g. Fish tapeworm disease:

_____

h. Blood fluke disease:

_____

i. Eyeworm disease:

j. Liver fluke disease:

3. In one or two sentences, distinguish between each term of the following pairs.

   a. Trematode/cestode:

   b. Miracidium/metacercaria:

   c. Rhabditiform larvae/filariform larvae:

   d. Nemathelminthes/Platyhelminthes:

   e. Definitive host/intermediate host:

   f. Scolex/proglottid:

4. Matching. Match the organism in the left-hand column with the disease it causes in the right-hand column. Entries in the right-hand column may be used more than once or not at all. (You may wish to review Table 27.3 before answering this exercise.)

____ a.	Trichuris trichiura	1. Blood fluke disease
____ b.	Schistosoma mansoni	2. Beef tapeworm disease
		3. Roundworm disease
____ c.	Loa loa	4. Whipworm disease
____ d.	Anculostroma duodenale	5. Fish tapeworm disease
____ e.	Taenia saginata	6. Pork tapeworm disease
____ f.	Schistosoma japonicum	7. Eyeworm disease
		8. Trichinosis
____ g.	Trichinella spiralis	9. Hookworm disease
____ h.	Ascaris lumbricoides	10. Filariasis
____ i.	Necator americanus	
____ j.	Taenia solium	

5. Fill in the blanks. The diagnosis of parasitic diseases may be difficult because unique (a) _____ rarely are present. Identification of the (b) _____ in (c) _____ _____ _____ such as the (d) _____ _____ is often the key to a correct diagnosis. This usually requires a (e) _____. Treatment generally consists of (f) _____ the worm burden to a (g) _____ _____ _____, since complete (h) _____ _____ of the parasite is not always possible. Various drugs are available to treat parasitic diseases, but they are often (i) _____ to body tissues.

CONCEPT EXERCISES

1. The way in which pigs are raised is important in the control of trichinosis. European practices have led to a much lower incidence of the disease there than occur in the United States. What precautions can be taken to reduce the frequency of trichinosis in pork?

_____

_____

_____

_____

_____

2. As discussed in Chapter 27 of your text, complete elimination of parasites from an infected person is often impossible. This is due, at least in part, to the small number of drugs available for the treatment of these diseases. What characteristics of these pathogenic organisms make their elimination so difficult?

_____ _____

_____

_____

3. Look at some of the pictures of tapeworms in your textbook. You will note that they are fairly complex multicellular animals, yet they have no mouth or digestive system. How does a tapeworm acquire food from the parasitic relationship it enjoys with its host?

_____ _____

_____

_____

POST-TEST

1. A disease transmitted by the eating of raw or poorly cooked fish is:
   a. Chinese liver fluke disease.
   b. trichinosis
   c. filariasis.
   d. blood fluke disease.

2. Whipworm disease is often accompanied by:
   a. appendicitis-like pain.
   b. rash.
   c. liver disease.
   d. intestinal obstruction.

3. Enterobius vermicularis causes:
   a. whipworm disease.
   b. roundworm disease.
   c. trichinosis.
   d. pinworm disease.

4. A roundworm disease transmitted by mosquitos is:
   a. eyeworm disease.
   b. filariasis.
   c. hookworm disease.
   d. whipworm disease.

5. Contact with dogs and other canines can transmit a disease caused by:
   a. Trichinella spiralis.
   b. Schistosoma japonicum.
   c. Echinococcus granulosus.
   d. Taenia saginata.

6. Trichinosis is a disease that in the United States, is most often acquired from meat whose source is a:
   a. restaurant or other public eating place.
   b. supermarket, butcher shop, or other commercial outlet.
   c. farm directly.
   d. hunter or trapper.

7. Helminths is a term applied to:
   a. parasitic roundworms.
   b. parasitic protozoa.
   c. parasitic flatworms.
   d. all multicellular parasites.

8. The head region of the flatworm is referred to as the:
   a. proglottid.
   b. miracidium.
   c. scolex.
   d. gravid proglottid.

9. Fasciola hepatica:
   a. is the causative agent of liver fluke disease.
   b. infects the gastrointestinal tract, where it may grow to 25 feet in length.
   c. is one of the species of flukes that cause bilharzia.
   d. causes the most common roundworm disease in the United States.

10. The beef tapeworm is:
    a. Taenia solium.
    b. Trichinella spiralis.
    c. Trichuris trichiura.
    d. Taenia saginata.

11. Cestodes are:
    a. nematodes.
    b. flukes.
    c. tapeworms.
    d. roundworms.

12. Hymenolepsis nana is:
    a. only 25 mm long and causes dwarf tapeworm disease.
    b. transmitted to humans by the eating of raw or poorly cooked fish.

c. often 25 feet long in the adult form and is transmitted to humans when they eat poorly cooked beef.

d. one of several species that causes hookworm disease.

13. The eggs of flukes first develop into a ciliated form called a
   a. metacercarium.
   b. miracidium.
   c. cercarium.
   d. microfilarium.

14. The trematode that causes intestinal fluke disease is:
   a. Fasciloa hepatica and is commonly found in sheep and cattle.
   b. the largest trematode occurring in humans, its length often reaching 8 cm.
   c. common to the United States, where more than 400,000 cases are known.
   d. transmitted by the eating of raw fish and is classified under the name Clonorchis sinensis.

15. Elephantiasis is:
   a. often associated with diseases caused by flukes.
   b. characteristic of filariasis.
   c. caused by Schistosoma mansoni.
   d. a disease that can have the elephant as an intermediate host.

ANSWERS TO EXERCISES

Pre-Test

1. d	6. c	11. b
2. c	7. d	12. a
3. a	8. c	13. c
4. d	9. c	14. c
5. a	10. a	15. a

Practice Exercises

1. a. F; b. T; c. T; d. F; e. T; f. F; g. F; h. T;
   i. T; j. T.

2. a. cattle; b. snail, fish; c. mosquito; d. pig; e. pig;
   f. dogs, cats; g. copepods, fish; h. snail; i. insects
   (deer fly, horse fly); j. snail. (All answers to this exercise
   can be found in Table 27.3.)

3. a. Trematodes are flukes, but cestodes are tapeworms;

b. A miracidium is the ciliated form that develops from the egg
    of a fluke; a metacercaria is an encysted form of the fluke
    released by the intermediate host (the snail).

c. Rhabditiform larvae are rod shaped and are the first form to
    emerge from the hookworm egg. Filariform larvae are hairlike
    or threadlike and develop from rhabditiform larve.

d. Nemathelminthes is the phylum name of the roundworms, while
    Platyhelminthes is the phylum name of the flatworms.

e. The definitive host harbors the adult, sexually mature form,
    but the intermediate host harbors the larval forms.

f. The scolex is the head region of a tapeworm; the proglottid
    is the name given to the bodysegments of the flatworm.

4. a. 4; b. 1; c. 7; d. 9; e. 2; f. 1; g. 8. h. 3;

   i. 9; j. 6.   (All answers to this exercise can be found in

   Table 27.3.)

4. a. symptoms; b. eggs; c. body specimens; d. feces;

   e. parasitologist; f. reducing; g. manageable level;

   h. eradication; i. toxic.

Concept Exercises

1. Pigs usually become infected with trichinosis by coming in contact
   with and ingesting human feces from infected persons. Pigs can
   be raised by methods that minimize this contact. In Europe, pigs
   are not fed with scraps and other garbage but are fed with food
   stuffs less likely to come in contact with human feces. This and
   other practices have reduced the frequency of trichinosis to a
   level that allows many Europeans to feel safe in eating rarer pork
   than would be considered safe in the United States.

2. As with the protozoan diseases, the parasite, as well as the host,
   is a eukaryote. This reduces the number of drugs and other treatments that can be used against the parasite without harm to the
   host.

3. The tapeworm obtains its nourishment by simply holding onto the
   lining of the gastrointestinal tract and absorbing nutriments from
   the intestine through its skin.

Post-Test

1. a 2. a 3. d 4. b 5. c 6. b 7. d 8. c 9. a 10. d

11. c 12. a 13. b 14. b 15. b

In reviewing the history and current state of industrial microbiology we are struck by an abiding theme: mutually beneficial relations between what we have come to call basic research and applied research. A century ago the largely practical investigations of Pasteur led to the establishment of microbiology, immunology and biochemistry. Much later the discovery of antibiotics by applied microbiologists provided tools crucial to the development of molecular biology. And now basic research in microbial genetics has returned the favor by supplying an array of new techniques for industrial applications. This synergy between science and technology, we believe, is the key to further progress in industrial microbiology.

Arnold L. Demain and Madine A. Solomon,
"Industrial Microbiology," Scientific American,
245 (no. 3):67-74, 1981.

CHAPTER OUTLINE

I. Microorganisms in Industry

A. Growth processes

II. Production of Organic Compounds

A. Organic acids

B. Amino acids and vitamins

C. Enzymes

D. Steroid transformations

E. Gibberellins

III. Alcoholic Beverage

A. Beer

B. Wine

C. Distilled spirits

IV. Other Products of Microorganisms

A. Antibiotics

B. Insecticides

OVERVIEW AND OBJECTIVES

Industrial microbiology began in the Neolithic period with the fermentation of beer, wine, bread, and cheese. Understanding of the process began with the experiments of Pasteur, who determined that the fermentation of wine was caused by the metabolic processes of yeasts. Today, the list of microbially produced products has expanded and includes yogurt, pickles, sauerkraut, single-cell protein, antibiotics, vitamins, and other industrial products. In this chapter, we will review several of these products and the organisms that produce them.

Industrial fermentations technically are any of a number of chemical transformations of organic compounds that are aided by enzymes (particularly those made by microorganisms). In most of these processes, the organic molecules to be converted are added to the culture medium in which the microorganism(s) is (are) being grown, and the products are harvested from the medium after growth of the organism(s) has taken place. These cultures may be either batch, in which a large tank is filled with the medium and the fermentation takes place, or continuous flow, in which the medium containing the compound to be fermented is continuously added to the incubation vessels to replace medium that has been fermented.

Many organic compounds are produced in this manner. Organic acids are produced by a number of bacterial fermentations. One of the most familiar is vinegar, which is produced by the fermentation of ethanol to acetic acid by Acetobacter aceti. Amino acids and vitamins are also produced for use as foodsupplements. Enzymes such as amylase, pectinase, and proteases are produced by bacterial and fungal fermentations for use in industrial processes, dry cleaners, and in baking. Steroids are transformed by fermentation for medical purposes, and gibberellins (plant hormones) are produced and used to increase the yield of fruit.

The production of alcoholic beverages such as beer and wine utilizes processes that are among the oldest of the industrial fermentations. Specific alcoholic beverages are produced by a number of yeasts and bacteria. Most of the organisms will not grow in media of greater than 10-12% ethanol. Fortified wines must be produced by the addition of ethanol to the wine after fermentation, and distilled spirits by the concentration of the alcohol by distillation, using heat and vacuum processes.

Among the bacterial fermentations most important to the medical profession is the production of antibiotics. Most antibiotics are produced by species of Streptomyces, Penicillium, and Bacillus. Bacillus thuringiensis is used as an insecticide because it produces toxic crystals that kill caterpillars of several destructive moths and related insects.

The development of recombinant DNA technology has opened a new horizon to industrial microbiology. In the future this technology may be used to produce insulin, interferon, vaccines, and human growth hormone, as well as other medically important proteins. Also, the addition of naturally occurring or engineered plasmids to bacterial species (and possibly plant and animal cells) may be used for many processes, such as the direct fixation of nitrogen by plants. This could eliminate the need for nitrogen fertilizers in agriculture.

After you have read Chapter 28 of your textbook, you should be able to:

1. Define or identify the following terms: enrichment medium, selective medium, batch technique, fermenter, fermentation, continuous flow technique, chemostat, turbidostat, citric acid, submerged culture, lactic acid, gluconic acid, acetic acid, glutamic acid, lysine, methionine, tryptophan, valine, riboflavin, cyanocobalamin, amylase, pectinase, protease, malt, wort, hops, top yeast, ale, bottom yeast, lager beer, sake, must, distilled spirits, proof number, brandy, whiskey, rum, neutral spirits, and plasmid.

2. List some of the important products produced by industrial fermentations and indicate how they are used.

3. Identify the microorganisms used in the various industrial fermentations discussed.

4. Distinguish between batch and continuous flow techniques for industrial fermentations.

PRE-TEST

1. Vinegar is produced when a bacterial fermentation of wine or other alcoholic beverages takes place. The product of this fermentation is:
   a. gluconic acid.
   b. ethanol.
   c. acetic acid.
   d. citric acid.

2. Microbial organisms can live in media containing alcohol in a concentration of up to:
   a. 5-8%.
   b. 10-12%.
   c. 15-17%.
   d. 20-22%.

3. A selective medium is one that:
   a. will inhibit other organisms in a mixture, while allowing certain organisms to grow.
   b. encourages growth of a particular organism in a mixture.
   c. supplies the needs of an organism to produce a selected product.
   d. inhibits an organism from producing a particular compound, while allowing it to produce other metabolic products.

4. If an aerobic organism is used industrially to produce a product

in the presence of oxygen, the process is called a:
a. fermentation.
b. respiration.
c. microbial synthesis.
d. batch technique.

5. Wine is produced by the fermentation of:
a. Saccharomyces cerivisiae.
b. Botrytis cinera.
c. Saccharomyces ellipsoideus.
d. Rhizobium.

6. If a distilled beverage has a proof number of 100, it contains
_____ alcohol.
a. 25%
b. 50%
c. 75%
d. 100%

7. Plasmids are:
a. a group of blood proteins.
b. tiny ringlets of DNA.
c. used in the fermentation of organic acids.
d. needed for the production of insecticides.

8. Distilled beverages produced from molasses are classified as:
a. whiskey.
b. neutral spirits.
c. brandy.
d. rum.

9. Common genera used for the production of antibiotics include all
of the following, except:
a. Penicillium.
b. Escherichia.
c. Bacillus.
d. Streptomyces.

10. Rhizopus is responsible for the industrial fermentation of:
a. amino acids.
b. lager beer.
c. sake.
d. hops.

11. Aspergillus species are used for the production of all of the
following, except:
a. amylase.
b. steroids.
c. pectinase.
d. proteases.

12. When an industrial fermentation is carried out in a large tank
into which a volume of medium is placed and inoculated with a
specific species of bacterium, the fermentation is referred to as

a(n) _____ fermentation.
a. batch technique
b. selective medium
c. enrichment medium
d. continuous flow

13. Aspergillus niger is used to produce _____ acid.
a. citric
b. lactic
c. gluconic
d. acetic

14. Botrytis cinera is:
a. a mold used to produce several antibiotics.
b. used in the fermentation of ale.
c. a mold that causes water loss from grapes and thereby increases the sugar concentration.
d. used to ferment fortified wines.

15. Lager beer is produced by:
a. Rhizobium.
b. top yeast.
c. Humulus lupulus.
d. bottom yeast.

PRACTICE EXERCISES

1. Identify the organism(s) that carries out each of the following industrial fermentations.

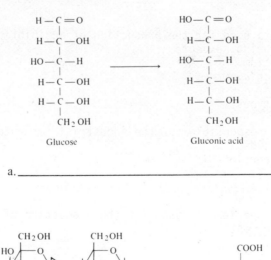

a. _____

b. _____

354

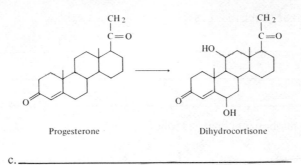

Progesterone   Dihydrocortisone

c. _____

2. In one or two sentences, distinguish between each term of the following pairs.

a. Malt/hops:

_____

_____

_____

b. Top yeast/bottom yeast:

_____

_____

_____

c. Enrichment medium/selective medium:

_____

_____

_____

d. Batch technique/continuous flow technique:

_____

_____

_____

355

e. Chemostat/turbidostat:

_____

_____

_____

f. Proof number/percent alcohol:

_____

_____

_____

g. Malt/wort:

_____

_____

_____

h. Whiskey/brandy:

_____

_____

_____

3. True or False. Indicate whether each of the following statements
   is true or false by placing a T for true or an F for false on the
   line provided.

_____ a. Enrichment medium inhibits other organisms in a mixture, while
          selecting out the desired organism.

_____ b. Amino acids (e.g., glutamic acid) are produced from Krebs
          cycle intermediates by bacteria such as Micrococcus.

_____ c. Gibberellins are produced by bacterial fermentations of
          Gibberella fujikuroi and are important in stimulating fruit
          production by plants. They are naturally occurring plant
          hormones.

_____ d. Ale is produced by bottom yeast.

_____ e. Bacillus thuringiensis produces a crystallin compound, which
          is toxic to many caterpillars and is used as an insecticide.

_____ f. Plasmids have been found only in prokaryotic organisms.

_____ g. An "industrial fermentation" can be either aerobic or anaerobic.

_____ h. Aspergillus niger is used to produce citric acid because it lacks the Krebs cycle enzymes.

_____ i. Amylase is produced industrially by a Clostridium fermentation. It is used in presoaks and dry cleaners.

_____ j. All alcoholic beverages are produced by the fermentation of carbohydrate to ethanol, carried out by Saccharomyces cerivisiae.

4. Fill in the blanks. Plasmids are tiny ringlets of (a) _____ material, apart from the (b) _____, which may contain between 2 and 250 (c) _____. They exist (d) _____ in the microorganism and usually number about (e) _____ per cell. Experimental research has demonstrated that their number may be increased to (f) _____ per cell with the result that their (g) _____ material and, hence, their (h) _____ can be significantly (i) _____.

5. Matching. Match the organism in the left-hand column with the industrial fermentation(s) in which they are used in the right-hand column. Each organism may be matched with more than one fermentation, and each fermentation may be used more than once or not at all.

_____ a. Bacillus thuringiensis	1.	Steroids
_____ b. Saccharomyces ellipsoideus	2.	Acetic acid
	3.	Gibberellens
_____ c. Rhizopus nigricans	4.	Lactic acid
_____ d. Rhizopus species	5.	Cyanocobalamin
_____ e. Lactobacillus bulgaricus	6.	Insecticides
_____ f. Aspergillus niger	7.	Riboflavin
_____ g. Aspergillus ochraceus	8.	Gluconic acid
_____ h. Acetobacter aceti	9.	Amylases
_____ i. Ashbya gossypii	10.	Citric acid
_____ j. Aspergillus oryzae	11.	Proteases
	12.	Alcoholic fermentations

CONCEPT EXERCISES

1. Explain how plasmids may be used in future industrial fermentations.

_____

_____

_____

_____

_____

_____

2. What characteristics of microorganisms make them so useful in the industrial production of organic compounds.

_____

_____

_____

_____

_____

3. In an article entitled "The Microbiological Production of Industrial Chemicals" (Scientific American, 245(No.3):155-178, 1981), Douglas D. Eveleigh states: "Often an organic substance with industrial applications can be made either biologically or by chemical synthesis. The decision to make it one way or the other is essentially an economic one." What are the major economic considerations in deciding whether to make a compound biologically or chemically?

_____

_____

_____

_____

_____

POST-TEST

1. A machine that measures the turbidity of a microbial population to indicate the extent of growth--and when a certain level is reached, adds new medium to the culture vessel while withdrawing the spent material--is called a:

a. turbidostat.
b. chemostat.
c. fermenter.
d. respirometer.

2. *Escherichia coli* and *Enterobacter aerogenes* are both necessary in the industrial production of:
   a. lactic acid.
   b. glutamic acid.
   c. lysine.
   d. methionine.

3. Ribofalvin is:
   a. an important vitamin produced by microbial fermentation.
   b. responsible for the biological production of steroids.
   c. a hormone that can stimulate the growth of fruit.
   d. used in the fermentation of sake.

4. The crushed grapes that form the substrate for the fermentation of wine are called the:
   a. malt.
   b. must.
   c. selective medium.
   d. wort.

5. Brandy is an alcoholic beverage that is:
   a. distilled from fermented fruit juice.
   b. made from molasses.
   c. fermented by *Rhizobium*.
   d. distilled from fermented grains.

6. Plasmids that can be transferred among and function in many gram(-) species have been found in:
   a. *Bacillus*.
   b. *Pseudomonas*.
   c. *Staphylococcus*.
   d. *Streptomyces*.

7. Bottom yeasts are responsible for the fermentation of:
   a. ale.
   b. sake.
   c. lager beer.
   d. acetic acid.

8. A medium that encourages the growth of a particular organism in a mixed culture is termed a(n) _____ medium.
   a. enrichment
   b. selective
   c. minimal
   d. complex

9. Lactic acid is produced industrially by:
   a. *Aspergillus niger*.
   b. *Lactobacillus bulgaricus*.

c. Acetobacter aceti.
d. Micrococcus species.

10. Species of all of the following organisms are used in the industrial biological transformations of steroids, except:
    a. Streptomyces.
    b. Phizopus.
    c. Escherichia.
    d. Mucorales.

11. An enzyme produced by Bacillus subtilis and Aspergillus oryzae in industrial fermentations and is used in the bating of hides is:
    a. amylase.
    b. protease.
    c. pectinase.
    d. cyanocobalamin.

12. Humulus lupulus is:
    a. used to ferment sake.
    b. a vine, the dryed petals of which are called hops.
    c. necessary in the biological production of vitamin B_{12}.
    d. a mold from which antibiotics are produced.

13. It is hoped that in the future products such as silk and casein can be produced by bacteria. To do this:
    a. the correct bacterial species must be isolated.
    b. an economical substrate must be found for the fermentation.
    c. a recombinant plasmid containing the correct gene must be produced and expressed in a bacterium.
    d. problems of contamination with other species of bacteria that can digest the products must be overcome.

14. A device that keeps a culture constantly in the logarithmic stage of growth by providing a constant flow of medium into the culture vessel is termed a:
    a. turbidostat.
    b. chemostat.
    c. fermenter.
    d. batch culture.

15. A submerged culture of Aspergillus niger is obtained in the production of citric acid by:
    a. sinking a screen onto which the mold can adhere into the culture medium.
    b. Keeping the culture medium anaerobic by covering it with mineral oil.
    c. providing an aerobic environment by piping sterile air through the tank.
    d. adding floccules to the medium to which the mold can attach.

ANSWERS TO EXERCISES

Pre-Test

1. c	6. b	11. c
2. b	7. b	12. a
3. a	8. d	13. a
4. a	9. b	14. c
5. c	10. c	15. d

Practice Exercises

1. a. <u>Aspergillus niger</u> or <u>Gluconobacter</u> (Figure 28.6);

   b. <u>Lactobacillus bulgarieus</u> (Figure 28.5);

   c. <u>Rhizopus nigricans</u> (Figure 28.10).

2. a. Malt is the digested grain from which beer is fermented; hops is the dried petals of the vine <u>Humulus lupulus</u>, which are added to give the beer flavor, color, and stability.

   b. Top yeast remains distributed throughout the beer and produces ale, while bottom yeast ferments more slowly and produces lager beer.

   c. Enrichment media encourage growth of a particular organism, but selective media inhibit the growth of many organisms while allowing the growth of selected organisms.

   d. In batch technique, a specific volume of medium is added and and fermented; in continuous flow technique, medium is being continuously added to replace fermented materials.

   e. In a chemostat, a constant flow of medium is added to replace fermented medium and the culture is kept in log phase growth. In a turbidostat, the turbidity (a measure of cell number) of the medium is kept constant and medium is added only when the turbidity exceeds a certain amount.

   f. Proof number is twice the percent of alcohol in a distilled beverage.

   g. Malt is the digested grain used to ferment beer; wort is the liquid produced when the malt is mashed with water. Hops is then added to the wort and the wort is fermented to produce beer.

   h. Whiskey is a distilled alcoholic beverage made from fermented malt cereal grains, and brandy is a distilled beverage made from fermented fruit and fruit juices.

3. a. F; b. T; c. T; d. F; e. T; f. F; g. T; h. T;

   i. F; j. F.

4. a. DNA; b. chromosome; c. genes; d. autonomously;

   e. 30; f. 300; g. genetic; h. product; i. amplified.

5. a. 6; b. 12; c. 1; d. 12; e. 4; f. 8, 10; g. 1;

   h. 2; i. 7; j. 9, 11, 12.

Concept Exercises

1. Plasmids are used as vectors to introduce foreign genes into bacteria. These genes may be of bacterial, plant, or animal origin. The bacterium carrying the recombinant plasmid can then be used to produce the industrially important product, the "cloned" gene.

2. A microorganism is a chemical factory that is able to grow rapidly, possesses a broad variety of enzymes that make an array of chemical conversions possible, has a high metabolic activity that permits conversions to take place rapidly, and has a high surface area for quick absorption of nutrients and release of end products.

3. Major considerations include the cost of raw materials, what fraction of the substrate is converted into the product, how long the conversion takes, how much it costs to recover the product from the fermentation medium, the potential value of by-products, and the cost of waste disposal.

Post-Test

1. a	6. b	11. b
2. c	7. c	12. b
3. a	8. a	13. c
4. b	9. b	14. b
5. a	10. c	15. c